CAROL PRAISE

Edited by
Michael Perry (Words) and David Peacock (Music)
with
Norman Warren and Noël Tredinnick

Marshall Pickering
An Imprint of HarperCollins*Publishers*

Marshall Pickering is an imprint of
HarperCollinsReligious
Part of HarperCollins*Publishers*
77-85 Fulham Palace Road
Hammersmith, London W6 8JB

First published in Great Britain in 1987 by
Marshall Morgan & Scott Publications Ltd
This edition published by Marshall Pickering in 1991

Reprinted: 95 94 93 92 91
Impression number: 10 9 8 7 6 5 4 3 2 1

ISBN 0 551 02513 1
Words edition: 0 551 01591 8 (single copy)
0 551 01453 9 (pack of 25)
Music edition (cased): 0 551 01452 0
Play Carol Praise: 0551 01989 1

Printed and bound in Great Britain by
The Bath Press, Avon

A catalogue record for this book
is available from the British Library

See 'Legal Information' for advice on reproducing individual items in this book

CONTENTS

PREFACE

'Praising God for all they had seen and heard'

They were ordinary people who heard the Christmas news; they may not even have been particularly religious. But it came in language they understood, and they were given clear directions. So, with music ringing in their ears, these shepherds – for that's what they were – went to see if it was true. And they were delighted and astonished at what they found. Without doubt it changed them; they could never be quite the same again, for they had found the saviour.

Getting the message over

As long as the news of Jesus is clearly told, and carols are sung from true hearts, then ordinary people today come to see what Christmas is all about. And by God's grace they too meet the saviour and are filled with joy.

Comprehensive collection

Carol Praise is the first major collection to combine both formal and informal carols for the winter season – Advent, through Christmas, to Epiphany. It can be used as the basic hymn book / song-book / carol book from November to February.

There never has been a book like it

All the greats are here. Alongside the traditional carols, now arranged with guitar chords, come the brightest and best of the recent crop of seasonal songs – drawn not only from the U.K. but, for example from Europe and North America. Worship songs related to the seasonal themes are a unique feature of this collection. Users will find here a rich variety of styles matched to all ages and tastes. There never has been a book like it!

Finding your way around

The carols are arranged alphabetically, but a 'chronological' index puts them back in narrative order, and a Bible index aids reference, for those who will be busy devising carol services using *Carol Praise*.

Of special interest will be new carols set to familiar melodies (see for instance: 'A messenger named Gabriel', 'All heaven rings', 'Christmas news', 'Come and hear the joyful singing', 'Hush little baby', 'Silver star', 'When God from heaven' . . . and many more). This approach means that visitors to carol occasions can join in straight away, without hesitation, because they know the tune.

Bright new possibilities

As well as straight carol arrangements, *Carol Praise* offers suggestions for bright presentation: over one hundred and twenty of its carols and worship songs include descants and instrumental obligatos. Additionally, there are several exciting rounds. The increasing use of instruments within worship is reflected not only in the obligatos, but in the occasional provision of melody and harmony lines for B♭ instruments. New and fresh harmonisations of well-known carols offer an added dimension and resource to the imaginative worship leader.

Who will use *Carol Praise*?

An international line-up of favourites adds yet another dimension to a comprehensive collection, making *Carol Praise* a vigorous resource for churches, schools, youth groups, house groups and clubs, and treasure for the musician to explore.

We know you will enjoy discovering the wealth of new carol material available, just as we did; and we trust it will enrich your presentation of the greatest news of all time.

Michael Perry and **David Peacock**

Our acknowledgements to those who helped
us with the compilation of this volume
will be found on page 637.

USING *CAROL PRAISE*

WORDS

* In *Carol Praise* there are: fresh translations of European carols, new English carols created for well-known secular Christmas melodies, revisions to minimise archaism and exclusive language, songs which are not as yet widely known. This means old word sheets and books won't match. So, for instance, in a carol service or school Christmas evening, the *Carol Praise* words booklets become necessary. Alternatively, to reproduce the words, please see the section 'Legal Information' (page 638) on how to obtain copyright permission etc..

* The 'Story Index' helps the planner of the carol service or event to match carols to the sequence of the Christmas story. The 'Bible Index' aids the speaker in his preparation or the leader who wishes to develop a theme.

* The beginning: A Christmas presentation is always made more interesting (and informative) by careful separation of the elements of the Christmas story. In other words, starting with the promise and expectation of the coming saviour builds up the excitement. There is a wide selection of material which refers to the prophets' promises to Israel, and the angel's annunciation to Mary.

* The middle: Carols which do not mention angels, shepherds or wise men are usefully placed before the story reaches the fields of Bethlehem. It's also good to keep carols about wise men where they should be. In other words, the wise men should never arrive in the stable with the shepherds (nor should the angels!). Only heartless parents would have kept their growing baby in a stable for a month until the magi arrived! Incidentally, the Bible story does not say how many wise men there were – so it's quite reasonable to stage a tableau with lots of people coming to bring gifts.

* The end: Finally, there are various 'reflective' carols which, if used at the end of the sequence, help to bring out the meaning of the story.

MUSIC

* It will be understood that many of the keyboard arrangements give only an outline of the accompaniment. Consequently, enterprising keyboard players will want to improvise and elaborate upon the given arrangements, in a style appropriate to the nature of the carol or worship song.

* The chords given in *Carol Praise* have been chosen with the average guitarist in mind. With many of the arrangements, capo markings are given to make the carols more accessible. '**Capo 5(C)**' means place the capo at the fifth fret and play the chords in brackets, which will be found to be in the key of **C**, rather than **F**.

* For chords marked '. . **sus**' assume they are sustained 4th chords.

* '**N.C.**' indicates no chords are to be played.

* For chords marked '. . +' play the equivalent augmented chord. For example '**C+**' = C aug. 5th.

* A guitarist may find it easier to dispense with the 'extras' of a chord – for example, instead of **C9** play C; instead of **Csus** play C; instead of **Cm7** play Cm.

* Bass notes are given where appropriate. Bass players are encouraged to follow these where possible.

* Certain carols have a fast harmonic rhythm, and a guitarist may have problems keeping up with the change of chords! These carols may be best left to the keyboard player.

* On a number of items, certain chords are in bold type. By playing these chords only, the average guitarist will be able to accompany the carols and songs with greater ease. However, these chords are not consistent with the keyboard harmony and are more suited to 'guitar-only' accompaniment.

1 A baby was born in Bethlehem

Capo 3(D)
Words: Ivor Golby
Music: Caribbean traditional melody
arranged Noël Tredinnick
Calypso style
Gm7 (Em7) C7 (A7) F (D)
Verses
1 A ba - by was born in Beth - le - hem, a ba - by was born in Beth - le - hem, a ba - by was born in Beth - le - hem — it was Je - sus Christ, our Lord.
2 They laid him in a man - ger, they laid him in a man - ger, they laid him in a man - ger — where the ox - en feed on hay.
3 Some shep - herds heard the glad tid - ings, some shep - herds heard the glad tid - ings, some shep - herds heard the glad tid - ings — from an an - gel in the sky.
4 They left their flocks a - sleep - ing, they left their flocks a - sleep - ing, they left their flocks a - sleep - ing — and hur - ried to Beth - le - hem.
C7 (A7) Gm7 (Em7) C7 (A7)
F (D) F7 (D7)
B♭ (G) Gm7 (Em7) C7 (A7) F (D)

Chorus

Descant
B♭ (G)
Am7 (F♯m7)
Gm7 (Em7)
C7 (A7)
Glo - ri - a, glo - ri - a in ex - cel - cis
Glo - ri - a, glo - ri - a in ex - cel - cis
F (D)
F7 (D7)
B♭ (G)
C7 (A7)
Am7 (F♯m7)
D7♭5 (B7♭5)
De - o; glo - ri - a, glo - ry,
De - o; glo - ri - a, glo - ri - a, sing
1–6.
7.
Gm7 (Em7)
C7 (A7)
F (D)
F (D)
glo - ry to God on high! high!
glo - ry to God on high! high!

5 Three wise men came from far lands . . .
they were guided by a star.
Gloria, gloria . . .

6 They laid their gifts before him . . .
and worshipped on bended knee.
Gloria, gloria . . .

7 Then everybody be happy . . .
on the birthday of our Lord!
Gloria, gloria . . .

2 A child is born for us

Christmas Communion Song

Words and music: Bernadette Farrell

Capo 3(D)
Very slow
F (D)
B♭/F (Em7/D)
F (D)
Gm7/F (Em7/D)
optional inst., descant after vv.2,3
Chorus (All)
Bread of life, hope of the world,
F (D)
Dm7 (Bm7)
Gm7 (Em7)
C (A)
F (D)
Je-sus Christ our bro - ther: feed us now,
last time to Coda
Gm7/F (Em7/D)
Csus (Asus)
C (A)
F (D)
B♭/F (Em7/D)
give us life, lead us to one an - oth - er.

Verses (solo/choir)
F (D)
B♭/F (Em7/D)
F (D)
Dm9 (Bm9)
1 A child is born for us, a son is given to us;
2 With our own eyes we see, with our own ears we hear
3 You are the hope of all, pro-mised since time be-gan,
Gm7 (Em7)
Csus (Asus)
C7 (A7)
Dm (Bm)
Fmaj7/C (Dmaj7/A)
in our midst Christ our Lord and God
the sal-va-tion of all the world,
ra-diant light in our dark-ness,
B♭ (G)
Gm7/D (G6/B)
F (D)
B♭/F (Em7/D)
D.C.
comes as one who serves.
God's in-car-nate Word.
truth to set us free.
CODA
F (D)
B♭/F (Em7/D)
Gm7/F (Em7/D)
F2 (D2)
one an-oth-er.
pp

3 A child is born for us today

(FIRST TUNE)

We'll call him Jesus

Words: from Isaiah 9
Pearl Beasley
Music: Brian Hoare

G Am7/G G Am7/G D7/G G D7/A D7
1 A child is born for us to-day, a son to us is
2 He comes to be the 'Prince of peace', to all the world a
3 On those who walk the dark-est way has dawned a shin-ing
G C G/B D7/A G Am/E Bm/D A/C♯ B/D♯
given; the sav-iour comes to guide our way and
friend; his migh-ty love will ne-ver cease, his
light far bright-er than the bright-est day, a
Em A7 D/F♯ D E7/D
lead us up to heaven. They'll call him
king-dom will not end. They'll call him
great and glo-rious sight. O come, Em-
Am/C D7/G G7/B
'Won-der-ful', heaven-ly 'Coun-sell-or'.
'Migh-ty God', 'E-ter-nal Fa-ther'.
-man-u-el, our God, be with us!

C Em/C♯ G/D Em7 Am7/C G
We'll call him 'Je - sus'.
We'll call him 'Je - sus'.
O come, Lord Je - sus!

Arrangement when sung in 4–parts: last two lines —

S
1 They'll call him 'Won - der - ful', heaven - ly
2 They'll call him 'Migh - ty God', 'E - ter - nal
3 O come, Em - man - u - el, our God be

A
1 They'll call him 'Won - der - ful', the heaven - ly
2 They'll call him 'Migh - ty God', 'E - ter - nal
3 O come, Em - man - u - el, our God be

T
1 They'll call him 'Won - der - ful', heaven - ly
2 They'll call him 'Migh - ty God', 'E - ter - nal
3 O come, Em - man - u - el, our God be

B
1 'Won - der - ful', hea - ven - ly
2 'Migh - ty God', 'E - ter - nal
3 Em - man - u - el, our God be

S
'Coun - sell - or'. We'll call him 'Je - sus'.
Fa - ther'. We'll call him 'Je - sus'.
with us! O come, Lord Je - sus!

A
'Coun - sell - or'. We'll call him 'Je - sus'.
Fa - ther'. We'll call him 'Je - sus'.
with us! O come, Lord Je - sus!

T
'Coun - sell - or'. We'll call him 'Je - sus', 'Je - sus'.
Fa - ther'. We'll call him 'Je - sus', 'Je - sus'.
with us! O come, Lord Je - sus, Je - sus!

B
'Coun - sell - or'. We'll call him 'Je - sus'.
Fa - ther'. We'll call him 'Je - sus'.
with us! O come, Lord Je - sus!

4 A child is born for us today

Troon Old

(SECOND TUNE)

Words: from Isaiah 9
Pearl Beasley
Music: Thomas Whitelaw

Introduction

Gm/B♭ A7 Dm C7 F

Dm/F Gm9/F C7 F

1 A child is
2 He comes to
3 On those who

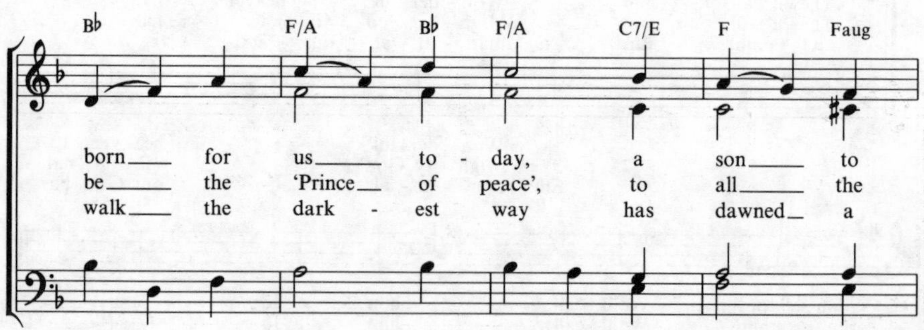
B♭ F/A B♭ F/A C7/E F Faug
born for us to - day, a son to
be the 'Prince of peace', to all the
walk the dark - est way has dawned a

Dm G9 Csus C F
us is given; the sav - iour
world a friend; his migh - ty
shin - ing light far bright - er

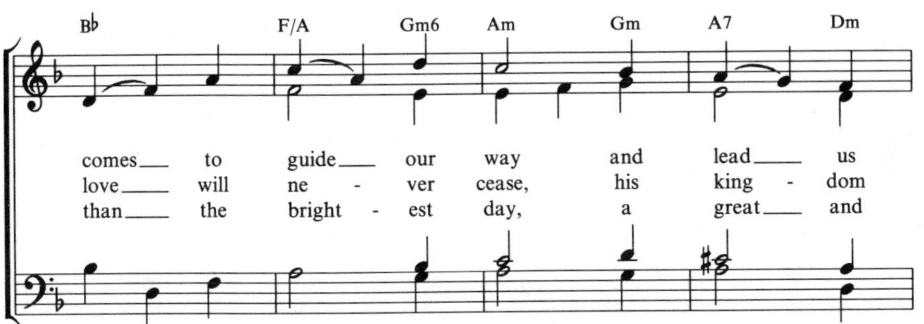
Bb F/A Gm6 Am Gm A7 Dm
comes to guide our way and lead us
love will ne - ver cease, his king - dom
than the bright - est day, a great and

C9 C7 Fsus F7/Eb Db
up to heaven. They'll call him
will not end. They'll call him
glor - ious sight. O come, Em -

Ab B F#
'Won - der - ful', hea - ven - ly 'Coun - sell - or'.
'Migh - ty God', 'E - ter - nal Fa - ther'.
- man - u - el, our God, be with us!

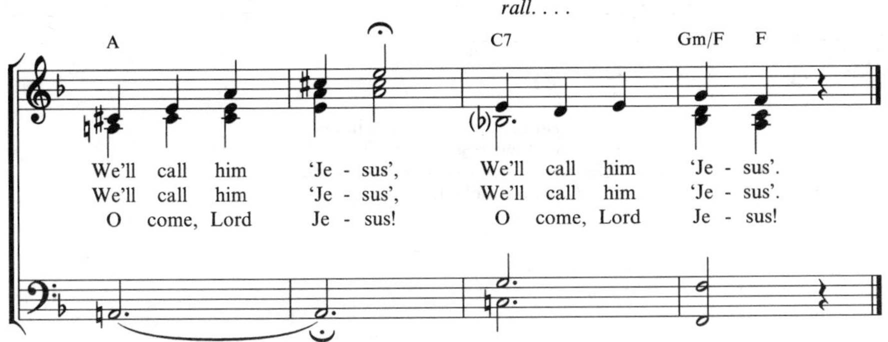
rall. . . .
A C7 Gm/F F
We'll call him 'Je - sus', We'll call him 'Je - sus'.
We'll call him 'Je - sus', We'll call him 'Je - sus'.
O come, Lord Je - sus! O come, Lord Je - sus!

5 A child is born in Bethlehem

A child is born

Words: from the Danish
Michael Perry
Music: Norman Warren

Brightly
Dm
G
Dm
1 A child is born in Beth - le - hem,
2 Sing prai - ses through the whole wide earth,
3 He lies with - in a man - ger bare,
4 He comes to be our hope of peace,
F
Am/E
Dm7
Am/C
B♭
Am
Sing__ no - well, sing__ no - well! the roy - al flower to
Sing__ no - well, sing__ no - well! for Ma - ry gives the
Sing__ no - well, sing__ no - well! and shep - herds kneel to
Sing__ no - well, sing__ no - well! to bring im - pris - oned
G7
Asus
Am
B♭
Dm/F
Gm
C7/G
Dm
Da - vid's stem. Al - le - lu - ia, al - le - lu - ia!
sav - iour birth. Al - le - lu - ia, al - le - lu - ia!
wor - ship there. Al - le - lu - ia, al - le - lu - ia!
souls re - lease. Al - le - lu - ia, al - le - lu - ia!

5 Our guilt has found a certain cure,
Sing nowell, sing nowell!
for Christ makes our salvation sure.
Alleluia, alleluia!

6 A great and mighty wonder

Words: after Germanus (c.634–732)
J M Neale (1818–1866)
and in this version Word & Music
Music: old German melody
harmonised M Praetorius (1571–1621)

Es ist ein' ros'

Capo 3(D)

F (D) B♭ (G) F (D) C (A) Dm (Bm) B♭ (G) F (D) C (A) Dm7 (Bm7) C (A) F (D)
1 A great and migh-ty won-der: re-demp-tion draw-ing near!
2 The Word be-comes in-car-nate and yet re-mains on high;
3 The an-gels sing the sto-ry: a-wake, O dis-tant lands!
4 He comes to save all na-tions: let all now hear his word!
B♭ (G) F (D) C (A) Dm (Bm) B♭ (G) F (D) C (A) Dm7 (Bm7) C (A) F (D)
the vir-gin bears the in-fant, the prince of peace is here!
the shep-herds hear the an-them as glo-ry fills the sky.
re-joice, you hills and val-leys; you o-ceans, clap your hands!
ap-proach and bring him wor-ship, the sav-iour and the Lord!
Gm (Em) Am (F♯m) F (D) G (E) C (A) F (D) B♭ (G) F (D)
Re-peat the hymn a-gain: 'To God on high be
C (A) D (B) Gm (Em) F (D) Gm (Em) Csus (Asus) C (A) F (D)
glo-ry, and peace on earth. A-men.'

7 A child this day is born

Wohin
Capo 5(C)

Words: traditional
and in this version Word & Music
Music: F Schubert (1797–1828)
arranged Norman Warren

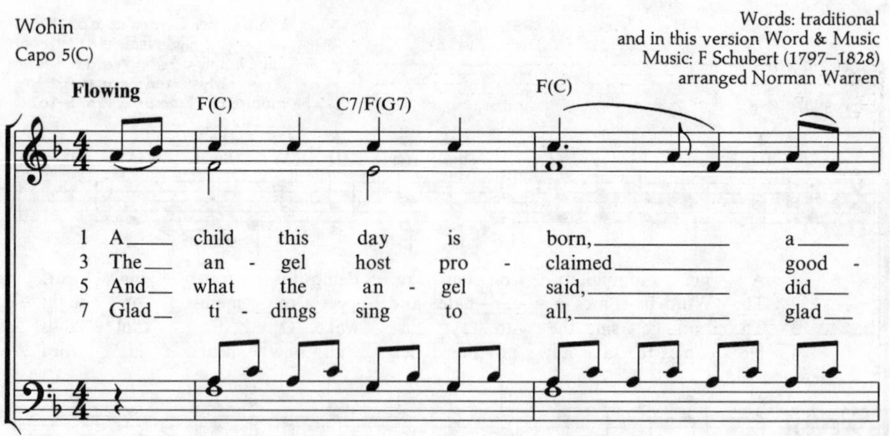
Flowing
F(C)
C7/F(G7)
F(C)
1 A child this day is born, a
3 The an - gel host pro - claimed good -
5 And what the an - gel said, did
7 Glad ti - dings sing to all, glad

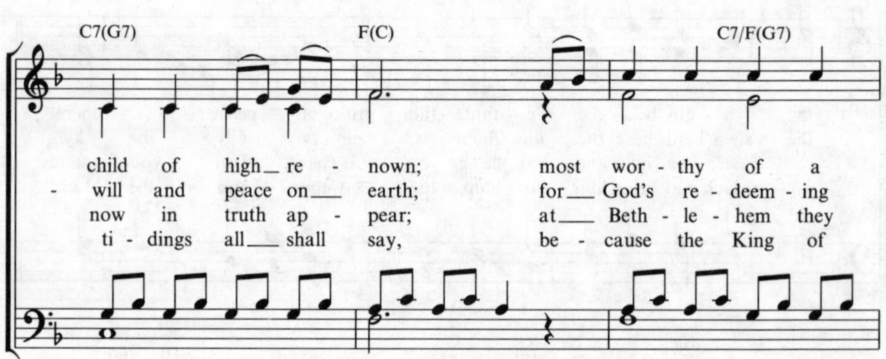
C7(G7)
F(C)
C7/F(G7)
child of high re - nown; most wor - thy of a
- will and peace on earth; for God's re - deem - ing
now in truth ap - pear; at Beth - le - hem they
ti - dings all shall say, be - cause the King of

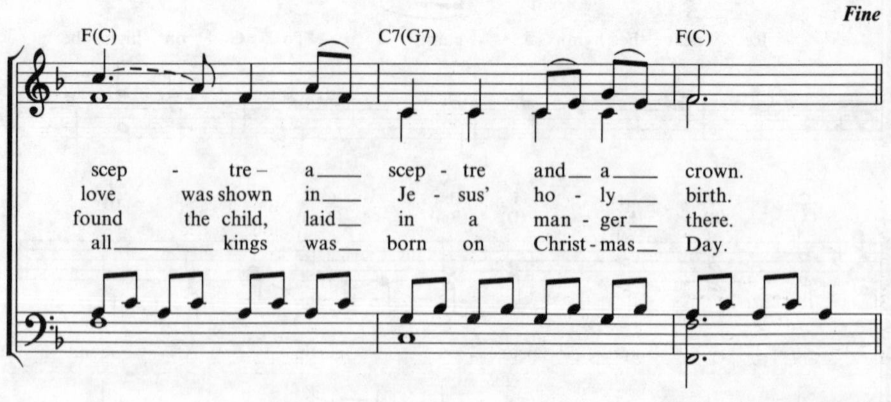
Fine
F(C)
C7(G7)
F(C)
scep - tre – a scep - tre and a crown.
love was shown in Je - sus' ho - ly birth.
found the child, laid in a man - ger there.
all kings was born on Christ - mas Day.

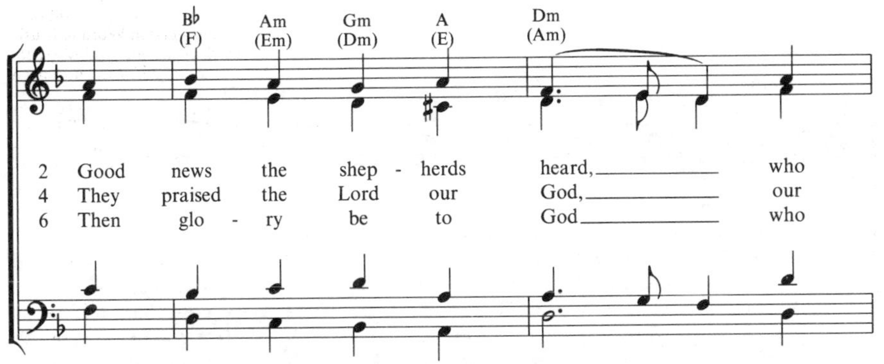
B♭ (F)
Am (Em)
Gm (Dm)
A (E)
Dm (Am)
2 Good news the shep - herds heard, who
4 They praised the Lord our God, our
6 Then glo - ry be to God who

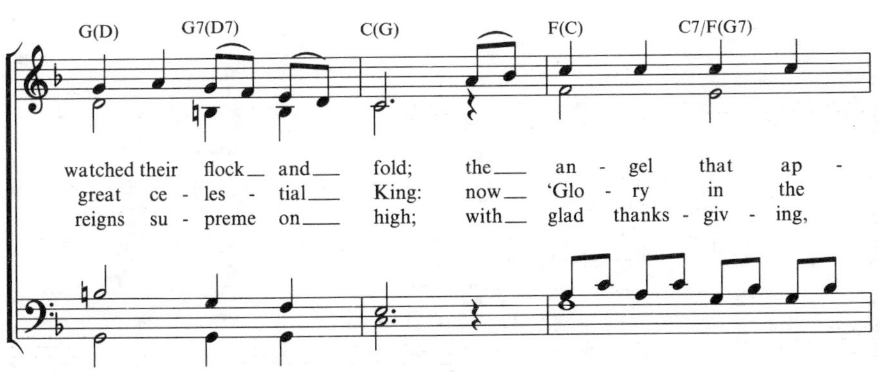
G(D)
G7(D7)
C(G)
F(C)
C7/F(G7)
watched their flock and fold; the an - gel that ap -
great ce - les - tial King: now 'Glo - ry in the
reigns su - preme on high; with glad thanks - giv - ing,

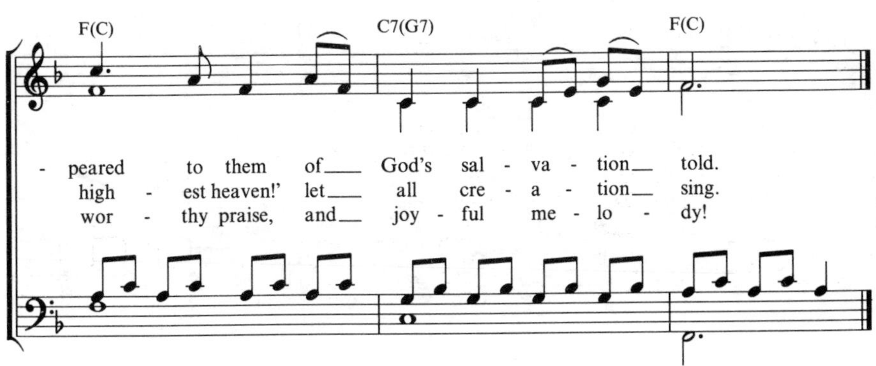
F(C)
C7(G7)
F(C)
- peared to them of God's sal - va - tion told.
high - est heaven!' let all cre - a - tion sing.
wor - thy praise, and joy - ful me - lo - dy!

8 A messenger named Gabriel

O Tannenbaüm

Capo 5(C)

Words: Michael Walker
Music: Traditional melody
arranged Noël Tredinnick

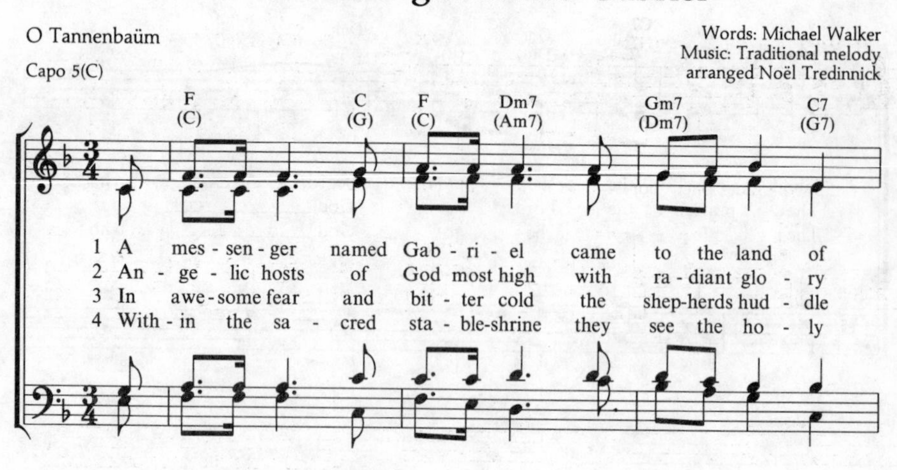

F (C) C (G) F (C) Dm7 (Am7) Gm7 (Dm7) C7 (G7)
1 A mes - sen - ger named Gab - ri - el came to the land of
2 An - ge - lic hosts of God most high with ra - diant glo - ry
3 In awe - some fear and bit - ter cold the shep-herds hud - dle
4 With - in the sa - cred sta - ble-shrine they see the ho - ly

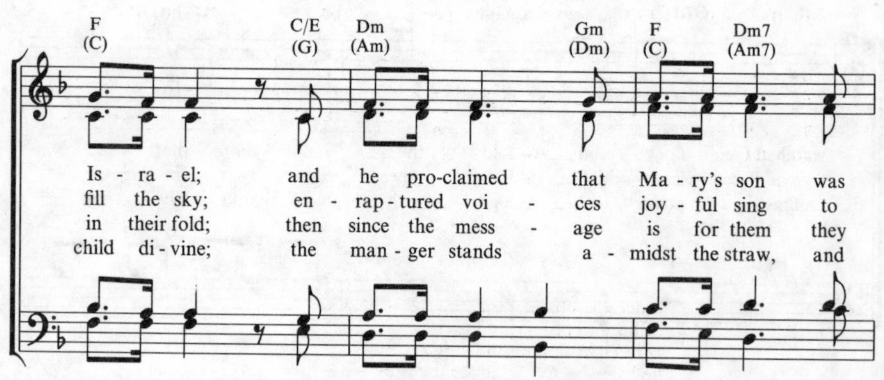

F (C) C/E (G) Dm (Am) Gm (Dm) F (C) Dm7 (Am7)
Is - ra - el; and he pro-claimed that Ma - ry's son was
fill the sky; en - rap - tured voi - ces joy - ful sing to
in their fold; then since the mess - age is for them they
child di - vine; the man - ger stands a - midst the straw, and

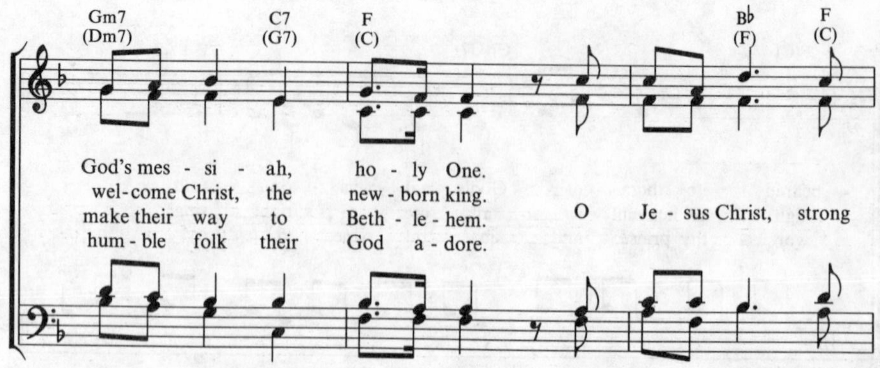

Gm7 (Dm7) C7 (G7) F (C) B♭ (F) F (C)
God's mes - si - ah, ho - ly One.
wel - come Christ, the new - born king.
make their way to Beth - le - hem.
hum - ble folk their God a - dore.
O Je - sus Christ, strong

Gm (Dm) C7 (G7) F (C) C/E (G) Dm (Am) Gm (Dm)
Son of God, once born for us at Beth-le-hem: we lis - ten to the
Dm/A (Am) A (E) D7 (A7) Gm (Dm) C (G) C7/F (G7) F (C)
an - gels' song and wor - ship you for ev - er.

5 Since then have passed two thousand years
of human misery and tears;
yet Christ alone can bring release:
he loves us still – the Prince of peace.
O Jesus Christ . . .

B♭ melody version
1.
2.

9 A song was heard at Christmas

Holy Apostles
Words: Timothy Dudley-Smith
Music: David Wilson
Bm9 Bm Bm9
1 A song was heard at Christ - mas to
2 A star was seen at Christ - mas, a
3 A tree was grown at Christ - mas, a
4 A child was born at Christ - mas when
Bm Bm6 Bm
wake the mid - night sky; a Sav - iour's birth, and
her - ald and a sign, that all might know the
sap - ling green and young; no tin - sel bright with
Christ - mas first be - gan; the Lord of all a
G♯dim/B Bm7 Bm7/A
peace on earth, and praise to God on high. The
way to go to find the child di - vine. The
can - dle - light up - on its branch - es hung. But
ba - by small, the Son of God made man. For
G Dmaj7 G
an - gels sang at Christ - mas with all the hosts a -
wise men watched at Christ - mas in some far east - ern
he who came at Christ - mas our sins and sor - rows
love is ours at Christ - mas, and life and light re -

F♯
Bm
G♯dim/B
- bove, and still we sing the new - born King, his
land, and still the wise in star - ry skies dis -
bore, and still we name his tree of shame our
- stored, and so we praise through end - less days the
F♯m7
B
glo - ry and his love.
- cern their Ma - ker's hand.
life for ev - er - more.
Sav - iour, Christ the Lord.

B♭ melody version
Fine
D.𝄋

10 A star in the sky

Words: Angela Draper
Music: traditional Malawi carol
arranged Noël Tredinnick

Introduction
F
Gm
C7
Dm Gm C7
F Dm Gm7 C7
Verse
F
1 A star in___ the sky
2 Gold, in - cense___ and myrrh
3 May Christ be___ our light -
B♭
Gm
C
F
led the Ma - gi on their way,
were the gifts they of - fered there,
- with us ev - er - more to stay,
a star in___ the sky
gold, in - cense___ and myrrh,
may Christ be___ our light
B♭
C7
Gm
C7
F
led them on - ward night and day;
giv - en with a rev - erent care:
guid - ing us up - on our way:
then at last it came to stay
cost - ly trea - sures they did share,
bring us home to God we pray,

Chorus
C7
F
ov - er the town of Beth - le - hem.
wor - ship-ping Christ in Beth - le - hem.
Christ who was born in Beth - le - hem.
Sing al - le - lu - ia, sing al - le - lu - ia,
Gm
C7
F
F♯dim7
sing out a song of praise; al - le - lu - ia,
Gm7
C7
Dm
Gm7
C7
sing out a song of praise – Christ is born in
F
Gm
C7
1.2.
F
Dm
Gm7
C7
3.
F
(link)
Beth-le-hem.

11 Across the desert sands

Pilgrim Carol
Capo 3(Em)
Words: Elizabeth Cosnett
Music: Adrian Cleaton
Flowing
Gm(Em)
D7/F♯(B7)
1 A - cross the de - sert sands, be-tween the fo - rest trees, through
(2) track that shep-herds tread, a half - re - mem-bered song, a
(3) ne - ver seen the place, no map de - scribes the way, but
(4) come, O come with me, all you whose hearts are stirred, to -
D7(B7)
Gm(Em)
fro - zen wastes and fer - tile lands and o - ver swell - ing seas; by
star that glim-mers gold and red – they're draw - ing me a - long; and
still I trust that by God's grace I shall not go a - stray; my
- ge - ther we shall sure - ly see the light of God's own word! And
Cm(Am)
vil - la - ges and towns, rough path and wind - ing road, by crag - gy
when the jour - ney's done I hope to meet my king and lay be -
Lord will show no scorn nor turn a - way from me, but glad - ly
as we go we'll raise with all our might and main a pil - grim
Gm/D(Em)
D7(B7)
Gm(Em)
peaks and roll - ing downs I bear a pre - cious load:
- fore him one by one the gifts I come to bring:
take what I have borne so far, so wea - ri - ly:
ca - rol full of praise, a ten - der, sweet re - frain:

Chorus
F/A (D)
Gm7 (Em7)
F7/A (D7)
B♭(G)
Gold of the world's wealth, in - cense for wor - ship,
E♭(C)
D7(B7)
Gm(Em)
myrrh mean - ing sor - row, love be-yond tell - ing.
1–3.
4.
2 A
3 I've
4 Now

12 All hail, king Jesus

Words and music: Dave Moody
Music arranged David Peacock

Worshipfully with strength
F C Bb/F F
All hail, king Je - sus; all hail, Em - man - u - el,
A/E Dm Dm/B G7 Gm7
King of kings, Lord of lords, bright morn-ing Star!
C7 Bb/C C7 F Fmaj7 F7 3 Bb
And through - out e - ter - ni - ty I'll sing your prai - ses
Eb9 F D7 Gm Bb/C C7 F Gm/F F
and I'll reign with you through - out e - ter - ni - ty.

13 All heaven rings

Barbara Allen

Words: Michael Perry
Music: English traditional melody
arranged Noël Tredinnick

Bm A7 D/F♯ A7 Bm G
1 All hea - ven rings with joy - ful songs as
2 The si - lent earth is filled with awe and
3 The Lord is born this ho - ly day of
4 Come, Christ-ians, greet the liv - ing Word, as -
D Bm7 E7 A A/E A/C♯ Bm Em A7
an - gels tell the sto - ry of one who comes to
mor - tal men stand trem - bling, for God is found a -
Ma - ry, vir - gin mo - ther, God's child of grace, his
- cribe him truth and me - rit; let heaven and earth with
Dmaj7 G (Em) D/A G A7 D G/D D
right our wrongs and take us up to glo - ry.
- mong the poor, our ve - ry selves re - sem - bling.
per - fect way, our sav - iour and our bro - ther.
one ac - cord praise Fa - ther, Son and Spi - rit!

14 All my heart this night rejoices

Words: after P Gerhardt (1607–1676)
C Winkworth (1827–1878),
in this version Word & Music
Music: David Peacock

All my heart
A7 D F♯m7 G A/G
1 All my heart this night re - joi - ces, as I hear, far and
2 Lis - ten! from a hum - ble man - ger comes the call, 'One and
3 Ga - ther, then, from ev - ery na - tion; here let all, great and
4 You, my Lord, with love I'll cher - ish, live to you, and with
F♯m Bm/F♯ C Em/B A7
near, sweet - est an - gel voi - ces. 'Christ is
all, run from sin and dan - ger! Christ - ians
small, kneel in a - dor - a - tion; love him
you dy - ing, shall not per - ish, but shall
Dmaj7 F♯m7 G A/G F♯m7 Bm7
born!' their choirs are sing - ing, till the air ev - ery - where now with
come, let no - thing grieve you: you are freed! All you need I will
who with love is yearn - ing: Hail the star that from far bright with
dwell with you for ev - er: joy di - vine shall be mine that can
Em Em7 1–3. Asus A7 4. Asus D9
joy is ring - ing.
sure - ly give to you.'
hope is burn - ing!
al - ter ne - ver.

15 All the way

Words and music: Mo Wilkinson
Music arranged David Peacock

Gently
A A7 D Bm E7
1 All the way, all the way, he came
2 From heaven a - bove to Beth - le - hem he came
3 From Beth - le - hem to Je - ru - sa - lem he came
4 From Je - ru - sa - lem to Cal - va - ry he came
A Bm A/C♯ D Esus E7
all the way for me;
from
from
from Je -
A A7 D Bm B7/D♯
all the way, all the way, he came
heaven a - bove to Beth - le - hem he came
Beth - le - hem to Je - ru - sa - lem he came
- ru - sa - lem to Cal - va - ry he came
A/E Bm7/E E7 Asus A
all the way for me.

5 From Calvary to heaven above
he came all the way for me . . .

6 From heaven above into my heart
he came all the way for me . . .

7 Jesus came, Jesus came,
he came all the way for me . . .

16 Alleluia, hear the angels sing

Alleluia to the King

Words: Michael Perry
Music: unknown
arranged David Peacock

Firmly
E
A
E
E/B
p 1 Al - le - lu - ia, hear the an - gels sing, al - le -
f 2 Al - le - lu - ia, let the whole world sing, al - le -

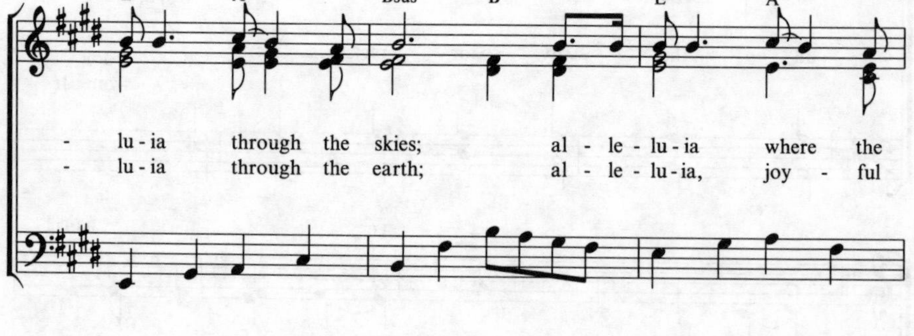
E
A
Bsus
B
E
A
- lu - ia through the skies; al - le - lu - ia where the
- lu - ia through the earth; al - le - lu - ia, joy - ful

E
C♯m
F♯7
E/B
A/B
E
in - fant king sleep-ing in a man - ger lies.
ca - rols bring – come to greet the sav - iour's birth!

17 Alleluia to the King of kings

Alleluia to the King

Words and music: unknown
arranged David Peacock

Firmly

E
A
E
E/B
Al - le - lu - ia to___ the King of kings; al - le -

E
A
Bsus
B
E
A
- lu - ia to___ the Lamb: al - le - lu - ia to___ the

E
C♯m
F♯7
E/B
A/B
E
Lord of Lords; who___ is the great___ 'I Am'!

18 Alleluia! Hurry the Lord is near

Hurry, the Lord is near

Words: Patrick Lee
Music: Ernest Sands
arranged Paul Inwood and David Peacock

Fast and urgent

Em D Em D C D

Optional 2nd voice part

Al - le - lu - ia!

Al - le - lu - ia! Hur-ry, the Lord is

Em D/E Em Am7 D Gmaj7

Hur-ry, the Lord is near. Al - le - lu - ia, al - le - lu -

near. Al - le - lu - ia, al - le - lu - ia!

last time **to Coda**

Am7 Bm7 Em D/E Em

- ia! Hur-ry, the Lord is near.

Verses

Hur-ry, the Lord is near.

1 Sound the trum-pet, the
2 Earth has longed for
3 Go out to meet him,
4 He is the migh-ty One,

Am
Em
C
D
Em
D/E
Lord ___ is near;
his ___ ap-proach:
shout ___ his name:
he is the Word;
Hur - ry, the Lord ___ is near;

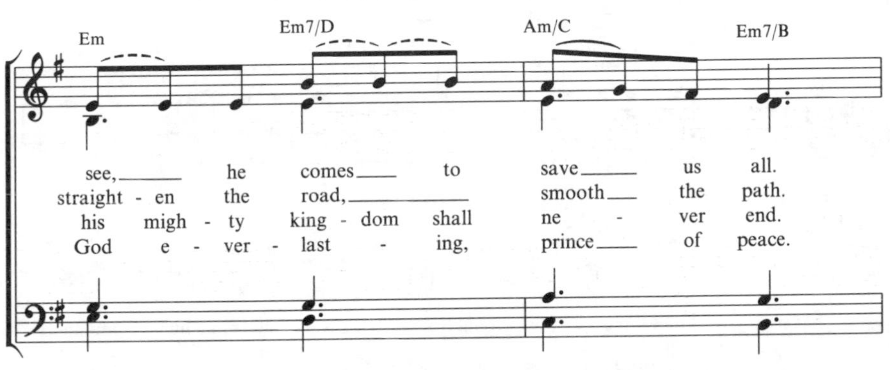
Em
Em7/D
Am/C
Em7/B
see, ___ he comes ___ to save ___ us all.
straight - en the road, ___ smooth ___ the path.
his migh - ty king - dom shall ne - ver end.
God e - ver - last - ing, prince ___ of peace.

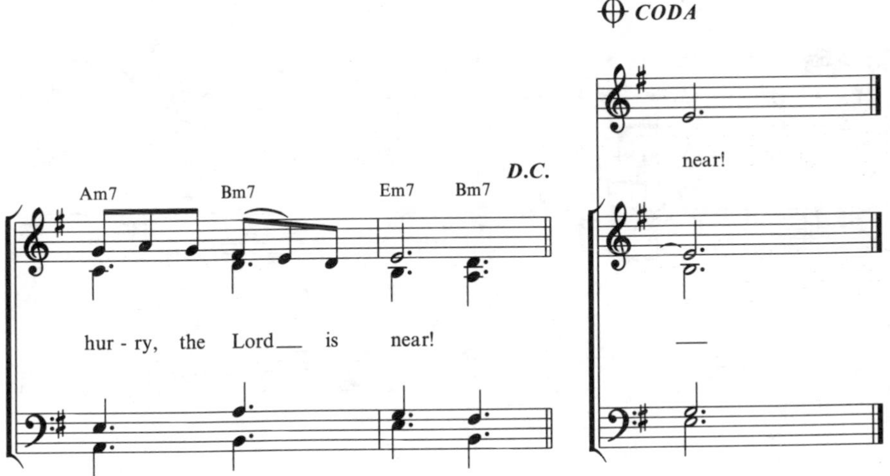
CODA
D.C.
Am7
Bm7
Em7
Bm7
hur - ry, the Lord ___ is near!
near!

19 Alleluia, my Father

Words and music: Tim Cullen
Music arranged David Peacock

With quiet devotion
E
B7
A
Al - le - lu - ia, my Fa - ther, for giv-ing us your
Son; send-ing him in - to the world to be giv-en up for
G♯m
C♯m
us, know - ing we would bruise him and smite him from the
earth: Al - le - lu - ia, my Fa - ther in his
1.
2.
death is my birth; al - le - life!
life

20 Alleluia . . . prepare the way

Alleluia for Advent

Words: from Isaiah 40
Music: Geoffrey Boulton Smith

Brightly
E D E (Bm7) E
last time to Coda
SOLO
Al - le-lu - ia, al - le-lu - ia;
ALL
al - le-lu - ia,
D E D E Bm E Bm
al - le-lu - ia! Pre-pare the way for the Lord, make his path straight: and all man -
SOLO/CHOIR
E D E Bm E (Bm7)
D.C.
CODA
- kind shall see the sal - va-tion of our God.
D E
al - le-lu - ia!

* Bm7 need only be used by guitars here if keyboard is played as well.

21 Angels from the realms of glory

Iris

Words: J Montgomery (1771–1854) in this version Jubilate Hymns
Music: French traditional melody arranged David Peacock

F C/E C7 F F/A
1 An - gels from the realms of glo - ry,
2 Shep - herds in the fields a - bid - ing,
3 Wise men, leave your con - tem - pla - tions!
4 Though an in - fant now we view him,

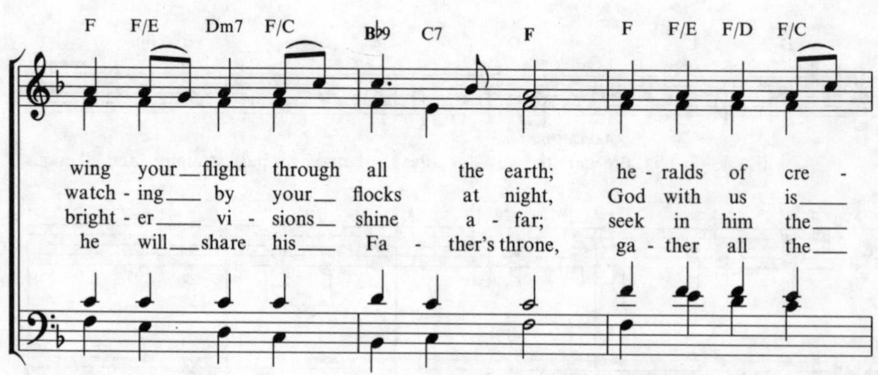
F F/E Dm7 F/C B♭9 C7 F F F/E F/D F/C
wing your flight through all the earth; he - ralds of cre -
watch - ing by your flocks at night, God with us is
bright - er vi - sions shine a - far; seek in him the
he will share his Fa - ther's throne, ga - ther all the

B♭9 C7/G F/A F F/E Dm7 F/C B♭9 C7 F
- a - tion's sto - ry now pro - claim Mes - si - ah's birth!
now re - sid - ing: see, there shines the in - fant light!
hope of na - tions, you have seen his na - tal star:
na - tions to him; ev - ery knee shall then bow down:

Descant or instrument
F D7 Gm C7 F B♭
Come and
Come and
C
1.
Dm C F B♭ F/C C
wor - ship Christ, the new - born king:
wor - ship Christ, the new - born king:
2. Dm C F B♭ F/C C F
wor - ship Christ the new - born king.
wor - ship Christ the new - born king.

22 As Joseph was awaking

As Joseph was a-walking
Words: English traditional
and in this version Word & Music
Music: Colin Fanshawe
arranged David Peacock
Capo 3(D)
Flowing
D7 (B7) Gm (Em) D7 (B7) Gm (Em) A7 (F♯7)
D (B) Gm (Em) C7 (A7)
1 As Jo-seph was a - wak-ing he heard an an-gel
(2) born in house nor yet in
F (D) Gm (Em) A7 (F♯7) Gm/E (Em) Gm7 (Em7)
sing, 'There shall be born to Ma-ry on earth your hea-ven-ly
hall, but cold-ly in a sta-ble, and in an ox-'s
Asus (F♯sus) A (F♯) 1. D7 (B7) 2. D (B) D/F♯ (B)
king.' 2 And nei-ther was he
stall. Glo-ry in the

Gm (Em)
Em (C♯m)
A7 (F♯7)
high - est: sing to God 'No - well'!
D (B)
D/F♯ (B)
Gm (Em)
E7/G♯ (C♯7)
E (C♯)
Glo - ry in the high - est: sing to God, 'No -
A7 (F♯7)
D (B)
Gm7 (Em7)
- well'!
3 And nei - ther was he cov - ered
4 And nei - ther was he cra - dled
C7 (A7)
F (D)
Gm (Em)
Asus (F♯sus)
A (F♯)
in fi - ne - ry or fair, but hum - bly in the cloth - ing
in sil - ver or in gold, but soft - ly in a man - ger
1.
Gm (Em)
A7 (F♯7)
D (B)
D/F♯ (B)
that all the bab - ies wear. Glo - ry in the
2.
Gm (Em)
A7 (F♯7)
D (B)
to keep him from the cold!

23 As with gladness

Dix
Words: W C Dix (1837–1898)
in this version Word & Music
Music: C Kocher (1786–1872)
arranged W H Monk (1823–1889),
descant S H Nicholson (1875–1947)
G D7 G C D7 G C D7 G C
1 As with glad - ness men of old did the guid - ing
2 As with joy - ful steps they sped to that low - ly
3 As they of - fered gifts most rare at your cra - dle
4 Ho - ly Je - sus, ev - ery day keep us in the
G/D D G Em Am G Am Bsus B
star be - hold, as with joy they hailed its light,
man - ger bed, there to bend the knee be - fore
plain and bare, so may we with ho - ly joy
nar - row way, and when earth - ly things are past,
C D7 G Am7 G Dsus D G D7 G
lead - ing on - ward, gleam - ing bright: so, most gra - cious
Christ whom heaven and earth a - dore: so with ev - er -
pure and free from sin's al - loy, all our cost - liest
bring our ran - somed souls at last: where they need no
D D7 G C D7 G C G/D D7 G
Lord, may we ev - er - more your splen - dour see.
- quick - ening pace may we seek your throne of grace.
trea - sures bring, Christ, to you, our heaven - ly king.
star to guide, where no clouds your glo - ry hide.

Descant
G D7 G C D7 G C D7 G C
5 In the heaven - ly coun - try bright none shall need cre -
5 In the heaven - ly coun - try bright none shall need cre -
G/D D G Em Am G Am Bsus B
- a - ted light – Christ, its light, its joy, its crown,
- a - ted light – Christ, its light, its joy, its crown,
C D7 G Am7 G Dsus D G D7 G
Christ its sun which goes not down: there for ev - er
Christ its sun which goes not down: there for ev - er
D D7 G C D7 G C G/D D7 G
may we sing al - le - lu - ias to our king.
may we sing al - le - lu - ias to our king.

24 At your feet we fall

Majestically
From Revelation 1
Words and music: Dave Fellingham
Music arranged Norman Warren
Capo 2(G)
Verse
A(G)
1 At your feet we fall, mighty risen Lord,
2 There we see you stand, mighty risen Lord,
3 Like the shining sun in its noon-day strength,
D/A (C/G)
A (G)
as we come before your throne to worship
clothed in garments pure and holy, shining
we now see the glory of your wondrous
D (C)
F♯7 (E7)
Bm (Am)
you! By your Spirit's power
bright; eyes of flashing fire,
face: once that face was marred,
you now draw our hearts, and we
feet like burnished bronze, and the
but now you're glorified; and your

E7 (D7) A(G) D(C) A(G)

hear your voice in tri - umph ring - ing clear: ______
sound of ma - ny wa - ters is your voice. ______
words, like a two-edged sword, have migh - ty power. ______

Chorus

F♯m (Em) B7 (A7) E (D)

'I am he that lives, that lives and was dead! Be -

A (G) Em6/G (Dm6/F) D/F♯ (C/E) F7 (E♭7) A/E (G/D) E7 (D7) A (G)

- hold I am a - live – a - live ev - er - more!' ______

B♭ version for chorus

25 Away in a manger

(FIRST TUNE)

Cradle Song

Capo 3(C)

Words: verses 1, 2 unknown (nineteenth century)
verse 3 J T McFarland (c.1906)
Music: W J Kirkpatrick (1838–1921)
arranged John Barnard

Eb (C) Bb/Eb (G/C) Eb (C) Cm (Am)
Verse 3 Descant or instrumental obligato
(Ah)
1 A - way in a manger, no crib for a
2 The cat - tle are low - ing, the ba - by a -
3 Be near me, Lord Je - sus; I ask you to
Fm (Dm) Bb7 (G7) Cm (Am)
bed, the lit - tle Lord Je - sus laid
- wakes, but lit - tle Lord Je - sus no
stay close by me for ev - er and
F7 (D7) Bb (G) Eb (C) Bb7/Eb (G/C)
down his sweet head; the stars in the
cry - ing he makes: I love you, Lord
love me, I pray; bless all the dear

E♭ (C)
B♭m/G (Gm/E)
C7 (A7)
Fm (Dm)
bright sky looked down where he lay, the
Je - sus – look down from on high and
child - ren in your ten - der care, and
B♭7 (G7)
Cm (Am)
F7 (D7)
B♭7 (G7)
E♭ (C)
lit - tle Lord Je - sus a - sleep on the hay.
stay by my side un - til morn - ing is nigh.
fit us for heaven to live with you there.
B♭ version of descant

26 Away in a manger

(SECOND TUNE)

Words: verses 1, 2 unknown (nineteenth century)
verse 3 J T McFarland (c.1906)
Music: Herbert Chappell

Flowing
Am
Am
Dm7
G7
SOLOIST A - way in a man - ger, no crib for a bed,
ALL A - way in a man - ger,
Cmaj7
Fmaj7
Dm/B
Dm/E
the lit-tle Lord Je - sus
no crib for a bed,
the lit-tle Lord Je -
E7
laid down his sweet head;
- sus laid down his sweet head;

Am
Dm7
G7
the stars in the bright sky
looked down where he lay,
the stars in the bright sky
Cmaj7
Fmaj7
the lit - tle Lord Je -
looked down where he lay,
Dm/B
Fmaj7/E
E7
sus
a - sleep on the hay.
2 The
the lit - tle Lord Je - sus
a - sleep on the hay.
C9
C6
C9
C6
A♭7
cat - tle are low-ing, the ba - by a - wakes, but lit - tle Lord
(legato)

C/G
D♭/G
C7
C9
C6
Je-sus no cry-ing he makes: I love you, Lord Je - sus – look
C9
C6
A♭7
C/G
G7
down from on high and stay by my side un - til morn-ing is
B7
E7
Am
Dm7
nigh.
3 Be near me, Lord Je - sus;
3 Be near me, Lord Je -
G7
Cmaj7
Fmaj7
I ask you to stay
close by me for ev -
- sus; I ask you to stay

Dm/B
Dm/E
E7
er
and love me, I pray;
close by me for ev - er
and love me, I pray;
Am
Dm7
G7
bless all the dear child - ren
in your ten-der care,
bless all the dear child - ren
Cmaj7
Fmaj7
Dm/B
Dm/E
and fit us for hea - ven
in your ten-der care,
and fit us for hea -
rall.
E7
A
to live with you there.
- ven
to live with you there.
rall.

27 Away in a manger

(THIRD TUNE)

Mueller

Capo 3(D)

Words: verses 1, 2 unknown (nineteenth century)
verse 3 J T McFarland (c.1906)
Music: J R Murray (1841–1905)

F(D)
B♭(G)
F(D)
1 A - way in a man - ger, no crib for a bed, the
2 The cat - tle are low - ing, the ba - by a - wakes, but
3 Be near me, Lord Je - sus; I ask you to stay close
C7(A7)
F(D)
lit - tle Lord Je - sus laid down his sweet head; the
lit - tle Lord Je - sus no cry - ing he makes: I
by me for ev - er and love me, I pray; bless
B♭(G)
F(D)
stars in the bright sky looked down where he lay, the
love you, Lord Je - sus – look down from on high and
all the dear child - ren in your ten - der care, and
C7(A7)
F(D)
Gm/B♭
(Em/G)
C7(A7)
F(D)
lit - tle Lord Je - sus a - sleep on the hay.
stay by my side un - til morn - ing is nigh.
fit us for hea - ven to live with you there.

28 Baby Jesus, sleeping softly

Words and music: Hilda Dodd

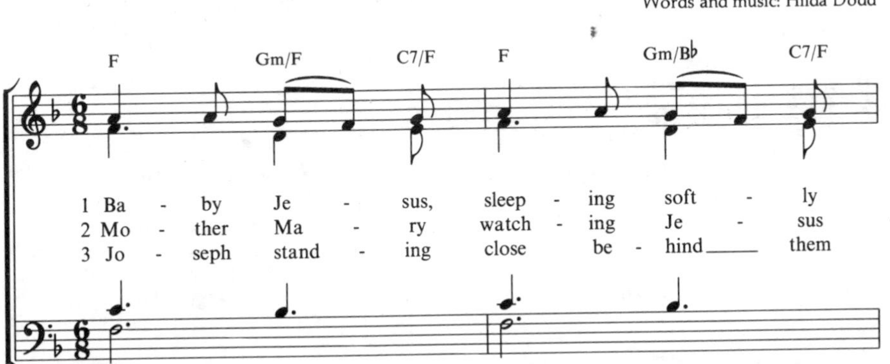
F Gm/F C7/F F Gm/B♭ C7/F
1 Ba - by Je - sus, sleep - ing soft - ly
2 Mo - ther Ma - ry watch - ing Je - sus
3 Jo - seph stand - ing close be - hind ___ them

F B♭ F/A F Dm Gm7 C7/B♭ F/A
on ___ the warm and fra - grant hay, child - ren all the
sleep - ing in the soft ___ warm hay, child - ren all the
hear - ing what the shep - herds say, child - ren all the

B♭ C7/B♭ F/A F B♭/D C7/G F/A F Gm7/B♭ F
wide world o - ver think ___ of you on Christ - mas Day.
wide world o - ver think ___ of you on Christ - mas Day.
wide world o - ver think ___ of you on Christ - mas Day.

29 Before the heaven and earth

(FIRST TUNE)

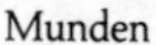
Munden

Words: from Philippians 2 *(The Song of Christ's Glory)*
Brian Black and Word & Music
Music: David Peacock

Flowing

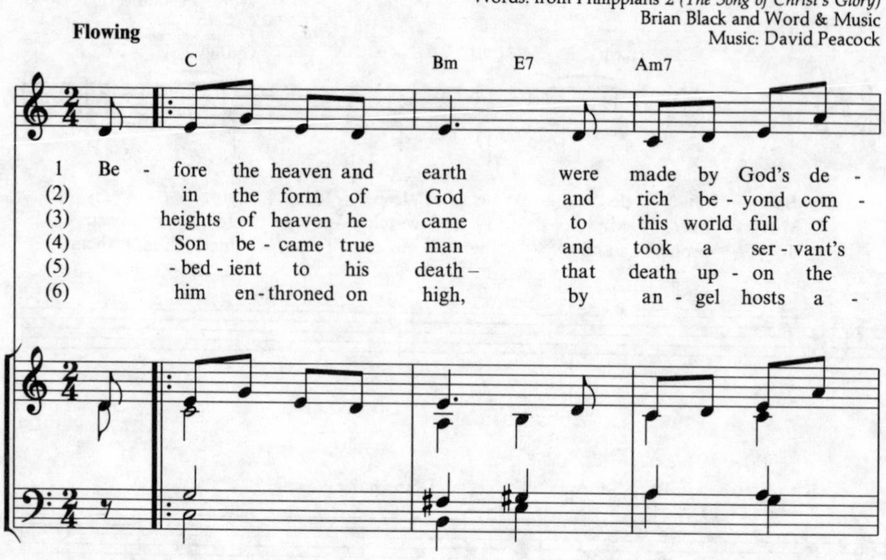
C
Bm
E7
Am7
1 Be - fore the heaven and earth were made by God's de -
(2) in the form of God and rich be - yond com -
(3) heights of heaven he came to this world full of
(4) Son be - came true man and took a ser - vant's
(5) - bed - ient to his death – that death up - on the
(6) him en - throned on high, by an - gel hosts a -

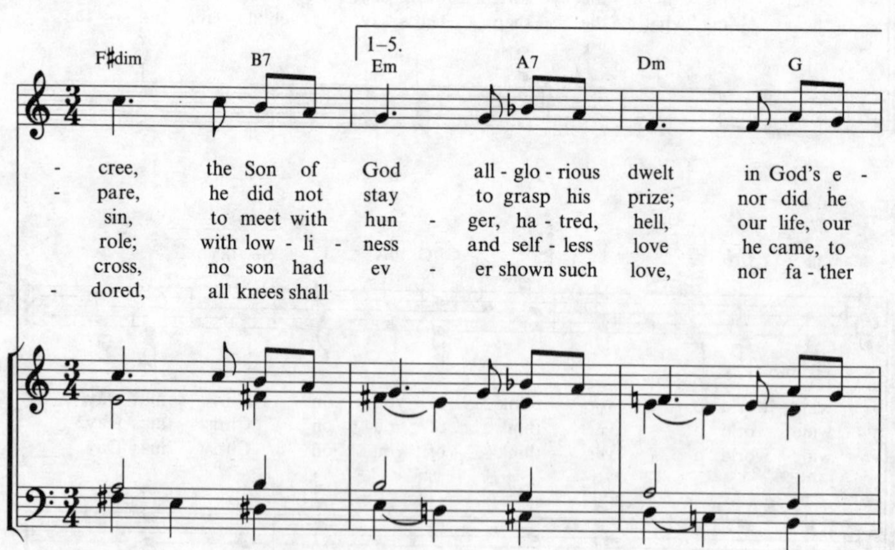
F♯dim
B7
1–5.
Em
A7
Dm
G
- cree, the Son of God all - glo - rious dwelt in God's e -
- pare, he did not stay to grasp his prize; nor did he
sin, to meet with hun - ger, ha - tred, hell, our life, our
role; with low - li - ness and self - less love he came, to
cross, no son had ev - er shown such love, nor fa - ther
- dored, all knees shall

6.
C D7 G Em D7
- ter - ni - ty. Though
lin - ger there. From
love to win. The bow, and tongues con -
make us whole. O -
known such loss. To
G Am D9 D7 G
- fess that Je - sus Christ is Lord.
B♭ melody version
1–5.
6.

30 Before the heaven and earth

(SECOND TUNE)

Words: from Philippians 2 (*The Song of Christ's Glory*)
Brian Black and Word & Music
Music: from J Leisentritt, *Catholicum Hymnologium,* (1584)
verse 6 arranged with descant John Barnard
Narenza
Capo 3(G)
B♭ (G) F (D) B♭ (G) E♭ (C) F7 (D7) B♭ (G)
1 Be - fore the heaven and earth were
2 Though in the form of God and
3 From heights of heaven he came to
4 The Son be - came true man and
5 O - bed - ient to his death – that
C (A) Dm (Bm) B♭ (G) C (A) F (D) B♭ (G) F7 (D7) B♭ (G) E♭ (C) F7 (D7)
made by God's de - cree, the Son of God all -
rich be - yond com - pare, he did not stay to
this world full of sin, to meet with hun - ger,
took a ser - vant's role; with low - li - ness and
death up - on the cross, no son had ev - er
Gm (Em) E♭ (C) D (B) B♭ (G) F (D) Gm (Em) Cm7 (Am7) F (D) B♭ (G)
- glo - rious dwelt in God's e - ter - ni - ty.
grasp his prize; nor did he lin - ger there.
ha - tred, hell, our life, our love to win.
self - less love he came, to make us whole.
shown such love, nor fa - ther known such loss.

B♭ (G) F (D) B♭/D (G/B) E♭ (C) F7/C (D7/A) B♭ (G) C7/B♭ (A7/G)
6 To him en - throned on high, by
6 To him en - throned on high, by
F (D) Dm (Bm) Gm (Em) C7 (A7) Fsus (Dsus) B♭ (G) F7/A (D7/F♯) B♭ (G) E♭ (C) F7/C (D7/A)
an - gel hosts a - dored, all knees shall bow, and
an - gel hosts a - dored, all knees shall bow, and
Gm (Em) E♭ (C) D (B) B♭ (G) F (D) Gm (Em) Cm/E♭ (Am/C) F (D) B♭ (G)
tongues con - fess that Je - sus Christ is Lord.
tongues con - fess that Je - sus Christ is Lord.

31 Behold I tell you a mystery

Capo 3(C)

From 1 Corinthians 15
Words and music: Phil Rogers

With strength
Verse
F(D)
E♭/F(C)
B♭/F(G)
1 Be - hold, I tell you a mys - te-ry; be - hold, I tell you a
F(D)
Dm(Bm)
Am(F♯m)
B♭(G)
mys - te-ry! We shall not all sleep, but
Gm7(Em7)
C(A)
B♭(G)
Gm7(Em7)
we shall all be changed – in a mo - ment, in a twink-ling of an
C7(A7)
B♭(G)
Gm7(Em7)
C7(A7)
eye; in a mo - ment, in a twink-ling of an eye.
Chorus
F(D)
E♭(C)
3
F(D)
B♭/F(G)
For the last trum-pet shall sound, and the dead shall be raised in-cor -

F(D)
E♭/F(C)
F(D)
- rup - ti-ble and we shall be changed,
E♭/F(C)
F(D)
Fine
Verse
F(D)
we shall be changed. 2 Death is swal-lowed up in
E♭/F(C)
B♭/F(G)
F(D)
Dm(Bm)
Am(F♯m)
vic - to-ry; death is swal-lowed up in vic-to-ry! O death, where is your
B♭(G)
Gm7(Em7)
C(A)
B♭(G)
Gm7(Em7)
sting? The sting of death is sin – but thanks be to God who gives us
C7(A7)
B♭(G)
Gm7(Em7)
C7(A7)
vic - to-ry through Je - sus Christ our Lord!

32 Behold the darkness shall cover the earth

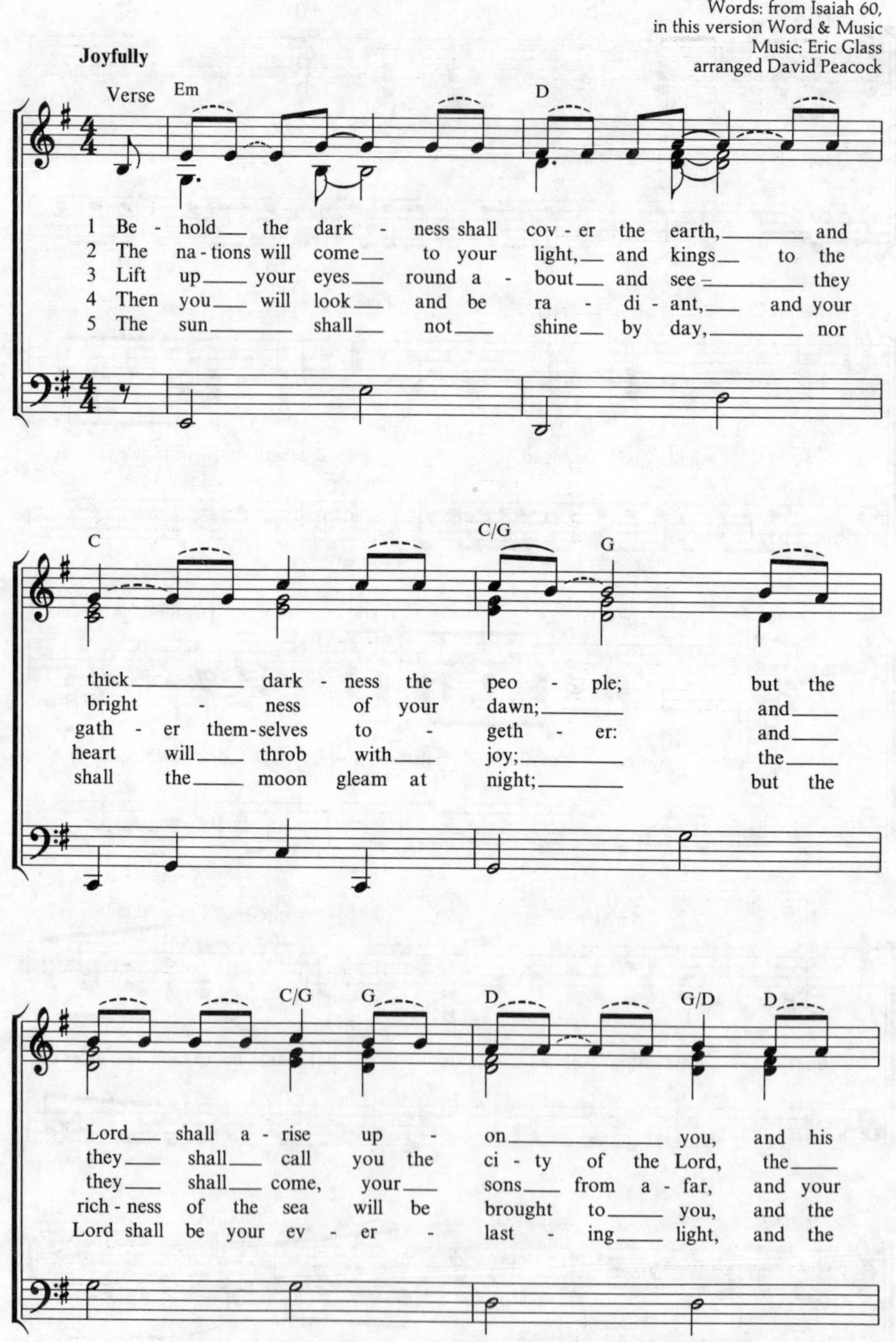
Words: from Isaiah 60,
in this version Word & Music
Music: Eric Glass
arranged David Peacock
Joyfully
Verse
Em
D
1 Be - hold the dark - ness shall cov - er the earth, and
2 The na - tions will come to your light, and kings to the
3 Lift up your eyes round a - bout and see they
4 Then you will look and be ra - di - ant, and your
5 The sun shall not shine by day, nor
C
C/G
G
thick dark - ness the peo - ple; but the
bright - ness of your dawn; and
gath - er them - selves to - geth - er: and
heart will throb with joy; the
shall the moon gleam at night; but the
C/G
G
D
G/D
D
Lord shall a - rise up - on you, and his
they shall call you the ci - ty of the Lord, the
they shall come, your sons from a - far, and your
rich - ness of the sea will be brought to you, and the
Lord shall be your ev - er - last - ing light, and the

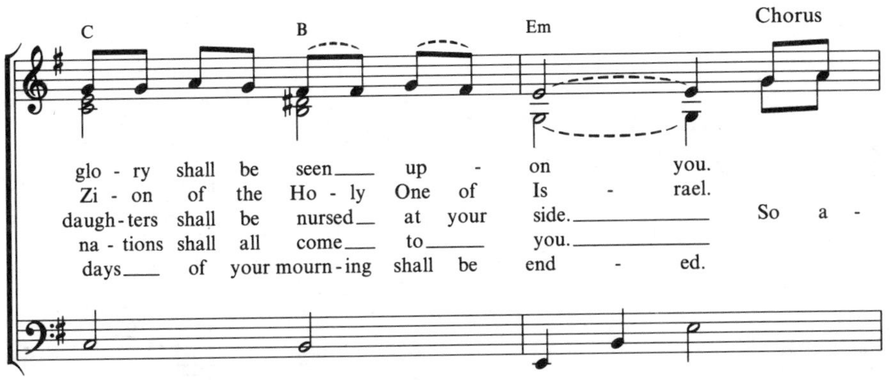

Chorus
C
B
Em
glo - ry shall be seen up - on you.
Zi - on of the Ho - ly One of Is - rael.
daugh-ters shall be nursed at your side. So a -
na - tions shall all come to you.
days of your mourn-ing shall be end - ed.

G C/G G D G/D D C
- rise, shine for your light is come and the glo - ry of the Lord is

B G C/G G D G/D D
ri - sen; so a - rise, shine for your light is come and the

C B Em
glo - ry of the Lord is up - on you!

33 Bethlehem, the chosen city

Words: Michael Perry
Music: Norman Warren

Plainsong feel
Em Am Bm7 Em
1&4 Beth - le - hem, the cho - sen ci - ty of our God,
2 Is - rael's land had suf - fered much in grief and pain
3 Ju - dah's hills their age - long vi - gil si - lent kept,
Am D Em7 Am
where the stem of faith - ful Jes - se du - ly flowered:
till the hand of God should touch the earth a - gain;
God ful - filled his pledge while Is - rael sul - len slept;
C Bm7/C C Em7/B Am Em7/G
there Mes - si - ah in a man - ger hum - bly lay,
then the roy - al star of Ja - cob would a - rise,
on - ly shep - herds watch - ing brave - ly through the night
C Am Bm7 Em
born of Ma - ry, born for us on Christ - mas Day!
Da - vid's scep - tre soon ap - pear be - fore their eyes.
found their Shep - herd, stooped to see the in - fant light.

34 Bethlehem, we come to bring

Words: after B de La Monnoye
Paul Wigmore
Music: Burgundian melody
arranged David Peacock

Patapan
Capo 1(G)
Lively
1 Beth - le - hem, we come to bring mer-ry dan - ces for your king!
2 Ma - ry, may we come to sing mer-ry songs to Christ our king?
3 Christ-ian peo-ple, now we say mer-ry Christ-mas on this day!
Step by step and drum by drum, pat-a-pat-a - pan, pat-a-pat-a - pan; step by step and drum by
drum step-ping brave-ly, here we come!
drum step-ping soft - ly, here we come!
drum step-ping glad - ly, here we come!

35 Bethlehem, what greater city

Stuttgart

Words: after Prudentius (348–c.413)
Michael Perry
Music: C F Witt (1660–1716)
arranged Kenneth D Smith, descant David Iliff

D G Am D7 G
1 Beth - le - hem, what great - er ci - ty
2 Was there ev - er beau - ty bright - er
3 From the East come men of learn - ing:
4 Migh - ty king their gold pro - claims him,

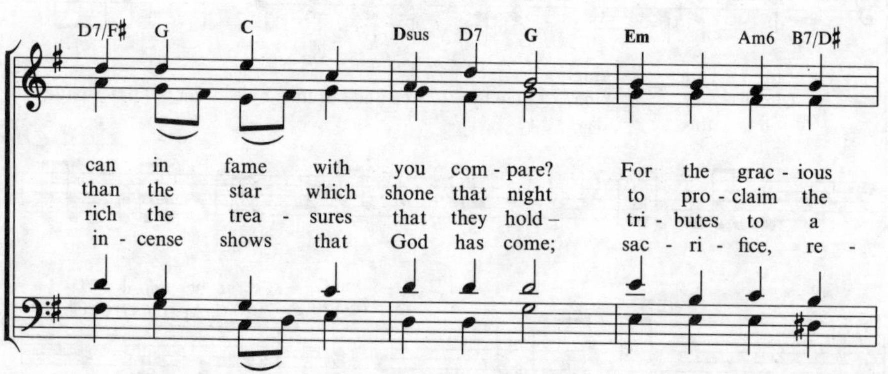
D7/F♯ G C Dsus D7 G Em Am6 B7/D♯
can in fame with you com - pare? For the grac - ious
than the star which shone that night to pro - claim the
rich the trea - sures that they hold – tri - butes to a
in - cense shows that God has come; sac - ri - fice, re -

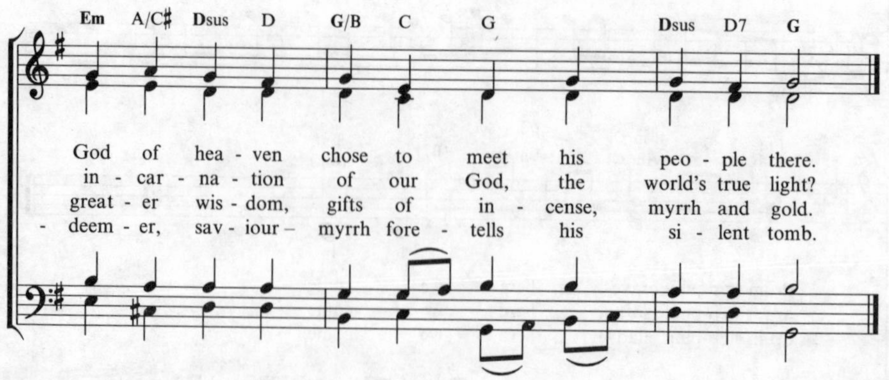
Em A/C♯ Dsus D G/B C G Dsus D7 G
God of hea - ven chose to meet his peo - ple there.
in - car - na - tion of our God, the world's true light?
great - er wis - dom, gifts of in - cense, myrrh and gold.
- deem - er, sav - iour – myrrh fore - tells his si - lent tomb.

D7 G Am D7 G
5 Je - sus Christ, to you be glo - ry,
5 Je - sus Christ, to you be glo - ry,

D/F♯ G C Dsus D7 G Em Am6 B7/D♯
Lord of lords whom we a - dore with the Fa - ther
Lord of lords whom we a - dore with the Fa - ther
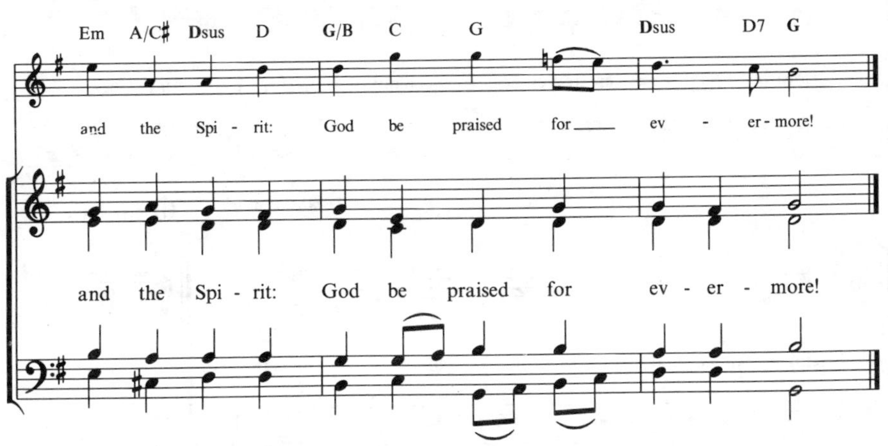
Em A/C♯ Dsus D G/B C G Dsus D7 G
and the Spi - rit: God be praised for ev - er - more!
and the Spi - rit: God be praised for ev - er - more!

36 Bless the Lord, O my soul

From Psalm 103
Words and music: Unknown
Music arranged David Peacock
With majesty
G C E7 A
Bless the Lord, O my soul, bless the Lord, O my
last time to Coda
D G C Am G/D Dsus
soul, and all that is with - in me bless his ho - ly
1. G C G/B D7/A
name; bless the
2. G C D7 G C G C G
name; King of kings (for ev-er and ev-er),
A D A D A B Em B Em B
Lord of lords (for ev-er and ev-er) King of kings (for ev-er and ev-er),
D.S. al Coda
CODA
Am G/B Am/C C/E G/D D7 G C G/B D7/A G
King of kings and Lord of lords! Bless the name.

37 Blow upon the trumpet

Philip James
Words: from Psalm 95, Joel 2 etc.
Michael Perry
Music: Norman Warren
Unison
1 Blow up-on the trum-pet!
2 Blow up-on the trum-pet!
3 Blow up-on the trum-pet!
4 Blow up-on the trum-pet!
clap your hands to - ge-ther, sound a-loud the prai-ses of the
let the na-tions trem-ble; see his power o - bli-ter-ate the
ar-rows in the light-ning fly the storm of bat-tle where he
Christ is sure-ly com-ing, hea-ven's for-ces mo-bil-i-zing
Harmony
Lord your king. He has kept his pro-mise, gran-ting us sal -
sun and moon. This is God's own ar-my bring-ing all to
mar-ches on. Glo-ry to our shep-herd keep-ing us through
at his word. We shall rise to meet him: death at last is
Unison
- va-tion: let his peo-ple ju-bil-ant-ly shout and sing!
judge-ment, for the day of Je-sus Christ is com-ing soon.
dan-ger, set-ting us like je-wels in his ro-yal crown!
con-quered, God gives us the vic-to-ry through Christ our Lord!
v.4

38 Born as a stranger

(FIRST TUNE)

Ginette

Words: Michael Perry
Music: Paul Whitell

With warmth, flowing

F A A7/D Dm7 Gm F/C C7
1 Born as a stranger, laid in a manger,
2 Infant so tender! Gone is the splendour,
3 Lord of all lowliness, perfect in holiness,
A Dm G7 Gm7/C C7/G
Jesus, the Lord of heaven and earth;
Jesus, that graced your Father's home;
Jesus the Christ, of whom we sing;
A Dm Dm/G Gm C Gm/B♭ A7
to us descending, sinners befriending,
our nature wearing, our sorrows bearing,
we bow before you, praise and adore you:
A7/D Dm B♭ F/A Gm7 C9 F
bring us to glory by your birth!
poor and alone for us you come.
be our true saviour and our king!

39 Born as a stranger

(SECOND TUNE)

Schönster Herr Jesu

Words: Michael Perry
Silesian Folk Songs. Leipzig 1842

D Bm D Em A D D Bm F♯m G A D
1 Born as a stran - ger, laid in a man - ger,
2 In - fant so ten - der! Gone is the splen - dour,
3 Lord of all low - li - ness, per - fect in ho - li - ness,
F♯m Bm G A D Em D Asus A
Je - sus, the Lord of heaven and earth;
Je - sus, that graced your Fa - ther's home;
Je - sus the Christ, of whom we sing;
D G D Am B Em Em A G A7/E D
to us de - scend - ing, sin - ners be - friend - ing:
our na - ture wear - ing, our sor - rows bear - ing,
we bow be - fore you, praise and a - dore you:
Bm D G D/F♯ Em/G D/A A7 D
bring us to glo - ry by your birth!
poor and a - lone to us you come.
be our true sav - iour and our king!

40 Born in the night

Mary's child

Words and music: Geoffrey Ainger
Music arranged Norman Warren

Moderately
G Gmaj7 Cmaj7/G Gaug
p
G Em7 Am Cm
1 Born in the night, Ma - ry's child, a
2 Clear shi - ning light, Ma - ry's child, your
3 Truth of our life, Ma - ry's child, you
4 Hope of the world, Ma - ry's child, you're
Gmaj7 Em Am Dsus D7 Bm Em
long way from your home; com - ing in need,
face lights up our way: light of the world,
tell us God is good: prove it is true,
com - ing soon to reign: king of the earth,

Words and music: © Stainer & Bell Limited †

1–3.

Cmaj7 Am 3 D9 G Gmaj7

Ma-ry's child, born___ in a bor-rowed room:
Ma-ry's child, dawn___ on our dark-ened day.
Ma-ry's child, go___ to your cross of wood.
Ma-ry's child, walk___ in our streets a -

3

𝆮.

4.

G Gmaj7 Am7/G 3 G

- gain, walk___ in our streets a - gain.

3

rall. e dim al fine **p**

B♭ version

3
1–3.
4.

41 Brightest and best

Epiphany Hymn

Words: R Heber (1783–1826)
in this version Jubilate Hymns
Music: J Thrupp (1827–1867)

D A/C♯ Bm A/C♯ D
1 Bright - est and best of the suns of the morn - ing,
2 What shall we give him, in cost - ly de - vo - tion?
3 Vain - ly we of - fer each lav - ish o - bla - tion,
4 Bright - est and best of the suns of the morn - ing,
A7/G D/F♯ A7/E D G Em A
dawn on our dark - ness and come to our aid;
Shall we bring in - cense and off - erings di - vine,
vain - ly with gifts would his fa - vour se - cure;
dawn on our dark - ness and come to our aid;
D/F♯ D A A7 Bm E7/G♯ A A7
star of the east, the ho - ri - zon a - dorn - ing,
gems of the mount - ain and pearls of the o - cean,
rich - er by far is the heart's a - dor - a - tion,
star of the east, the ho - ri - zon a - dorn - ing,
D/F♯ Em7 D/F♯ Em7/G D/A A7 D
guide where our in - fant re - deem - er is laid!
myrrh from the fo - rest or gold from the mine?
dear - er to God are the prayers of the poor.
guide where our in - fant re - deem - er is laid!

42 Child in the manger

Words: after M MacDonald (1789–1872)
L Macbean (1853–1931)
Music: Gaelic melody
arranged Noël Tredinnick
Bunessan
Gently
C C/E Dm/F G Dm7 G7
1 Child in the man - ger, in - fant of Ma - ry,
2 Once the most ho - ly child of sal - va - tion
3 Pro - phets fore - told him, in - fant of won - der;
C G/B Am C/E D7/F♯ Gsus G7
out - cast and stran - ger, Lord of all!
gen - tle and low - ly lived be - low:
an - gels be - hold him on his throne:
Em Am Dm7 C/E F Dm7 G7/D
child who in - her - its all our trans - gress - ions,
now as our glo - rious migh - ty re - deem - er,
worth - y our sav - iour of all their prai - ses;
C C/G Dm7/F Gsus G7 C
all our de - mer - its on him fall.
see him vic - tor - ious ov - er each foe.
hap - py for ev - er are his own.

43 Child in a stable

Dans cette etable
Capo 2(G)

Words: after E Flèchier (1632–1710)
Michael Perry
Music: French traditional melody
arranged Norman Warren

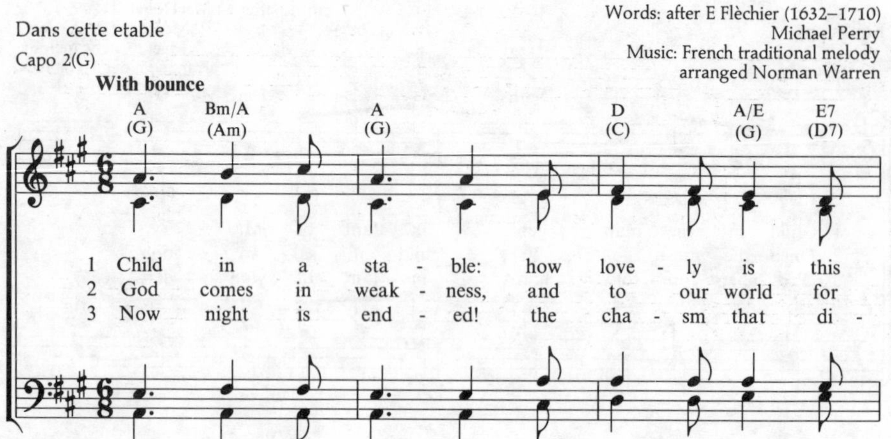

With bounce
A (G) Bm/A (Am) A (G) D (C) A/E (G) E7 (D7)
1 Child in a sta - ble: how love - ly is this
2 God comes in weak - ness, and to our world for
3 Now night is end - ed! the cha - sm that di -

A (G) D (C) A/E (G) E (D)
place where God is a - ble to show such per - fect
love de - scends with meek - ness from realms of light a -
- vides at last is mend - ed, and God with us a -

A (G) Dsus (Csus) D (C) B (A)
grace! No prince - ly babe that smiled or
- bove. This Child shall heal our wrong, for
- bides. For on this hap - py morn new

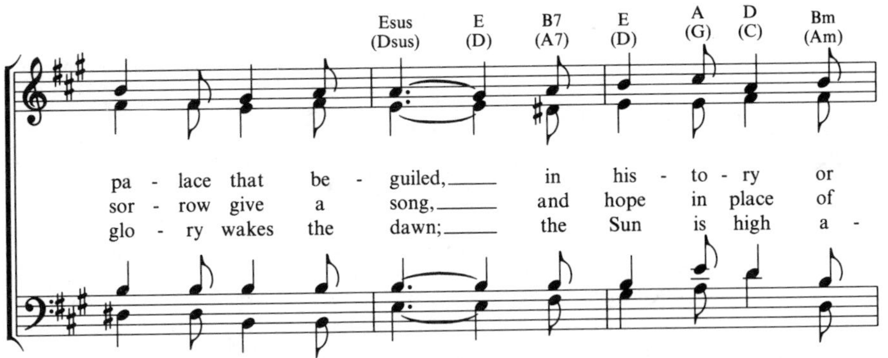
Esus
(Dsus)
E
(D)
B7
(A7)
E
(D)
A
(G)
D
(C)
Bm
(Am)
pa - lace that be - guiled, in his - to - ry or
sor - row give a song, and hope in place of
glo - ry wakes the dawn; the Sun is high a -

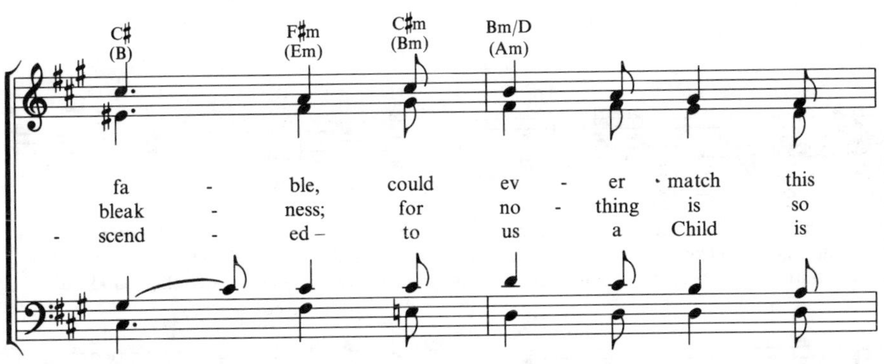
C♯
(B)
F♯m
(Em)
C♯m
(Bm)
Bm/D
(Am)
fa - ble, could ev - er match this
bleak - ness; for no - thing is so
- scend - ed – to us a Child is

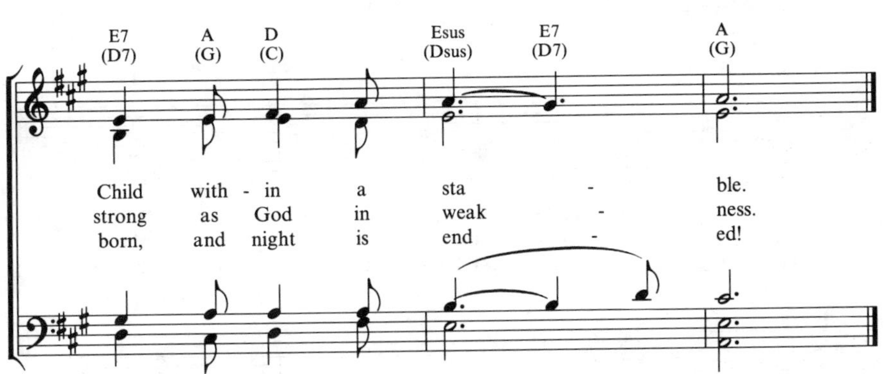
E7
(D7)
A
(G)
D
(C)
Esus
(Dsus)
E7
(D7)
A
(G)
Child with - in a sta - ble.
strong as God in weak - ness.
born, and night is end - ed!

44 Child of gladness

(FIRST TUNE)

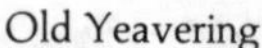
Old Yeavering

Words: Michael Perry
Music: Noël Tredinnick

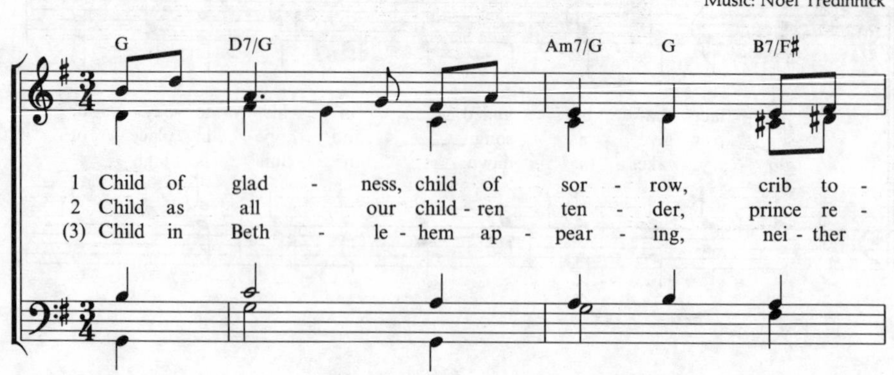
G D7/G Am7/G G B7/F♯
1 Child of glad - ness, child of sor - row, crib to -
2 Child as all our child - ren ten - der, prince re -
(3) Child in Beth - le - hem ap - pear - ing, nei - ther

Em A7 Em7/D D G Dm7 G7
- day and cross to - mor - row; ho - ly child who comes to
- moved from hea - ven's splen - dour: wealth and glo - ry you sur -
hurt nor ha - tred fear - ing: you we wor - ship, God re -

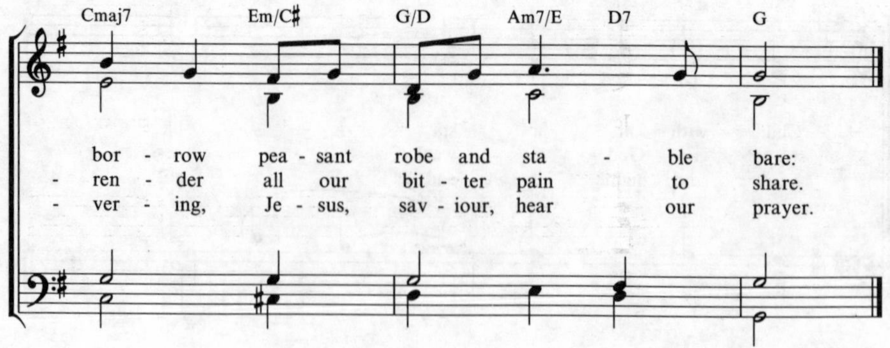
Cmaj7 Em/C♯ G/D Am7/E D7 G
bor - row pea - sant robe and sta - ble bare:
- ren - der all our bit - ter pain to share.
- ver - ing, Je - sus, sav - iour, hear our prayer.

Verse 3 (melody in tenor)

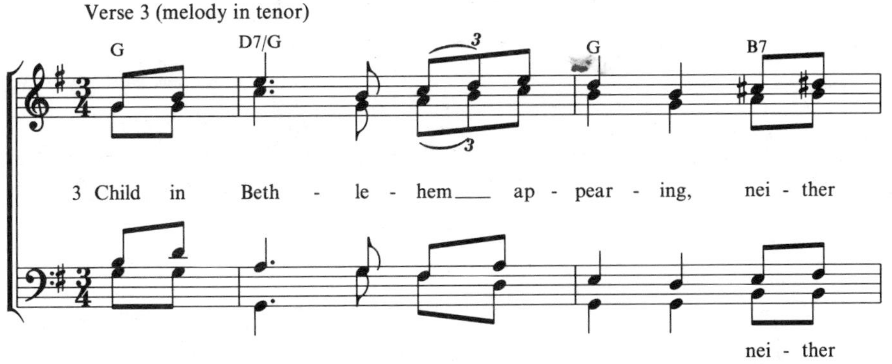
G
D7/G
G
B7
3 Child in Beth - le - hem___ ap - pear - ing, nei - ther
nei - ther

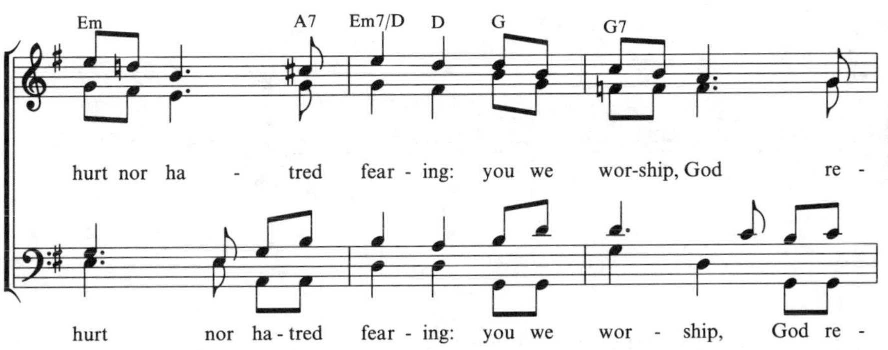
Em
A7
Em7/D
D
G
G7
hurt nor ha - tred fear - ing: you we wor-ship, God re -
hurt nor ha-tred fear - ing: you we wor - ship, God re -

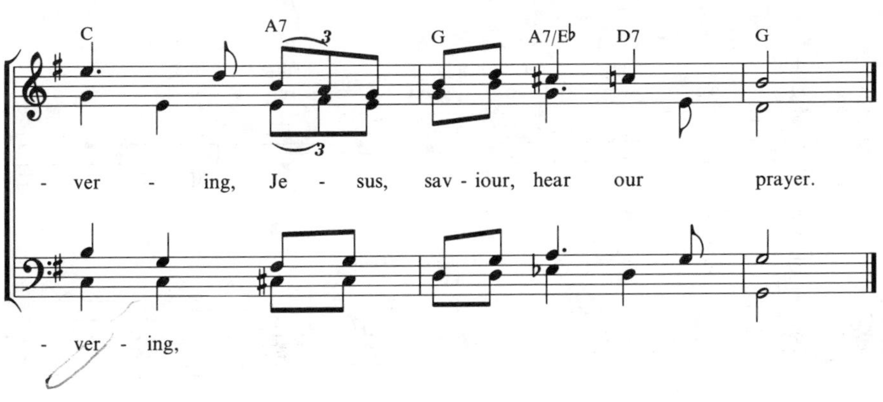
C
A7
G
A7/E♭
D7
G
- ver - ing, Je - sus, sav - iour, hear our prayer.
- ver - ing,

45 Child of gladness

(SECOND TUNE)

Quem pastores laudavere

Capo 3(D)

Words: Michael Perry
Music: German carol melody
arranged R Vaughan Williams (1872–1958)

F (D) C/E (A) F (D) B♭/D (G) B♭ (G) Csus (Asus) C7 (A7)
1 Child of glad - ness, child of sor - row,
2 Child as all our child - ren ten - der,
3 Child in Beth - le - hem ap - pear - ing,
F (D) Gm (Em) C7 (A7) Dm (Bm) G (E) C (A)
crib to - day and cross to - mor - row;
prince re - moved from hea - ven's splen - dour:
nei - ther hurt nor hat - red fear - ing:
F (D) B♭/D (G) F/A (D) B♭ (G) Csus (Asus) C7 (A7) A/C♯ (F♯) Dm (Bm)
ho - ly child who comes to bor - row
wealth and glo - ry you sur - ren - der
you we wor - ship, God re - ver - ing,
Gm (Em) Am (F♯m) Dm (Bm) Gm7 (Em7) C7 (A7) F (D)
pea - sant robe and sta - ble bare.
all our bit - ter pain to share.
Je - sus, sav - iour, hear our prayer.

46 Christ is born for us today

Words: J M Neale (1818–1866), in this version Word & Music
Music: Fourteenth-century German melody arranged Noël Tredinnick

Resonet in laudibus

Capo 5(C)

F (C) Dm (Am) F/A (C) B♭ (F) C (G) Am (Em) Dm (Am)
1 Christ is born for us to - day – rough the man - ger,
2 Child of grace at Ma - ry's knee, he is born to
3 Christ - ians all, re - joice and sing with the com - ing
F/A (C) G7 (D7) C (G) Gm (Dm) C (G) B♭/F (F) F (C) Gm (Dm) Dm (Am)
soft the hay; all who will con - fess him may re -
set us free; he is born our hope to be, our
of our King; let the bells of hea - ven ring to
Am7 (Em7) B♭maj7 (Fmaj7) Gm7 (Dm7) C7 (G7) B♭/F (F) F (C)
- ceive the Son, the ho - ly One of Ma - ry.
God, our Lord, by all a - dored for ev - er.
tell the earth of Je - sus' birth to Ma - ry!

Music arrangement: Noël Tredinnick / Jubilate Hymns

47 Christ is born to be our king

Christ is born
With warmth
Words: Michael Perry
Music: David Sanderson
G Am7/G F♯m7 Em7 C/D Bm/D D7 Em
1 Christ is born to be our king –
2 Shep - herds in the fields at night
3 Christ - ians down the a - ges tell
G/B Am7/E G Am7 D
list - en, as the an - gels sing,
hear the ti - dings, see the light,
Christ can break the powers of hell,
Am Am7 D D7 Bm Bm7 Em Em7
to the hea - vens ech - o - ing,
find the child, in praise u - nite:
so that we may sing as well,
1. Am7 Gmaj7 Am7/E Em/D Am/C Dsus D9 G
'Glo - ry be to God on high!'

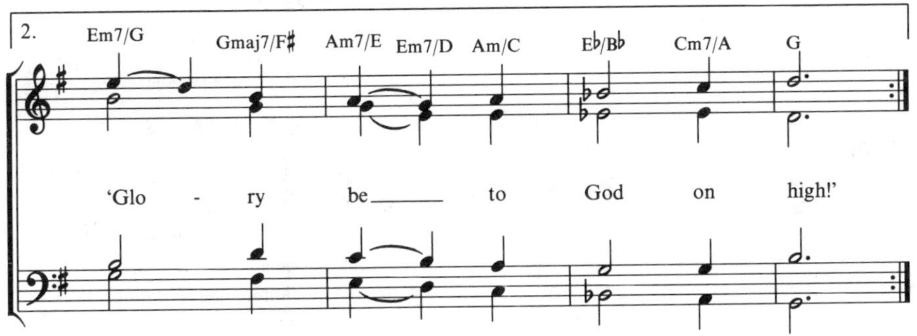
2.
Em7/G
Gmaj7/F♯
Am7/E
Em7/D
Am/C
E♭/B♭
Cm7/A
G
'Glo - ry be___ to God on high!'

3.
Em7/G
Gmaj7/F♯
Am7/E
Em7/D
Am/C
E♭/B♭
Cm7/A
G
'Glo - ry be___ to God on high!'

B♭ melody version

1.
2.
3.

48 Christ is born within a stable

Russian Air

Words: Michael Perry
Music: Russian traditional melody
arranged Norman Warren and David Peacock
descant David Iliff

D Em7 A D Em7/G A D A/C♯ G/B Em/G
1 Christ is born with - in a sta - ble: greet the day when
2 East - ern skies are bright - ly shin - ing, hope has come up -
D/A A7 D D Em7 A D Em7/G A
hea - ven smiled! Shep - herds, fast as they are a - ble,
- on the earth; an - gel songs with ours com - bin - ing
D A/C♯ G/B Em/G D/A A7 D D A7/E D/F♯
run to see the ho - ly Child. Al - le - lu - ia,
tell the world of Je - sus' birth. Al - le - lu - ia,
G/B A/C♯ D A D A7/E D/F♯ G A D
al - le - lu - ia, al - le - lu - ia! A - men.
al - le - lu - ia, al - le - lu - ia! A - men.

Descant or instrument
D Em7 A D Em7/G A D A/C♯ G/B Em/G
3 Peal the bells and spread the joy - ful
3 Peal the bells and set them ring - ing, spread the joy - ful
D/A A7 D D Em7 A D Em7/G A
news a - broad; come with sing - ing
news a - broad; come with faith and join our sing - ing
D A/C♯ G/B Em/G D/A A7 D D A7/E D/F♯
to ac - claim the in - car - nate Lord! Al - le - lu - ia,
to ac - claim the in - car - nate Lord! Al - le - lu - ia,
G/B A/C♯ D A D A7/E D/F♯ G A D
al - le - lu - ia, al - le - lu - ia! A - men.
al - le - lu - ia, al - le - lu - ia! A - men.

49 Christ is surely coming

Land of hope and glory

Words: from Revelation 22
Christopher Idle
Music: E Elgar (1857–1934)
arranged Noël Tredinnick

Capo 3(G)

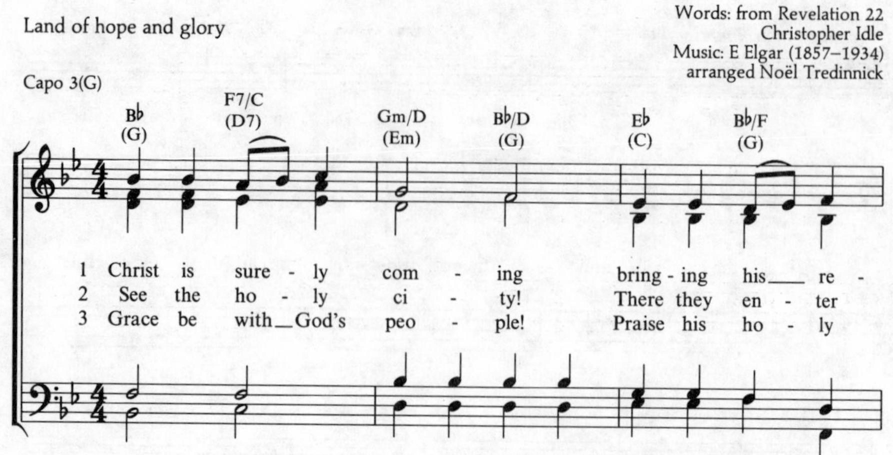

B♭ (G)
F7/C (D7)
Gm/D (Em)
B♭/D (G)
E♭ (C)
B♭/F (G)
1 Christ is sure - ly com - ing bring - ing his__ re -
2 See the ho - ly ci - ty! There they en - ter
3 Grace be with__God's peo - ple! Praise his ho - ly

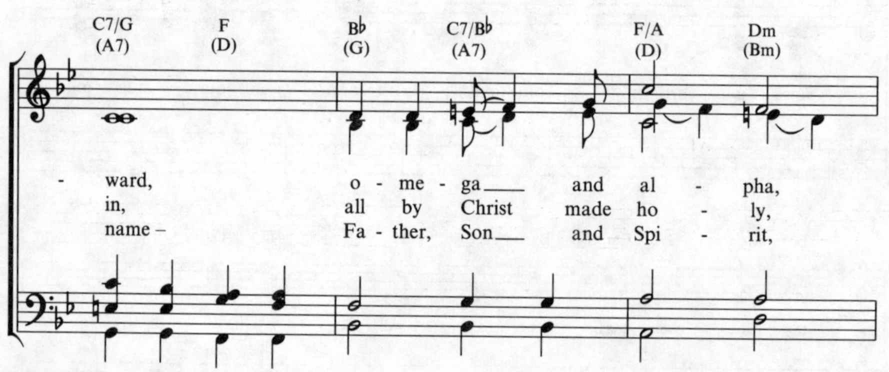

C7/G (A7)
F (D)
B♭ (G)
C7/B♭ (A7)
F/A (D)
Dm (Bm)
- ward, o - me - ga___ and al - pha,
in, all by Christ made ho - ly,
name – Fa - ther, Son___ and Spi - rit,

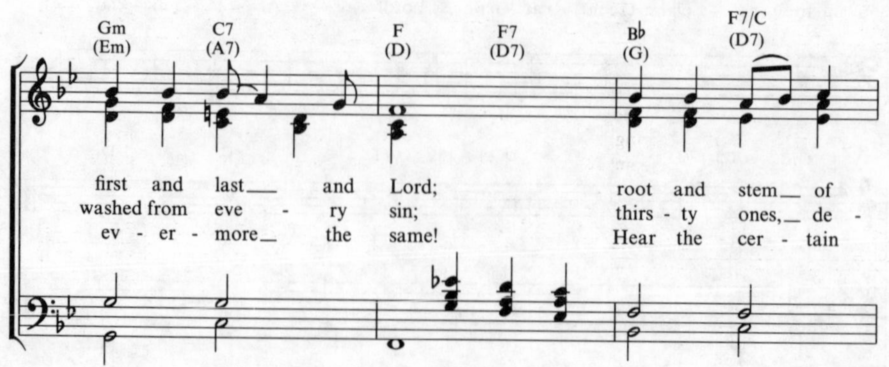

Gm (Em)
C7 (A7)
F (D)
F7 (D7)
B♭ (G)
F7/C (D7)
first and last___ and Lord; root and stem__ of
washed from eve - ry sin; thirs - ty ones,__ de -
ev - er - more__ the same! Hear the cer - tain

Gm/D (Em) B♭/D (G) E♭/G (C) B♭/F (G) C7/E (A7) F7 (D7) B♭ (G) C7/B♭ (A7)
Da - vid, brill-iant morn-ing star – Meet your judge and
- sir - ing all he loves to give: Come for liv - ing
pro - mise from the e - ter - nal home: 'Sure - ly I___ come
F/A (D) Dm (Bm) E♭/G (C) F7 (D7) B♭ (G) B♭7 (G7)
sav - iour, na - tions near___ and far;
wa - ter, free - ly drink, and live;
quick - ly!' – Come, Lord Je - sus, come;
E♭ (C) F7/E♭ (D7) B♭/D (G) Gm (Em) Cm7 (Am7) F7 (D7) B♭ (G)
meet your judge and sav - iour, na - tions near___ and far!
come for liv - ing wa - ter, free - ly drink, and live!
'Sure - ly I___ come quick - ly!' – Come, Lord Je - sus, come!

50 Christ was born on Christmas day

Words and music: P Shaw (1917–1977)
Music arranged David Peacock

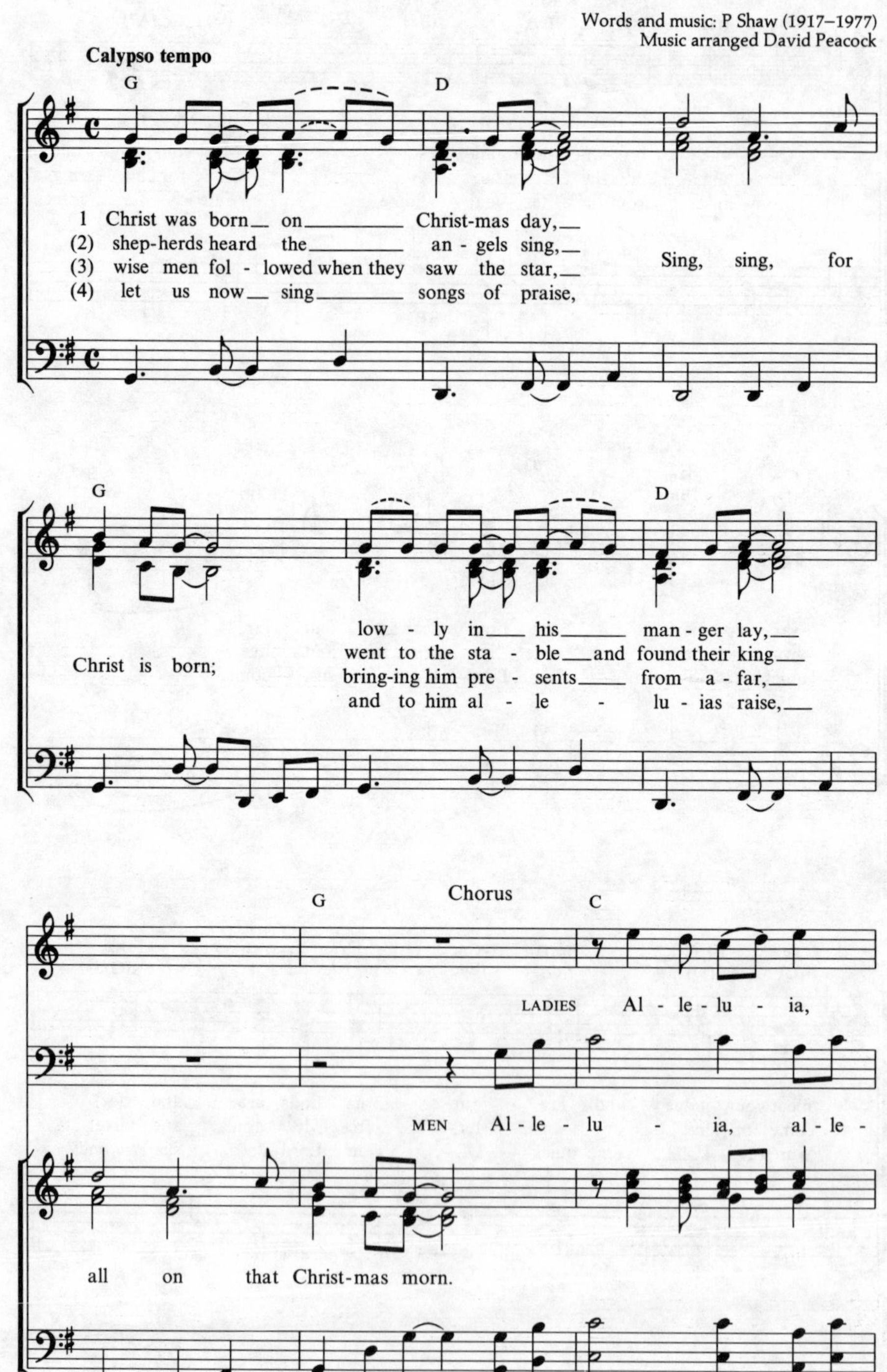
Calypso tempo
G
D
1 Christ was born on Christ-mas day,
(2) shep-herds heard the an - gels sing,
(3) wise men fol - lowed when they saw the star,
(4) let us now sing songs of praise,
Sing, sing, for
G
D
Christ is born;
low - ly in his man - ger lay,
went to the sta - ble and found their king
bring-ing him pre - sents from a - far,
and to him al - le - lu - ias raise,
G
Chorus
C
LADIES Al - le - lu - ia,
MEN Al - le - lu - ia, al - le -
all on that Christ-mas morn.

G/D
D7
al - le - lu - ia, al - le - lu - ia,
- lu - ia, al - le - lu - ia, for
G
G/B
C
Christ is born; al - le - lu - ia,
Christ is born; al - le - lu - ia, al - le -
G/D
G
D7
G
Fine
al - le - lu - ia, all on that Christ - mas morn.
2 The
3 The
4 So
- lu - ia, all on that Christ - mas morn.

51 Christians, awake

Yorkshire

Words: J Byrom (1692–1763)
in this version Word & Music
Music: J Wainwright (1723–1768)
arranged W H Monk (1823–1889)

C G C G7 C G7 C F
1 Christ - ians, a - wake, sa - lute the hap - py morn
2 Then to the watch - ful shep - herds it was told,
3 To Beth - le - hem these shep - herds swift - ly run
4 O may we keep and pon - der in our mind
C F G7 C G7 C Dm C/G G C
on which the sav - iour of the world was born;
who heard the her - ald an - gel's voice: 'Be - hold,
to see the won - der of God's on - ly Son;
God's gra - cious love in sav - ing lost man - kind:
F C Dm C Dm G
rise to a - dore the my - ste - ry of love
I bring good tid - ings of a ho - ly birth
they find with Jo - seph and the low - ly maid,
trace we his foot - steps who re - trieved our loss,

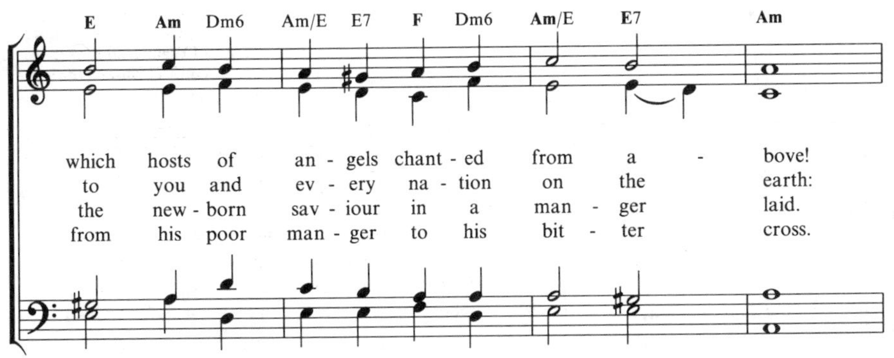
E Am Dm6 Am/E E7 F Dm6 Am/E E7 Am
which hosts of an - gels chant - ed from a - bove!
to you and ev - ery na - tion on the earth:
the new - born sav - iour in a man - ger laid.
from his poor man - ger to his bit - ter cross.

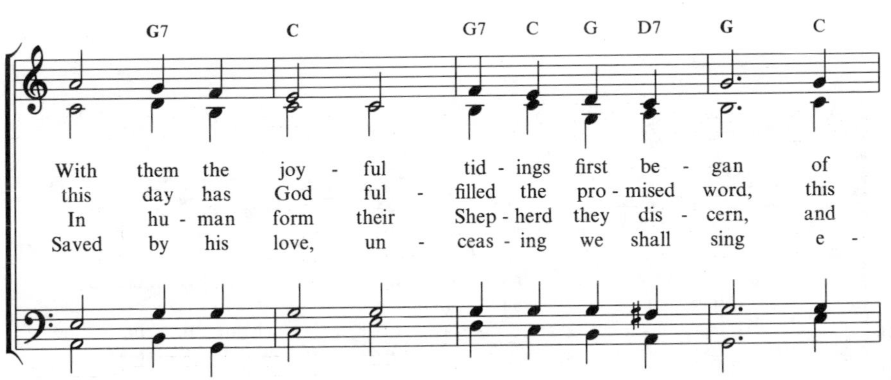
G7 C G7 C G D7 G C
With them the joy - ful tid - ings first be - gan of
this day has God ful - filled the pro - mised word, this
In hu - man form their Shep - herd they dis - cern, and
Saved by his love, un - ceas - ing we shall sing e -

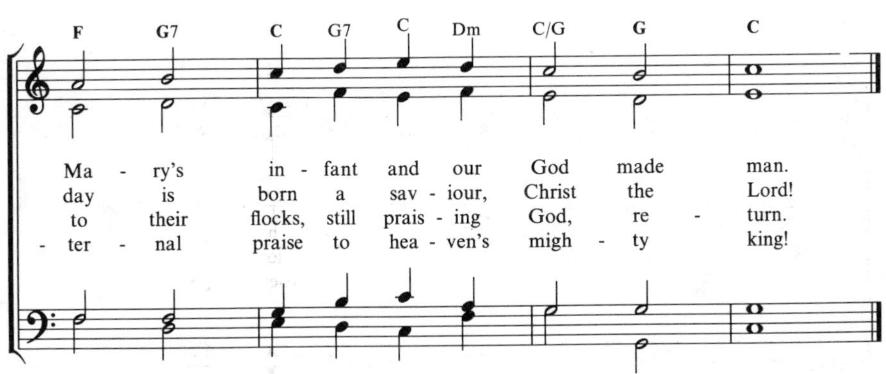
F G7 C G7 C Dm C/G G C
Ma - ry's in - fant and our God made man.
day is born a sav - iour, Christ the Lord!
to their flocks, still prais - ing God, re - turn.
- ter - nal praise to hea - ven's migh - ty king!

52 Christians, make a joyful sound

Resonet in laudibus (extended version)

Capo 3(C)

Words: from the Latin (c.1500)
Michael Perry
Music: Fourteenth-century German melody
arranged Noël Tredinnick

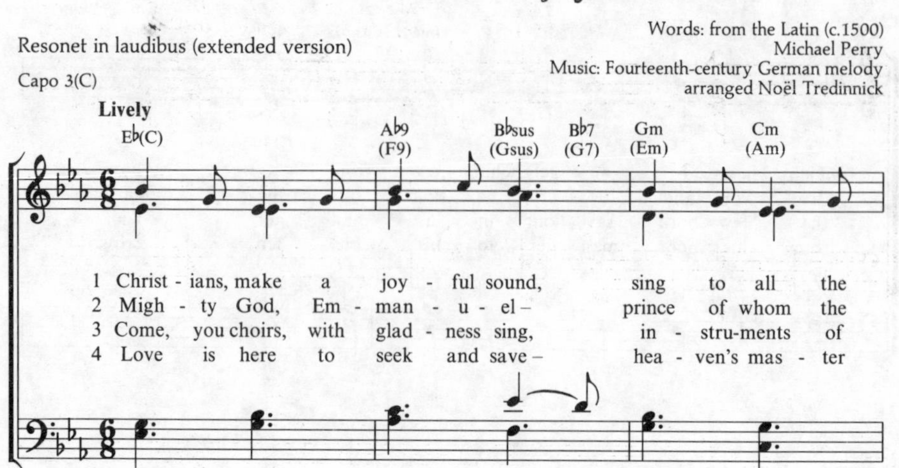
Lively
E♭(C)
A♭9
(F9)
B♭sus
(Gsus)
B♭7
(G7)
Gm
(Em)
Cm
(Am)
1 Christ - ians, make a joy - ful sound, sing to all the
2 Migh - ty God, Em - man - u - el – prince of whom the
3 Come, you choirs, with glad - ness sing, in - stru-ments of
4 Love is here to seek and save – hea - ven's mas - ter

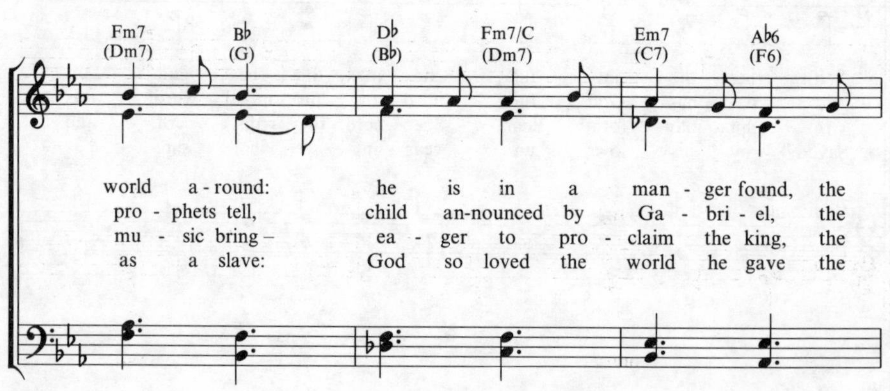
Fm7
(Dm7)
B♭
(G)
D♭
(B♭)
Fm7/C
(Dm7)
Em7
(C7)
A♭6
(F6)
world a - round: he is in a man - ger found, the
pro - phets tell, child an-nounced by Ga - bri - el, the
mu - sic bring – ea - ger to pro - claim the king, the
as a slave: God so loved the world he gave the

Gm7
(Em7)
Cm
(Am)
Fm
(Dm)
B♭
(G)
A♭/E♭
(F)
E♭
(C)
ho - ly One, the in - fant son of Ma - ry.

Chorus
B♭ (G)
Gm (Em)
E♭ (C)
A♭ (F)
B♭ (G)
Cm (Am)
G7 (E7)
Cm (Am)
Edim7 (C♯dim7)
Let the peo - ple join and say that Christ the Lord is
F7 (D7)
B♭ (G)
Cm (Am)
E♭7 (C7)
D♭ (B♭)
Edim7 (C♯dim7)
Cm (Am)
born to - day, till the ve - ry earth shall raise the
D♭ (B♭)
A♭ (F)
Gm (Em)
Cm (Am)
B♭ (G)
E♭ (C)
song of praise: 'No - well, no - well –
A♭ (F)
Cm/G (Am)
Fm7 (Dm7)
B♭sus (Gsus)
B♭ (G7)
A♭/E♭ (F)
E♭ (C)
Christ is born, the in - fant son of Ma - ry!'

53 Christmas for God's holy people

Every star shall sing a carol

Words: Michael Saward
Music: Sydney Carter
arranged David Peacock

Capo 3(Em)
Descant or instrumental part
1 Christ-mas for God's ho - ly peo-ple is a time of joy and peace: so, all Christ - ian men and wo-men, hymns and ca - rols let us raise to our God
2 Child of Ma - ry, vir - gin mo-ther, pea - sant ba - by, yet our king, cra - dled there a - mong the ox - en: joy - ful ca - rols now we sing to our God
3 An - gel ar - mies sang in cho - rus at our Christ's na - ti - vi - ty; he who came to share our na - ture: so we sing with gai - e - ty to our God
4 Shep-herds hur - ried to the man-ger, saw the babe in Beth - le - hem, glo - ri - fied the God of hea - ven: now we join to sing with them to our God
5 In - fant low - ly, born in squa-lor, pro - phet, king and great high priest, Word of God, to us de - scend-ing: still we sing, both great and least, to our God
Chorus

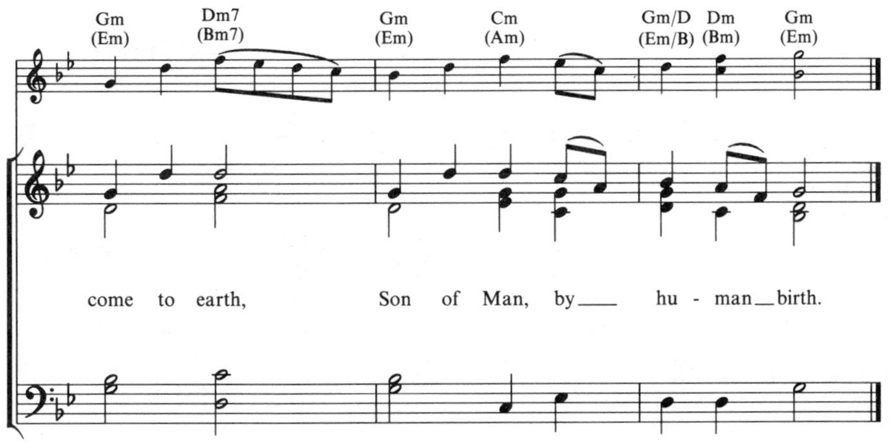
Gm
(Em)
Dm7
(Bm7)
Gm
(Em)
Cm
(Am)
Gm/D
(Em/B)
Dm
(Bm)
Gm
(Em)
come to earth, Son of Man, by___ hu - man___birth.

Suggested percussion accompaniment for chorus

Triangle
Tambourine
tr
(shake)
Side Drum
Cymbals
roll (soft sticks)
Bass Drum

54 Christmas news

Personent hodie

Words: David Mowbray
Music: from *Piae Cantiones*
arranged G Holst (1874–1934)

Brightly
Em
Bm
1 Christ - mas news!
2 Christ - mas news!
3 Christ - mas news!
4 Christ - mas news!
(octaves ad lib.)

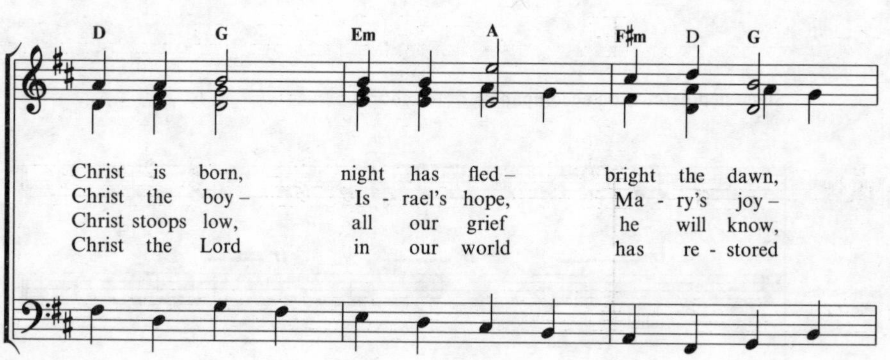
D
G
Em
A
F♯m
D
G
Christ is born, night has fled – bright the dawn,
Christ the boy – Is - rael's hope, Ma - ry's joy –
Christ stoops low, all our grief he will know,
Christ the Lord in our world has re - stored

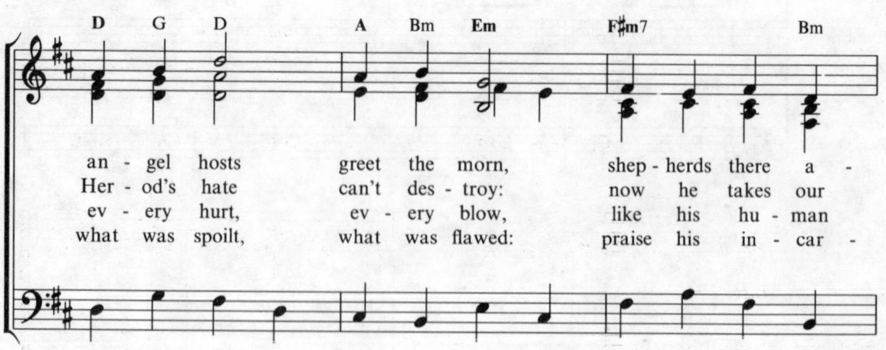
D
G
D
A
Bm
Em
F♯m7
Bm
an - gel hosts greet the morn, shep - herds there a -
Her - od's hate can't des - troy: now he takes our
ev - ery hurt, ev - ery blow, like his hu - man
what was spoilt, what was flawed: praise his in - car -

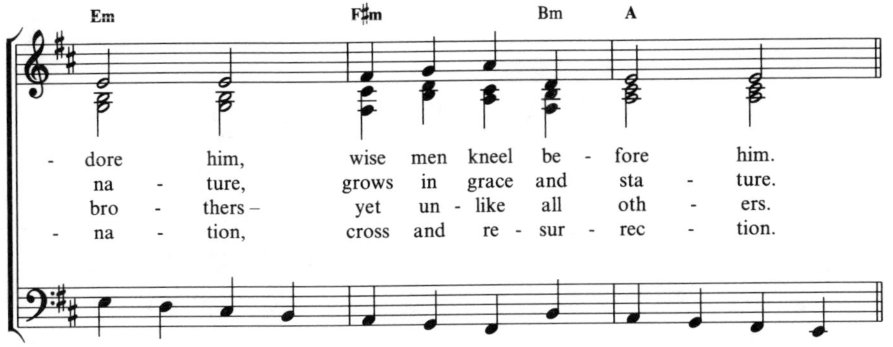
Em
F♯m
Bm
A
- dore him, wise men kneel be - fore him.
na - ture, grows in grace and sta - ture.
bro - thers – yet un - like all oth - ers.
- na - tion, cross and re - sur - rec - tion.

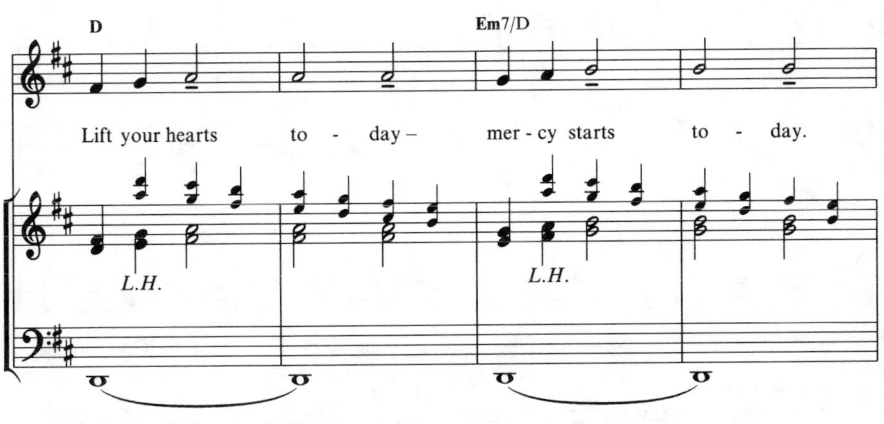
D
Em7/D
Lift your hearts to - day – mer - cy starts to - day.
L.H.
L.H.

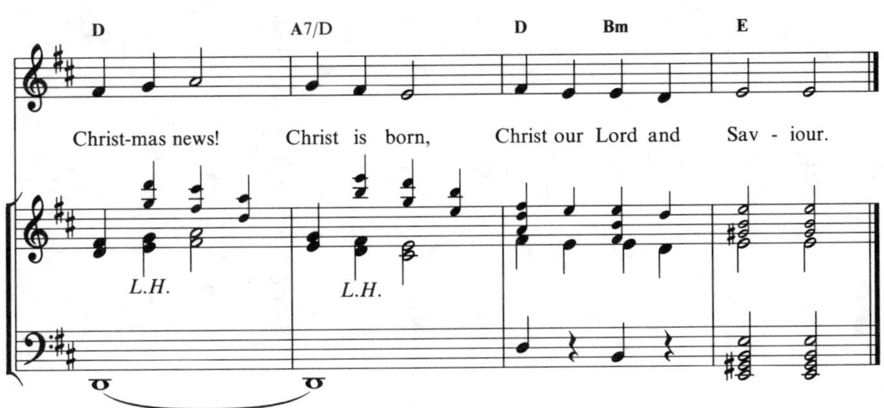
D
A7/D
D
Bm
E
Christ-mas news! Christ is born, Christ our Lord and Sav - iour.
L.H.
L.H.

55 Clap your hands

♩ = 120
With excitement

From Psalm 47
Words and music: Herbert Chappell

Dm7/G
(marcato)
F/G
Dm7/G
ff
(stacc.)
(sim. stacc.)
F/G
Dm/G
C6
C
p
SOLO
Clap your hands,
clap your hands;
shout to God with the
G7/C
voice of tri - umph.
ALL
Clap your hands,
clap your hands;

C6 C G7/C C Ab/Eb Db/Eb
shout to God with the voice of tri-umph. For the Lord most high is
sfz ff
Ab/Eb Db/Eb Ab/Eb Db/Eb
pow-er-ful. He's the king of all the earth. For the Lord most high is
ff
sfz
Ab/Eb Db/Eb Dm7/G F/G
pow-er-ful. He's the king of all the earth.
(stacc.)
Dm7/G F/G Dm/G

C6
C
C6
C
C6
C
G7/C
C
He'll sub-due the peo-ple un-der us, and the na-tions un-der our feet.
p subito
C6
C
C6
C
C6
C
G7/C
C
p
He'll sub-due the peo-ple un-der us, and the na-tions un-der our feet.
Fmaj7
G7
Cmaj7
C6
God is gone up with a shout,
f
Fmaj7
G7
Cmaj7
and the Lord with sounds of trum-pets.

Fmaj7
G7
God is gone up with a shout,
Cmaj7
C6
Fmaj7
G7
and the Lord with sounds of
Dm7/G
F/G
Dm7/G
trum-pets.
F/G
Dm/G
C6
C
C6
C
Clap your hands, clap your hands,

C6 C G7/C C C6 C C6 C
shout to God with the voice of tri-umph. Clap your hands, clap your hands,
C6 C G7/C C D♭maj7
shout to God with the voice of tri - umph. O clap your
ff
C6
hands. your hands.
O clap your hands.
8va
fff

56 Clap your hands, you people

From Psalm 47
Words and music: Judy Davies
Music arranged David Peacock

Joyfully

C Am7 F G7 C Am7 F Em/G G7/F

Clap your hands, you peo-ple; shout to God with a voice of tri-umph!

E7 Am/C Am A♭ C/G Dm7 Gsus G7 C *Fine*

Sing to God, sing prai - ses,_ for he is high-ly ex - al - ted!

Verses

Am F Dm G C Am7 F Gsus G7/F

1 For the Lord most high is migh-ty, he is king in all the earth;
2 God in ma - jes - ty is reig-ning: praise the Lord with shout and song!
3 Kings and no - bles, pay him hom-age, bow be - fore_ his ho - ly throne:

E Am/E E Am D/F♯ C/E D G ***D.C.***

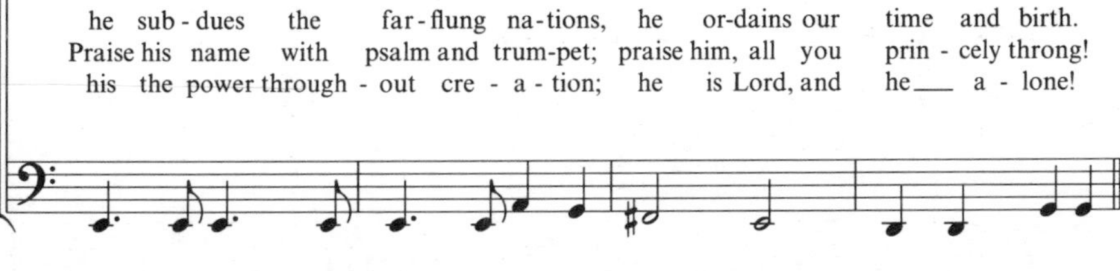
he sub - dues the far - flung na - tions, he or-dains our time and birth.
Praise his name with psalm and trum-pet; praise him, all you prin - cely throng!
his the power through - out cre - a - tion; he is Lord, and he_ a - lone!

57 Clothed in kingly majesty

Kingly majesty
Capo 3(G)

Words: from Psalm 93
Michael Saward
Music: Norman Warren

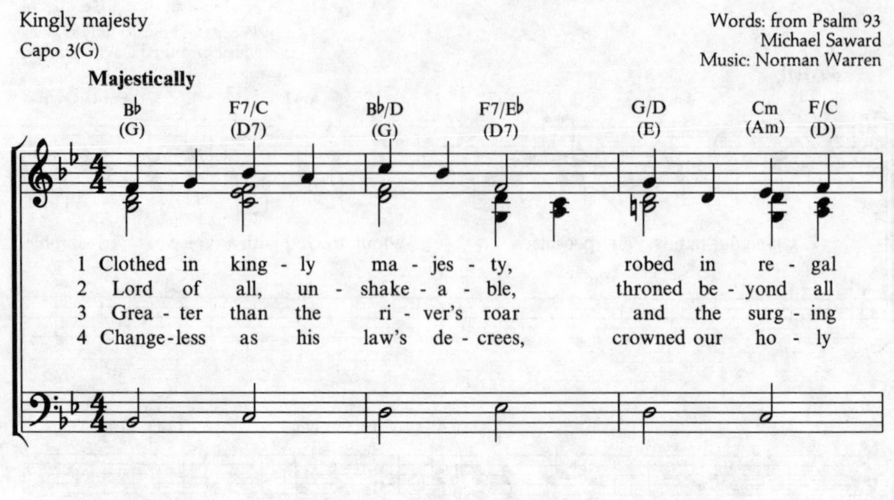

Majestically
B♭ (G) F7/C (D7) B♭/D (G) F7/E♭ (D7) G/D (E) Cm (Am) F/C (D)
1 Clothed in king - ly ma - jes - ty, robed in re - gal
2 Lord of all, un - shake - a - ble, throned be - yond all
3 Grea - ter than the ri - ver's roar and the surg - ing
4 Change-less as his law's de - crees, crowned our ho - ly

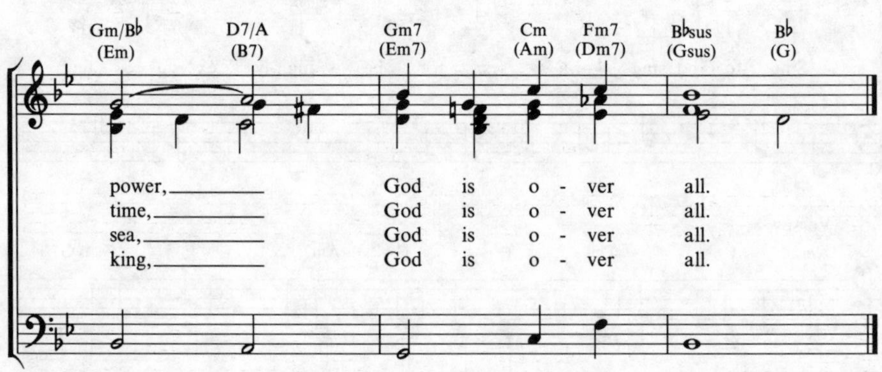

Gm/B♭ (Em) D7/A (B7) Gm7 (Em7) Cm (Am) Fm7 (Dm7) B♭sus (Gsus) B♭ (G)
power, God is o - ver all.
time, God is o - ver all.
sea, God is o - ver all.
king, God is o - ver all.

4 part B♭ brass accompaniment

marcato

58 Come all you good people

Gallery Carol
Capo 5(C)
Brightly
From an old Dorset Carol
Words: Michael Saward
Music: English traditional melody
arranged David Peacock
1 Come all you good people and burst into song! be joyful and happy, your praises prolong; remember the birthday of Jesus our king,
2 His mother, a virgin so gentle and pure, was told of God's promise, unchanging and sure, foretelling the birthday of Jesus our king,
3 To Bethlehem hurried the shepherds amazed, with stories of angels and heavens that blazed, proclaiming the birthday of Jesus our king,
4 So come let us honour the babe in the hay and give him our homage and worship today, recalling the birthday of Jesus our king,
who brings us salvation: his glory we sing.

59 Come and hear the joyful singing

Nos Galan
Capo 3(C)
Words: Michael Perry
Music: Welsh traditional melody
arranged David Peacock
Joyfully
Instrumental obligato (8ve higher ad lib.)
E♭ (C) B♭ (G) Cm (Am) B♭/D (G) E♭ (C)
Fm/A♭ (Dm) B♭7 (G7) E♭ (C) Fm/A♭ (Dm) E♭/B♭ (C) B♭7 (G7) E♭ (C) E♭ (C) B♭ (G)
Cm (Am) B♭/D (G) E♭ (C) Fm/A♭ (Dm) B♭7 (G7) E♭ (C) Fm/A♭ (Dm)
1 Come and hear the joy - ful sing - ing,
2 An - gels of his birth are tell - ing,
3 Choir and peo - ple, shout in won - der,
Al - le - lu - ia, glo - ri - a, set the bells of
Al - le - lu - ia, glo - ri - a, prince of peace all
Al - le - lu - ia, glo - ri - a, let the mer - ry
heav - en ring - ing: al - le - lu - ia,
powers ex - cel - ling; al - le - lu - ia,
or - gan thun - der; al - le - lu - ia,

Eb/Bb Bb7 Eb Bb7 Eb Bb/D
(C) (G7) (C) (G7) (C) (G)
glo - ri - a, God the Lord has shown us fa - vour –
glo - ri - a, death and hell can not de-feat him:
glo - ri - a, thank our God for love a-maz - ing,
Eb Bb/D Cm Bb7/F F7 Bb7 Eb/G Bb7/F Eb Bb/D
(C) (G) (Am) (G7) (D7) (G7) (C) (G7) (C) (G)
al - le - lu - ia, glo - ri - a, Christ is born to
al - le - lu - ia, glo - ri - a, go to Beth - le -
al - le - lu - ia, glo - ri - a, Fa - ther, Son and
Cm Fm/Ab G Cm Fm/Ab Bb7/F Eb/G Fm/Ab Eb/Bb Bb7 Eb
(Am) (Dm) (E) (Am) (Dm) (G7) (C) (Dm) (C) (G7) (C)
be our sav - iour. Al - le - lu - ia, glo - ri - a!
- hem and greet him. Al - le - lu - ia, glo - ri - a!
Spi - rit prais - ing. Al - le - lu - ia, glo - ri - a!

60 Come and hear the news . . .

Paschal Procession

1
Come and hear the
2
'Go to - day, find your re-deem - er:
3
An - gels sing, good news they bring,
go to Beth - le-hem and find him ly - ing in a
4
Let's go to Beth - le-hem and find him; the
ly - ing in a man - ger –
Christ the
5
Prai - ses sing to our King
prai - ses sing to our King for his
6
'Glo - ry in the
peace on earth, good
Capo 3(D)
F (D)
Gm (Em)
C (A)
F (D)
Keyboard

The piece works well with any combination of these lines. With small numbers, try singing just two or three. Divide the congregation into groups. . . .

. . . (Christmas Procession)

Words: from Luke 2
Michael Perry
Music: Christopher Walker

news, the news of Christ-mas joy for all peo - ple!
he is born in Beth - le - hem!'
joy - ful news of the sav - iour:
man - ger – Christ the Lord! List - en . . .
sav - iour pro - phets have fore - told. He is
sav - iour who is born for us: let's . . .
praise to the Prince of peace. Let us
name is Won - der - ful Coun - sel - lor, so . . .
high - est heaven;
will to all!'
B♭ (G)
Gm (Em)
C7 (A7)

. . . Each group repeats its line again and again. To start with, establish line 1 firmly, then add others gradually, saving line 6 to the last. Lines 3, 4, and 5 can be sung in canon.

61 Come and join the celebration

Celebrations

Words and music: Valerie Collison
Music arranged David Peacock

Lively
C C/E F F/A C C/E
Instrumental obligato
Chorus
Come and join the cel - e-bra - tion – it's a
F Dm7 G C C/E F F/A C
ve - ry spe - cial day; come and share our ju - bil - a - tion –
Am7 F G7 C Fine G7
there's a new king born — to - day! —
Verses
1 See the
2 Wise men
3 'God is

C/G F Dm7 G7 C
shep - herds hur - ry down to Beth - le - hem,
jour - ney, led to wor-ship by a star,
with us!' – round the world the mes - sage bring;
Dm/F Dm G7 C C/E
gaze in won - der
kneel in hom - age,
he is with us –
D.C.
D7 G7
at the Son of God who lies be - fore them:
bring - ing pre - cious gifts from lands a - far, so
'Wel - come!' all the bells on earth are peal - ing:

62 Come and see the shining hope

Marching through Georgia

Words: from Revelation 4–5
Christopher Idle
Music: American traditional melody
arranged David Wilson and David Peacock

G C G
1 Come and see the shin - ing hope that Christ's a - post - le saw;
2 All the gifts you send us, Lord, are faith - ful, good, and true;
3 Po - wer and sal - va - tion all be - long to God on high!
C G/B Asus A Dsus D7
on the earth, con - fus - ion, but in heaven an o - pen door,
ho - li - ness and right - eous - ness are shown in all you do:
So the migh - ty mul - ti - tudes of hea - ven make their cry,
G G7 C G Am7 B7/F♯ E7
where the liv - ing crea - tures praise the Lamb for ev - er - more:
who can see your great - est Gift and fail to wor - ship you?
sing - ing Al - le - lu - ia! where the ech - oes ne - ver die:
Am D7 Gsus G
Love has the vic - tory for ev - er!
Love has the vic - tory for ev - er!
Love has the vic - tory for ev - er!

Chorus

G/B
C
G
A - men, he comes! to bring his own re-ward! A -

Bm
Asus/E
A7
Dsus
D
- men, praise God! for just - ice now re - stored;

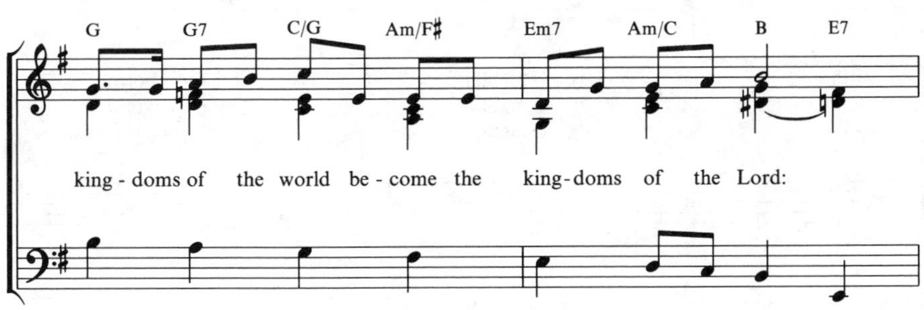
G
G7
C/G
Am/F♯
Em7
Am/C
B
E7
king - doms of the world be - come the king-doms of the Lord:

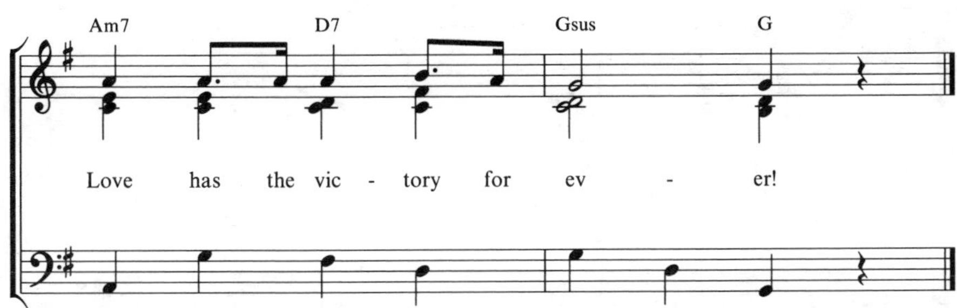
Am7
D7
Gsus
G
Love has the vic - tory for ev - er!

63 Come and sing the Christmas story

All through the night
Words: Michael Perry
Music: Welsh traditional melody
arranged David Peacock
Instrumental obligato
G C G/B Am D
1 Come and sing the Christ - mas sto - ry
2 Je - sus, Sav - iour, child of Ma - ry
3 Lord of all! Let us ac - claim him
Am/C Am D7 G C G/B
this ho - ly night! Christ is born: the
this ho - ly night, in a world con -
this ho - ly night; king of our sal -
A7 D Am/C Am D7 G G7
hope of glo - ry dawns on our sight.
- fused and wea - ry you are our light.
- va - tion name him, throned in the height.

C/E G C/E G7/D C Am/E E Am E7/B Am/C Em
Al - le - lu - ia! earth is ring - ing with a thou - sand
God is in a man - ger ly - ing, man - hood tak - ing,
Son of Man – let us a - dore him: all the earth is
Cmaj7 Am G/D D7 G C G/B
an - gels sing - ing – hear the mes - sage
self de - ny - ing, life em - brac - ing,
wait - ing for him; Son of God – we
A7 D Am/C Am D7 G
they are bring - ing this ho - ly night.
death de - fy - ing this ho - ly night.
bow be - fore him this ho - ly night.

64 Come and praise the Lord our king

Michael, row the boat

Words: Michael Perry
Music: traditional melody
arranged David Peacock

Flowing
G/A
D
Dmaj7
1 Come and praise the Lord our king, Al - le -
(2) news the an - gels tell, Al - le -
(3) shep - herds make your way, Al - le -
(4) gifts the wise men hold – Al - le -
(5) prai - ses take your part, Al - le -
(6) praise the Lord our king, Al - le -

G
A7/G
D
F♯m
- lu - ia, let the world with ca - rols
- lu - ia, Christ is born, and all is
- lu - ia, find the Son of God to -
- lu - ia, they bring in - cense, myrrh and
- lu - ia, thank him with a joy - ful
- lu - ia, let the world with ca - rols

1-5.
6.
Em
E7
G/A
A7
D
G/A
D
ring. al - le - lu - ia! Hear the
well. al - le - lu - ia! With the
- day. al - le - lu - ia! See the
gold. al - le - lu - ia! In our
heart. al - le - lu - ia! Come and
ring. al - le - lu - ia!

65 Come, let us glorify the Lord

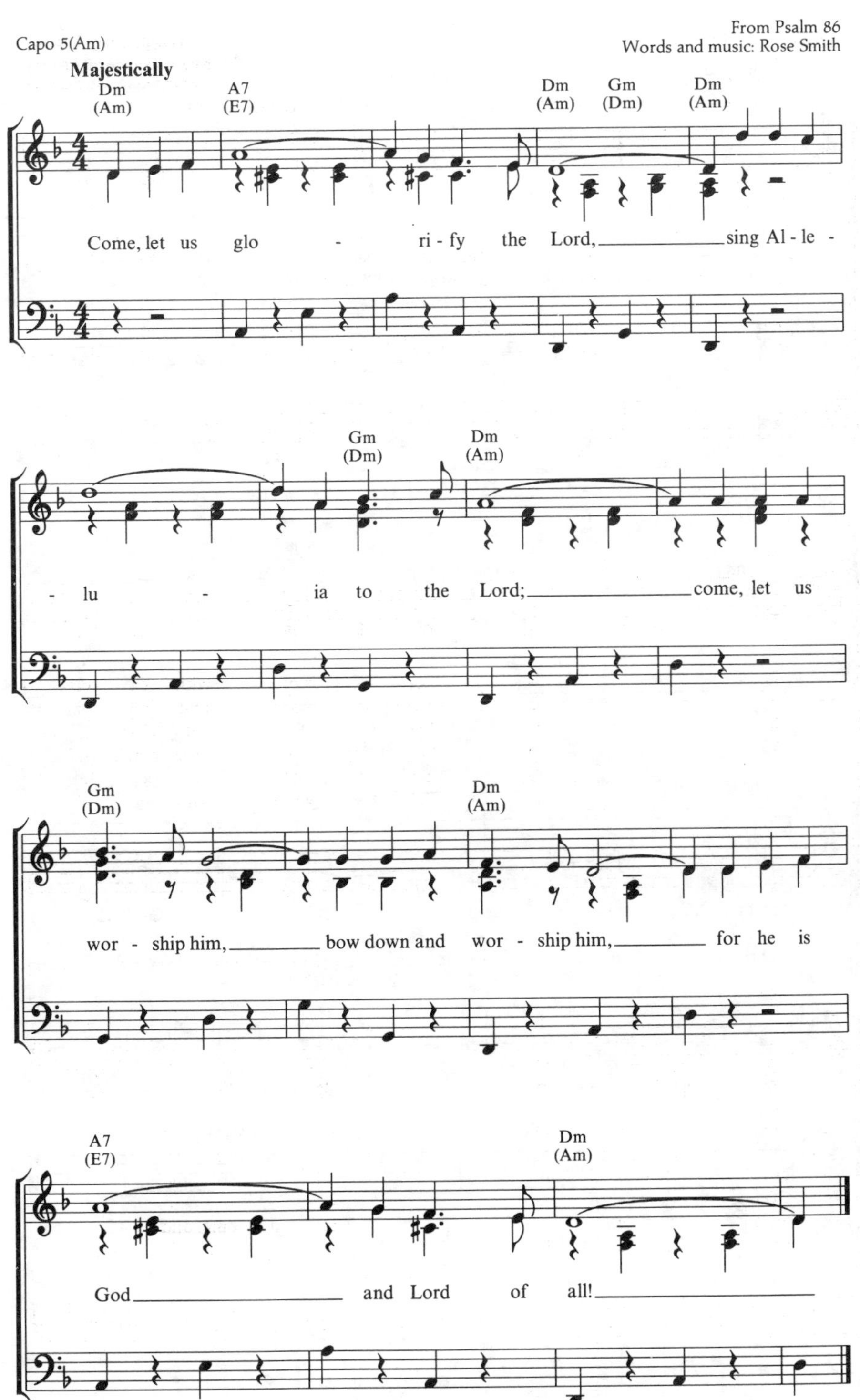

From Psalm 86
Words and music: Rose Smith
Capo 5(Am)
Majestically
Dm (Am) A7 (E7) Dm (Am) Gm (Dm) Dm (Am)
Come, let us glo - ri - fy the Lord, sing Al - le -
Gm (Dm) Dm (Am)
- lu - ia to the Lord; come, let us
Gm (Dm) Dm (Am)
wor - ship him, bow down and wor - ship him, for he is
A7 (E7) Dm (Am)
God and Lord of all!

66 Come, let us kneel before him

Capo 3(C)
Flowing
Words and music: Pat Ogle
Music arranged David Peacock
E♭(C) A♭(F) E♭(C) A♭(F)
1 Come, let us kneel be - fore him,
2 For he has borne our sor - rows,
3 Wake, all who live in Zi - on;
E♭(C) A♭(F) E♭(C) A♭(F)
come, let us praise his name;
and he has borne our griefs, that
sing, all you war - torn lands: the
Gm7(Em7) Cm(Am) A♭(F) B♭7(G7)
wor - ship the Lord our God:
we might walk re - deemed.
Prince of peace is come!
A♭/C(E/A) 1.2. E♭/B♭(C/G) A♭(F) 3. E♭(C)

67 Come, Lord Jesus

Words and music: Norman Warren

Worshipfully
Am
Am/G
F
F/E
Dm7
1 Come, Lord Je-sus, come Lord Je-sus; come and
2 come and
make our hearts your home!
make this world your own!
G7
C
E7
A
F♯m/A
We bow be - fore you, we
love and a - dore you, ac - know-ledge that you are Lord of
D/A
A
F♯m
F
E
E7
all:
Come, Lord Je-sus, come Lord
Je-sus; come and make our hearts your home.
2 come and make this world your own.
Fine
D.C.

68 Come, let us worship

Words: from Psalm 95
Sarah Turner-Smith
Music: Paul Herrington
arranged David Peacock

Gently
Chorus
C G/B Am Em/G
Come, let us wor-ship our re - deem - er,
F Dm Gsus G C
let us bow down be-fore his throne; come, let us
4th time to Coda
G/B Am Am7/G F C/E Dm7 G7
kneel be-fore our ma - ker – ho - ly is his
C C7 F Dm7 G7
name.
1 Come in - to his pres-ence with thanks -
2 We are the peo - ple of his
3 All prai - ses be to God the

Em7 Am Dm G G7/F Csus2 C
- giv - ing, make a joy - ful noise
pas - ture, the sheep of his hand,
Fa - ther, praise to Christ his Son;
C7 F Dm7 G7 Em7
for the Lord is a great
for Christ the Lord is our shep -
praise be to God the Ho - ly Spir -
A D F/G G F/G G7
God – king a - bove all Gods.
- herd, he will lead us home.
- it: bless the Three - in - One!
CODA
Am G F C/E Dm7 G7 C
name. Ho - ly is his name!

69 Come on, let us sing to the Lord

Capo 4(C)
With exuberance
From Psalm 95
Words and music: David Williams
Chorus
E(C)
C♯m(Am)
Come on, let us sing to the Lord,
E(C)
A(F)
B7(G7)
E(C)
come on, let us wor-ship the king; come on, let us
C♯m(Am)
F♯m(Dm)
A(F)
B7(G7)
shout a - loud and come be - fore him with thanks-giv-ing.
last time to Coda
Verse
A(F)
B7(G7)
E(C)
1 We will ex - tol him with
2 Let us kneel be-fore our God in

A(F)
B7(G7)
E(C)
C♯m(Am)
mus - ic and with song, we will
praise and a - dor - a - tion: he is the
G♯m(Em)
A(F)
bow be - fore him; the Lord he is our
king of kings, he is the lord of
B7(G7)
D.C.
CODA
E(C)
God.
Lords.
Easy B♭ clarinet accompaniment
last time to Coda
D.C.
CODA

Arranged David Peacock

70 Come, O long-expected Jesus

Cross of Jesus

Words: C Wesley (1707–1788)
in this version Jubilate Hymns
Music: J Stainer (1840–1901)

G D7/G D7 G Em G/D D7
1 Come, O long - ex - pect - ed Je - sus,
2 Is - rael's strength and con - so - la - tion,
3 Born your peo - ple to de - liv - er,
4 By your own e - ter - nal Spi - rit
G C G D7 G G/D D Em Am D7 G7
born to set your people free! from our fears and
born sal - va - tion to im - part; dear de - sire of
born a child and yet a king; born to reign in
rule in all our hearts a - lone; by your all suf -
Am Em G7 C Am B7 Em G/D D7 G
sins re - lease us, Christ in whom our rest shall be.
ev - ery na - tion, joy of ev - ery long - ing heart:
us for ev - er, now your gra - cious king - dom bring:
- fi - cient me - rit raise us to your glo - rious throne.

71 Come ride with kings

Words: David Mowbray
Music: David Boarder

Fast and lively 𝅗𝅥 = 92
Dm G7 Dm G7 Dm C
Dm Dm
1 Come ride with kings to
(2) join the an - gels
(3) Ma - ry's won - der
(4) ce - le - brate, come
C Dm Am G
Beth - le - hem and kneel in com - pa -
ga - ther - ing and lis - ten to the
o - ver - flow that all God's pro - mi -
dance and sing! This child is here God's

Music: © David Boarder / Jubilate Hymns

Words: © David Mowbray / Jubilate Hymns

Dm
- ny with them; fol - low the shep - herds
songs they sing; help spread the news for
- ses are true; come see by her hu -
peace to bring; his truth and joy for
C Dm Am G
with de - light and find the child they
all to hear of Christ be - neath the
- ma - ni - ty God's pre - sence and di -
all to grant, his king - dom in our
Dm
Chorus
found that night.
shin - ing star.
- vi - ni - ty.
lives to plant.
God so loved the world,

C
he gave his Son man -

1–3.
Dm G7 Dm G7 Dm C
- kind _ to save.

Dm
4.
Dm G7 Dm
2 Come
3 Let
4 Then
- kind _ to save.

72 Come now with awe

Finlandia
Capo 3(C)
Words: Timothy Dudley-Smith
Music: J Sibelius (1865–1957)
1 Come now with awe, earth's an - cient vi - gil keep - ing: cold un - der star - light lies the sto - ny way. Down from the hill - side see the shep - herds creep - ing,
2 Come now with joy to wor - ship and a - dore him; hushed in the still - ness, won - der and be - hold – Christ in the sta - ble where his mo - ther bore him,
3 Come now with faith, the age - long se - cret guess - ing, hearts rapt in won - der, soul and spi - rit stirred – see in our like - ness love be - yond ex - press - ing,
4 Come now with love: be - yond our com - pre - hend - ing love in its ful - ness lies in mor - tal span! How should we love, whom Love is so be - friend - ing?

Eb/Bb (C)
Ab (F)
hear in our hearts the whis - pered news they
Christ whom the pro - phets faith - ful - ly fore -
all God has spo - ken, all the pro - phets
Love rich in mer - cy since our race be -
G (E)
Eb (C)
Cm (Am)
say: 'Laid in a man - ger
- told: High King of a - ges,
heard; born for us sin - ners,
- gan now stoops to save us,
Eb (C)
Bb (G)
Fm (Dm)
lies an in - fant sleep - ing, Christ our Re -
low we kneel be - fore him, star - light for
bear - er of all bless - ing, flesh of our
sighs and sor - rows end - ing, Je - sus our
Eb/Bb (C)
Bb7 (G7)
Eb (C)
- deem - er, born for us to - day.'
sil - ver, lan - tern - light for gold.
flesh, be - hold the e - ter - nal Word!
Sav - iour, Son of God made man.

73 Cradle rocking

Christmas Lullaby
Words and music: Jodi Page Clark
Music arranged David Peacock
Gently
C Em Am Em7 Dm7 G7
1 Cra - dle rock - ing, cat - tle low - ing, bright star
2 Mo - ther Ma - ry, watch - ing care - fully by the
3 Who could guess, to see you lie there, that you
4 Do you know – so weak and help - less – of the
C Dm/F G C Em
guid - ing men to see lit - tle Christ - child
light of one bright star; Bread of hea - ven,
came to bring a sword? Prince of peace, born
grace you bear to us; do you dream yet
Am Em7 Dm7 G7 C Am F G7 C
in the man - ger, light of all the world to be:
soft - ly sleep - ing, gen - tle gift of God to man:
in a man - ger, with a price up - on your soul.
of the king - dom you will some day bring to pass?
Chorus
F C
Al - le - lu - ia, ho - ly Child, ho -

Dm G7 C C7
- san - na in the high - est; glo - ri -
F C Dm
- a, Em-man - u - el, ho - san -
G7 C
1–3.
last time
- na in the high - est! - est!
B♭ version of chorus

74 Come to set us free

Advent Entrance Song

Words and music: Bernadette Farrell

Brightly ♩ = 88+
Chorus
Dm Am Dm G A
Come to set us free, come to make us your own;
Dm Am Dm G A
come to show the way to your peo-ple, your cho - sen:
B♭ C Fmaj7 Dm Gm C Am
o - pen our lives to the light of your pro - mise.

last time to Coda
Bb C Dm Bb
Come to our hearts with heal-ing, come to our minds with po-wer;
Dm Am Dm Am Dm
come to us and bring us your life.
1 You are
2 You are
3 You are
Bb C F Gm7 C Dm
light which shines in dark-ness, Morn-ing Star which ne-ver sets:
hope which brings us cour-age, you are strength which ne-ver fails:
pro-mise of sal-va-tion, you are God in hu-man form:

G 3 F/G G F/G G F/G G F/G
o - pen our eyes which on - ly dim - ly see the truth which
o - pen our minds to ways we do not know, but where your
bring to our world of emp - ti - ness and fear the word we
D.C.
B♭ Gm7 C
sets us free.
Spi - rit grows.
long to hear.
CODA
Dm Am Dm Am Dm
come to us and bring us your life.

75 Down from the height

Purpose

Words: from Philippians 2 *(The Song of Christ's Glory)*
Michael Perry
Music: Noël Tredinnick

With breadth, not too slow
G C Am D Bm Em
1 Down from the height of his glo - ry he came,
2 All through those days his re - solve was the same –
3 Now God has grant - ed him hon - our and fame,
Dm7 G7 Cmaj7 Em7 F/A Bm E7
will - ing - ly leav - ing his right - ful do - main:
Je - sus the ser - vant, the shar - er of pain:
tak - en him up to the high - est to reign:
A D Bm C♯m F♯m
Je - sus was born in the i - mage of man,
per - fect o - be - dience, the path of dis - dain,
'Je - sus is Lord!' ev - ery voice shall main - tain,
Am Dm G7 C Am D7 G
love was his mo - tive and mer - cy his aim.
down to a death of de - ri - sion and shame.
all of cre - a - tion shall bow to his name.

Can also be sung to 'Slane'

76 Darkness like a shroud

Arise, shine

Words and music: Graham Kendrick
Music arranged David Peacock

Subdued, becoming bright

C♯m B/C♯ C♯m A B E
1 Dark - ness like a shroud co - vers the earth,
2 Child - ren of the light, be clean and pure;
3 Here a - mong us now, Christ the Light
4 Like a ci - ty bright, so let us blaze;
C♯m B/C♯ C♯m A B G♯sus G♯
e - vil like a cloud co - vers the peo - ple; but the
rise, you sleep - ers, Christ will shine on you: take the
kin - dles brigh - ter flames in our tremb - ling hearts: Liv - ing
lights in ev - ery street turn - ing night to day: and the
E F♯m7 B E F♯m7
Lord will rise u - pon you, and his glo - ry will ap -
Spir - it's flash - ing two - edged sword and with faith de - clare God's
Word, our lamp, come guide our feet – as we walk as one in
dark - ness shall not o - ver - come, till the full - ness of Christ's
B E C♯m7 F♯m Bsus B
- pear on you, na - tions will come to your light.
migh - ty word; stand up, and in his strength be strong!
light and peace, jus - tice and truth shine like the sun.
king - dom comes, dawn - ing to God's e - ter - nal day.

Chorus
F♯m/B
B
E
G♯m
C♯m G♯m C♯m
A
A - rise, shine, your light has come, the glo-ry of the Lord has
F♯m
A/B
E
G♯m
A G♯m
Amaj7
risen on you; a - rise, shine, your light has come –
A♯dim
E/B
G♯m
1-3.
A
A/B
Je - sus the light of the world has
E
G♯7
4.
A
A♯dim
E/B G♯m
come.
world, Je - sus the light of the
A A♯dim
E/B
G♯m
A A/B
E
world, Je-sus the light of the world has come.

77 Ding dong! Merrily on high

Branle de l'Official
Words: G R Woodward (1848–1934)
Music: sixteenth-century French melody
arranged Noël Tredinnick
G Am Bm G7 C D
1 Ding dong! Mer-ri-ly on high in heaven the bells are
2 E'en so, here be-low, be-low, let stee-ple bells be
3 Pray you, du-ti-ful-ly prime your ma-tin chime, you
G A7 Bm G7
ring - ing. Ding dong! Ve-ri-ly the sky is
swung - en; and i-o, i-o, i-o, by
ring - ers; may you beau-ti-ful-ly rhyme your
C G/B Dsus D7 C/G G Bm7 Em7
riven with an-gels sing - ing:
priest and peo-ple sung - en! Glo -
eve-time song, you sing - ers:
Am7 D7 Gmaj7 Cmaj7 F♯m7 B7
- - - - - - -

Em7 A7 D7 G C Em D7
- - - - ri - a, ho - san - na in ex -
G Dm7 G7 Cm F7
- cel - sis; Glo - - -
Bm7 Em7 Am7 D7 Gmaj7 Cmaj7
- - - - - - -
F♯ Bm G C G/B Dsus D7 C/G G
- - ri - a, ho - san - na in ex - cel - sis!

78 Ding, dong, ring out the carillon

Carol of the Bells
Capo 5(C)
♩ = c.84
Words: I Mawby (1903–1983)
Music: Norman Bearcroft
arranged David Peacock
Descant / instrument
Chorus
F (C) Fmaj7 (Cmaj7) Gm/B♭ (Dm) Gm (Dm) C (G) C/E (G)
Ding, dong, ding, dong, ring out the car - il - lon;
Ding, dong, ring out the car - il - lon;
F (C) Fmaj7 (Cmaj7) G (D) C (G) F (C) Fmaj7 (Cmaj7)
ding, dong, ding, dong, joy is here: ding, dong, ding, dong,
ding, dong, joy is here: ding, dong,
Fine
Gm/B♭ (Dm) Gm (Dm) C (G) C/E (G) F (C) Fmaj7 (Cmaj7) Gm (Dm) C7 (G7) F (C)
let ev - ery care be gone; ding, dong, ding, dong, Christ - mas cheer!
let ev - ery care be gone; ding, dong, Christ - mas cheer!

C
(G)
G7
(D7)
C
(G)
Verses
1 In a man - ger see him ly - ing – lit - tle babe so
2 See the star so clear - ly shin - ing, in the dark - ness
3 Hear the an - gel voi - ces sing - ing, 'Peace on earth, good
G7
(D7)
C
(G)
ding - a - dong ding!
weak and small: on his mo - ther's
of the night; wise men of the
will to men!' All the bells of
G7
(D7)
C
(G)
G7
(D7)
C7
(G7)
D.C.
ding - a - dong - a
care re - ly - ing cra - dled in a cat - tle stall.
east it's guid - ing, by its rad - iance led a - right.
heaven are ring - ing, ec - ho - ing to earth a - gain.

79 Emmanuel, God is with us

Emmanuel
Capo 5(C)
Words and music: Dave Fellingham
With a rocky feel
C/F (G) F (C) C/F (G) F (C)
Em - man - u - el, God is with us, Em -
C/F (G) F (C) F/E (Cmaj7) Dm (Am)
- man - u - el, God is with us. The
B♭maj7 (Fmaj7) Am7 (Em7) Gm (Dm)
Lord of hosts – he is with us, the God of Jac - ob is
Dm (Am) A7 (E7) Dm (Am) B♭ (F) C/B♭ (G7) F/A (C)
our strong - hold, the Lord most high is our re - fuge and strength:

Gsus
(Dm)
C7
(G7)
F
(C)
B♭/F
(F)
F
(C)
Gsus/F
(Dm)
F
(C)
B♭/F
(F)
God is with us, God is

F
(C)
G7sus/F
(Dm)
F
(C)
F♯dim7
(C♯dim7)
G7sus
(Dm7)
Gm
(Dm)
with us dwell-ing in the midst of his

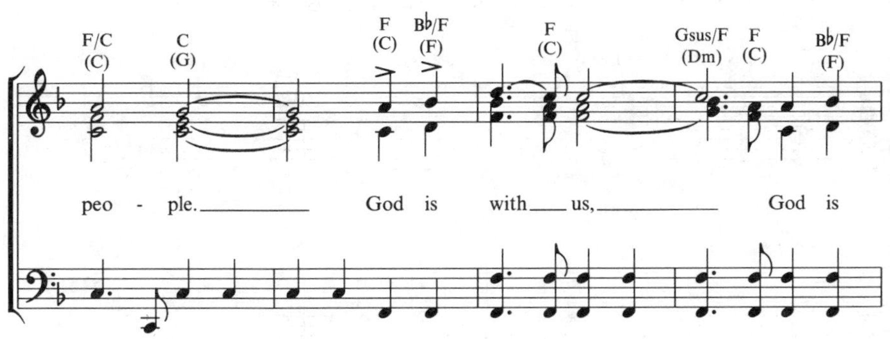
F/C
(C)
C
(G)
F
(C)
B♭/F
(F)
F
(C)
Gsus/F
(Dm)
F
(C)
B♭/F
(F)
peo - ple. God is with us, God is

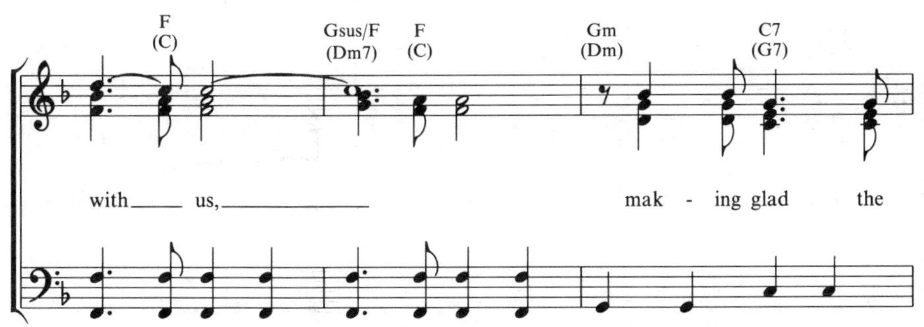
F
(C)
Gsus/F
(Dm7)
F
(C)
Gm
(Dm)
C7
(G7)
with us, mak - ing glad the

Am (Em) Dm (Am) Gm (Dm) C7 (G7) Am (Em) D (A)
ci - ty of God as the ri - ver of life flows from the throne,
B♭ (F) C (G) Dm (Am) C/E (G) F (C) Gm (Dm) C7 (G7)
bring - ing life and strength to all. We shall not be moved
C (G) F (C) B♭ (F) B♭/F (F) F (C) Gsus/F (Dm) F (C) Gm7♭5 (Dm7♭5)
God is with us. Em - man - u - el,
E♭m/G♭ (B♭m) E♭sus/G♭ (B♭m) F6 (Am) Gm7/F (Dm) F/C (G) C (G) F (C) B♭ (F) F (C)
God with us. God is now with us.

80 Emmanuel . . . he is here

From Isaiah 9 and 53
Words and music: Graham Kendrick

With feeling
Chorus
D
D♯dim7
Em
Em-man - u-el — God is with — us, —
Em7
A7
Em-man - u-el — he is
D
here;
Em-man - u-el —
D♯dim7
Em
Em7
— he is a - mong — us; —

last time
Fine
A7
D
Em-man - u-el his king-dom is here.
Verses
D♯dim7
1 Won-der-ful Coun-sell - or, they laughed at his
2 He was des - pised and re -
3 But he was woun-ded for our trans -
4 He was op - pressed, he was af -
Em
Em7
A7
wis - dom, the Migh - ty God
- ject - ed, a man of sor -
- gress - ions, he was bruised
- flic - ted, and yet he o -
D
on a dus - ty road;
- rows ac-quain-ted with grief:
for our in - i - quit - ies:
- pened not his mouth:

D♯dim7
Ev - er - last - ing Fa - ther, a friend of
from him we turned and hid our
on him was the pun - ish - ment that
like a lamb that is led to the
Em
Em7
sin - ners,
fa - ces;
made us whole,
slaugh - ter,
A7
a Prince of peace in a cat - tle stall.
he was des-pised, him we did not es - teem.
and by his stripes we are healed.
like a sheep be - fore his shear - ers he did not speak.
1.3.
D
2.4.
D
D.C.

81 Emmanuel, Emmanuel

From Isaiah 7
Words and music: Bob McGee
Music arranged David Peacock

With warmth
C F G7 C
Em-man - u - el, Em-man - u - el,
A7 Dm Dm7 G7 C
his name is called Em-man - u - el
F G7 Em
God with us, re-vealed in us
A7 Dm Dm7 G7 C
his name is called Em-man - u - el.

82 Empty he came

Kenosis

Words: from Philippians 2 (*The Song of Christ's Glory*)
Gavin Reid
Music: Norman Warren

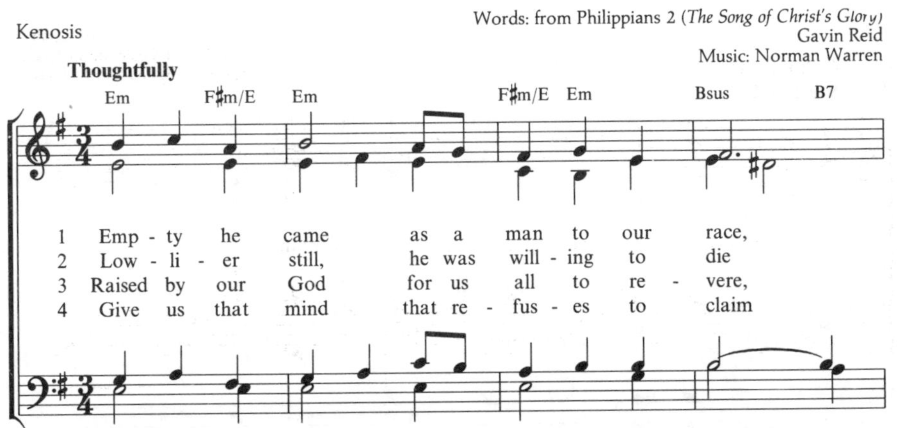
Thoughtfully
Em F♯m/E Em F♯m/E Em Bsus B7
1 Emp - ty he came as a man to our race,
2 Low - li - er still, he was will - ing to die
3 Raised by our God for us all to re - vere,
4 Give us that mind that re - fus - es to claim

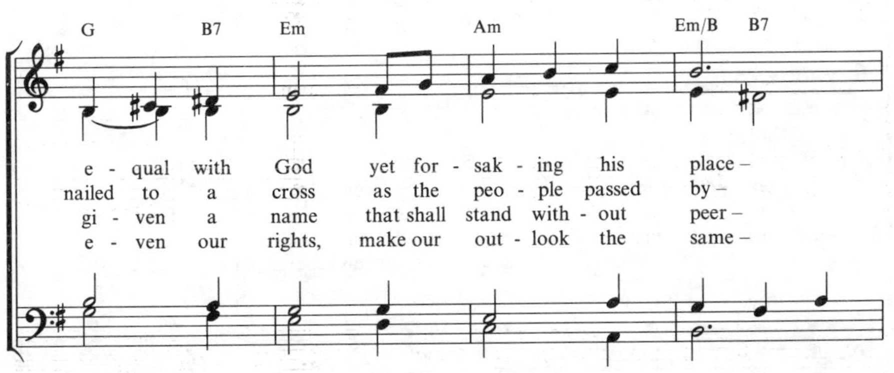
G B7 Em Am Em/B B7
e - qual with God yet for - sak - ing his place –
nailed to a cross as the peo - ple passed by –
gi - ven a name that shall stand with - out peer –
e - ven our rights, make our out - look the same –

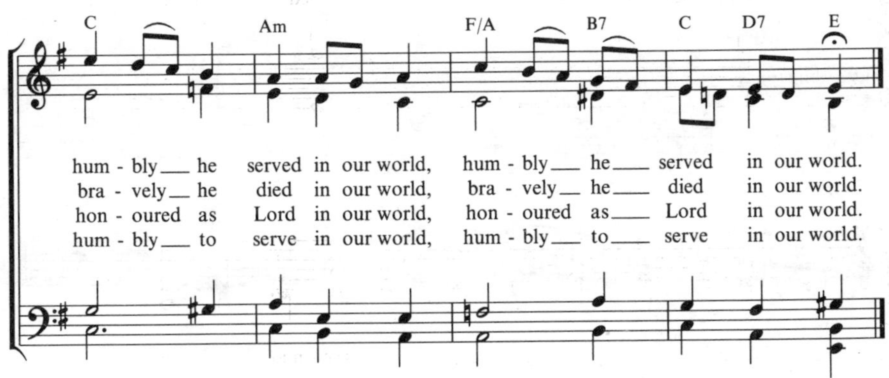
C Am F/A B7 C D7 E
hum - bly he served in our world, hum - bly he served in our world.
bra - vely he died in our world, bra - vely he died in our world.
hon - oured as Lord in our world, hon - oured as Lord in our world.
hum - bly to serve in our world, hum - bly to serve in our world.

83 Faithful vigil ended

Faithful vigil

Words: from Luke 2 *(The Song of Simeon / Nunc dimittis)*
Timothy Dudley-Smith
Music: David Wilson

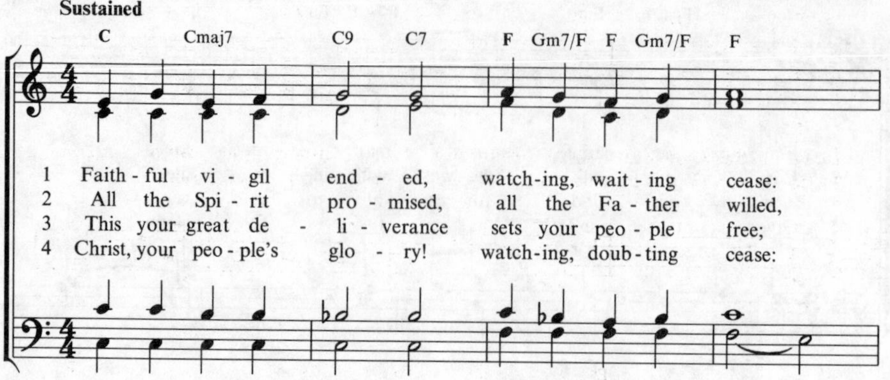

Sustained
C Cmaj7 C9 C7 F Gm7/F F Gm7/F F
1 Faith - ful vi - gil end - ed, watch - ing, wait - ing cease:
2 All the Spi - rit pro - mised, all the Fa - ther willed,
3 This your great de - li - verance sets your peo - ple free;
4 Christ, your peo - ple's glo - ry! watch - ing, doub - ting cease:

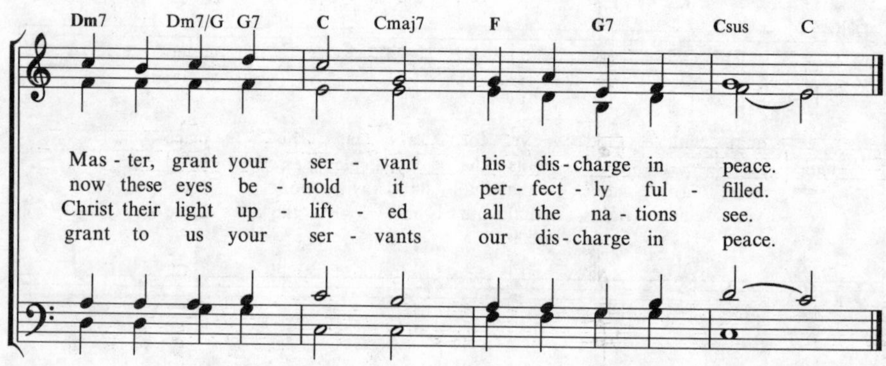

Dm7 Dm7/G G7 C Cmaj7 F G7 Csus C
Mas - ter, grant your ser - vant his dis - charge in peace.
now these eyes be - hold it per - fect - ly ful - filled.
Christ their light up - lift - ed all the na - tions see.
grant to us your ser - vants our dis - charge in peace.

Flute obligato

84 Father God, we worship you

Words and music: Geoff Baker

Flowing
F C/E E♭ B♭ Gm7 C9 C F C9
1 Fa - ther God, we wor - ship you, ev - er-more the same:
2 Je - sus, Lord, we wor - ship you, ev - er-more the same:
F C/E E♭ B♭ Gm7 C9 C F F9 F
may the things we say and do, glo - ri - fy your name;
may the things we say and do, glo - ri - fy your name;
B♭maj7 Am A♭ E♭ B♭maj7 Gm7 C9 C
from the shel-ter of your love let our prai - ses ring,
make us dai - ly more like you, till your face we see,
F C/E E♭ B♭ Gm7 C9 C F
lift - ing up the name we love – chil - dren of the King.
and in heaven with you we'll reign, for e - ter - ni - ty.

85 Fear not, for I bring all people

Come into his presence

Words: from Luke 2
Michael Perry
Music: Source unknown,
arranged David Peacock

① C C/E ② F Em7 Am7

1 'Fear not, for I bring all peo - ple good news of joy,
2 'On this day in Da - vid's ci - ty Je - sus is born,
3 'Glo - ry in the high - est hea - ven, peace on the earth,

③ Dm7 G7 Asus A ④ Dm7 G7 C

good news of joy, good news of joy:
Je - sus is born, Je - sus is born.
peace on the earth, peace on the earth!'

This may be sung as an unaccompanied round

B♭ melody version

86 Fling wide the gates

Crucifer

Words: from Psalm 24
Michael Perry
Music: S H Nicholson (1875–1947)

Triumphantly
C Dm7 G C D7 G G7
Fling wide the gates, un - bar the an-cient doors; sa -
Fine
C G7 C F G7 Dm G7 Csus C
- lute your king in his tri - um - phant cause!
Verse
Em Am D7 G C Am B Em
1 Now all the world be - longs to Christ our Lord: let
2 Who has the right to wor - ship him to - day? All
3 He comes to save all those who trust his name, and
4 Who is the vic - tor glor - ious from the fight? He
D.C.
Am D7 G C Dsus D G G7
all cre - a - tion greet the liv - ing Word!
those who glad - ly serve him and o - bey.
will de - clare them free from guilt and shame.
is our king, our life, our Lord, our right!

87 From heaven above

Lindow

Brightly

Words: after M Luther (1483–1546)
Michael Perry
Music: Norman Warren

Am
G
Am7
1 'From heaven a - bove I come to bring the
2 'For know that God has kept his word and
3 'The One by whom the world was made is

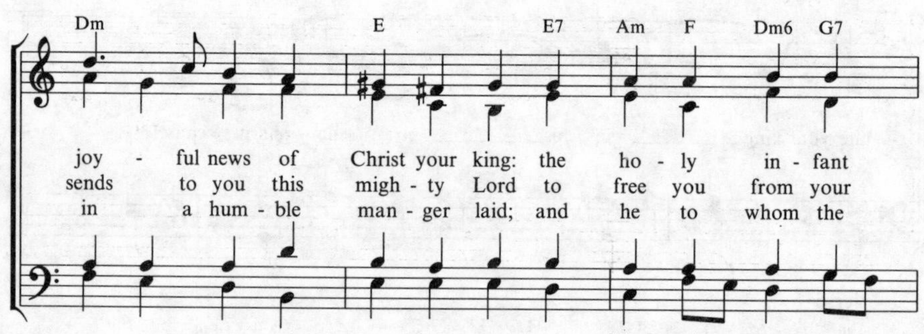

Dm
E
E7
Am
F
Dm6
G7
joy - ful news of Christ your king: the ho - ly in - fant
sends to you this migh - ty Lord to free you from your
in a hum - ble man - ger laid; and he to whom the

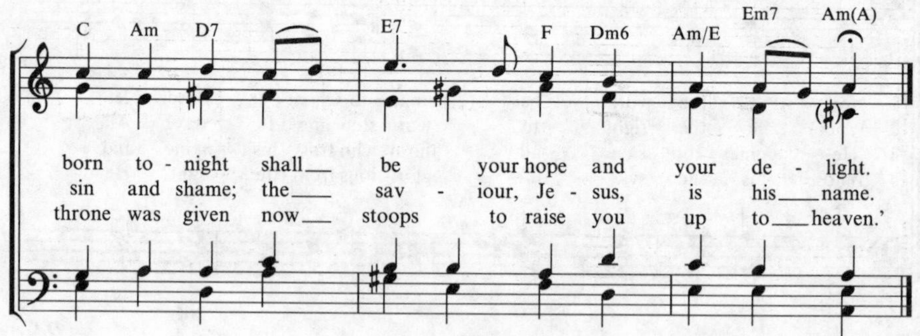

C
Am
D7
E7
F
Dm6
Am/E
Em7
Am(A)
born to - night shall be your hope and your de - light.
sin and shame; the sav - iour, Je - sus, is his name.
throne was given now stoops to raise you up to heaven.'

4 So with the shepherds make your way,
and find in Bethlehem today
the child of peace, the ever-blessed,
your master and your gracious guest.

5 Then bear the news that angels tell
to all the weary world as well;
let human power and pomp and pride
be vanquished at this Christmastide.

6 Sing praises to the Father, Son,
and Holy Spirit – Three in One;
let God made known in Christ our Lord
be worshipped, honoured, and adored.

88 For this purpose

Capo 2(C)

Words and music: Graham Kendrick

Flowing
D(C)
Introduction
A(G)
Bm(Am)
F♯m(Em)
G(F)
Asus
(Gsus)
A(G)
Verse
D(C)
A(G)
1 For this
2 In the
Bm(Am)
F♯m(Em)
G(F)
A(G)
D(C)
pur - pose Christ was re - vealed,
name of Je - sus we stand;
Bm(Am)
Bm/A
(Am7)
Asus/E
(Gsus)
to de - stroy all the works of the ev - il
by the power of his blood we now claim this

A(G)
D(C)
A(G)
Bm(Am)
F♯m(Em)
one; Christ in us has
ground: Sa - tan has no au -

G(F)
F♯(E)
Bm(Am)
Bm/A
(Am7)
ov - er - come, so with glad-ness we sing
- tho - ri - ty here, powers of dark-ness must flee,

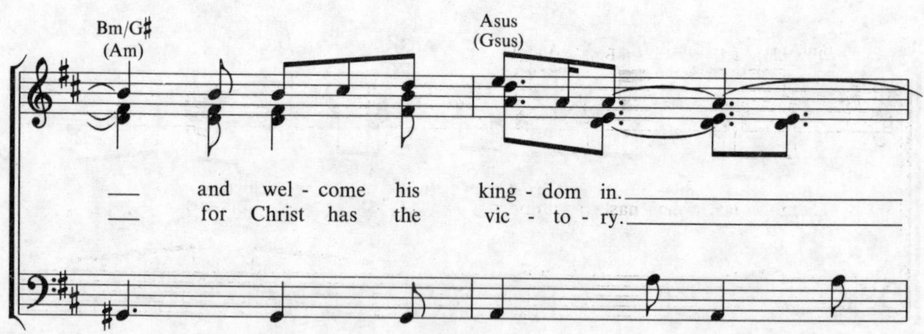
Bm/G♯
(Am)
Asus
(Gsus)
and wel - come his king - dom in.
for Christ has the vic - to - ry.

Rhythmic
A(G)
Chorus
D(C)
G(F)
D(C)
MEN
WOMEN
Ov - er sin he has con-quered: Al - le -

G(F) D(C) G(F) D(C) E(D) A(G) E(D)
MEN
WOMEN
- lu - ia! he has con-quered. Ov - er death vic - tor - ious: Al - le -

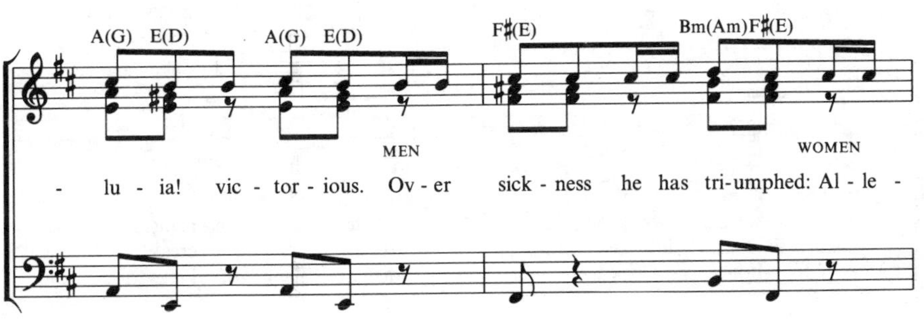
A(G) E(D) A(G) E(D) F♯(E) Bm(Am) F♯(E)
MEN
WOMEN
- lu - ia! vic - tor - ious. Ov - er sick - ness he has tri-umphed: Al - le -

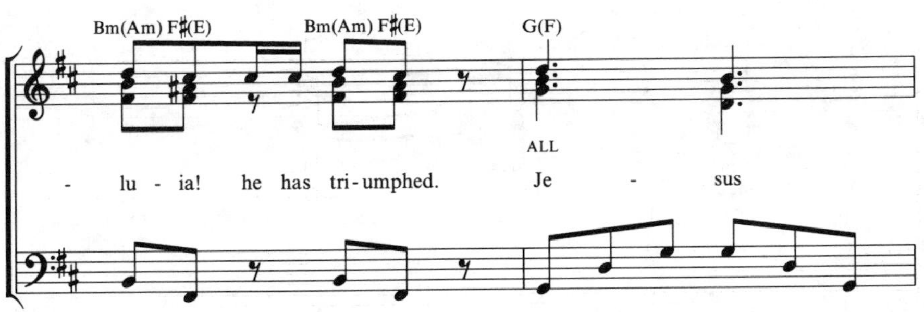
Bm(Am) F♯(E) Bm(Am) F♯(E) G(F)
ALL
- lu - ia! he has tri-umphed. Je - sus

Asus (Gsus) A7(G7) D(C) G(F) D(C) Asus (Gsus) D(C)
reigns ov - er all!

89 For unto us a child is born

From Isaiah 9
Words and music: David J Hadden
Music arranged David Peacock

Flowing and expressive
C
Cmaj7
1 For un - to us a child__ is born,___ un - to
(2) there shall be___ no end___ to the
(3) is the Migh - ty God,___ he___
F9
Gsus
us a son__ is given,__ and the gov - ern - ment___ shall
in - crease of___ his rule,___ to the in - crease of his
is the Prince of peace,__ the__ King of kings___ and
G7
C
G7
be up - on___ his shoul - der;___ for un - to
gov - ern - ment__ and peace;___ for he shall
Lord___ of lords:___ all___
C
Cmaj7
F9
us a child__ is born,___ un - to us a son__ is given,__
sit on Da - vid's throne__ up - hold - ing right - eous-ness,__
hon - our to___ the king,___ all___ glo - ry to___ his name,__

Gsus
G7
C
and the gov-ern-ment shall be up-on his shoul - der.
our God shall ac - comp-lish this.
for now and for ev - er-more!
Chorus
G7
C
F
And he will be called Won-der-ful, Won-der-ful Coun-sel-lor,
Dm
G
C
Migh - ty God,
Gsus
G
C
F
Dm
the Ev-er-last - ing Fa-ther, Prince of peace,
C/G
G7
1.2.
C
Gsus
G
3.
C
Migh - ty God.
2 And
3 For he

90 From east to west

Words: after Sedulius (died c.450) and J Ellerton (1826–1893), in this version Word & Music
Music: David Peacock
Matthew
Moderately
Instrumental obligato
B♭/C F C/F B♭ F/A Gm7
1 From east to west, from shore to shore, let earth a-wake and
(3) us the world's Cre - a-tor wears the fash-ion of a
(5) glo-ry be to God a-bove, and on the earth be
Csus C B♭/C F C/F B♭ F/A Dm7
sing: the ho-ly child that Ma-ry bore is
slave; our hu-man flesh the Ma-ker shares, his
peace to all who long to taste his love, till
Gm7 Csus C F Fine F/A B♭
Christ, the Lord and King! 2 He did not spurn the
crea-ture, comes to save. 4 To shep-herds poor, their
time it-self shall cease!

Am Dm7 Gm7 Csus C7 F
ox - 's stall, nor scorn the man - ger bed; there
Lord most high – their Shep- herd – was re - vealed, while
Em7 A7 D D/F♯ Gm7 B♭ Csus C B♭/C
God whose mer - cy feeds us all, by Ma-ry's love was fed. 3 For
an - gel choirs sang in the sky a - cross the si - lent field: 5 All
B♭ melody version
vv.1,3,5
Fine
vv.2,4

91 From heaven you came

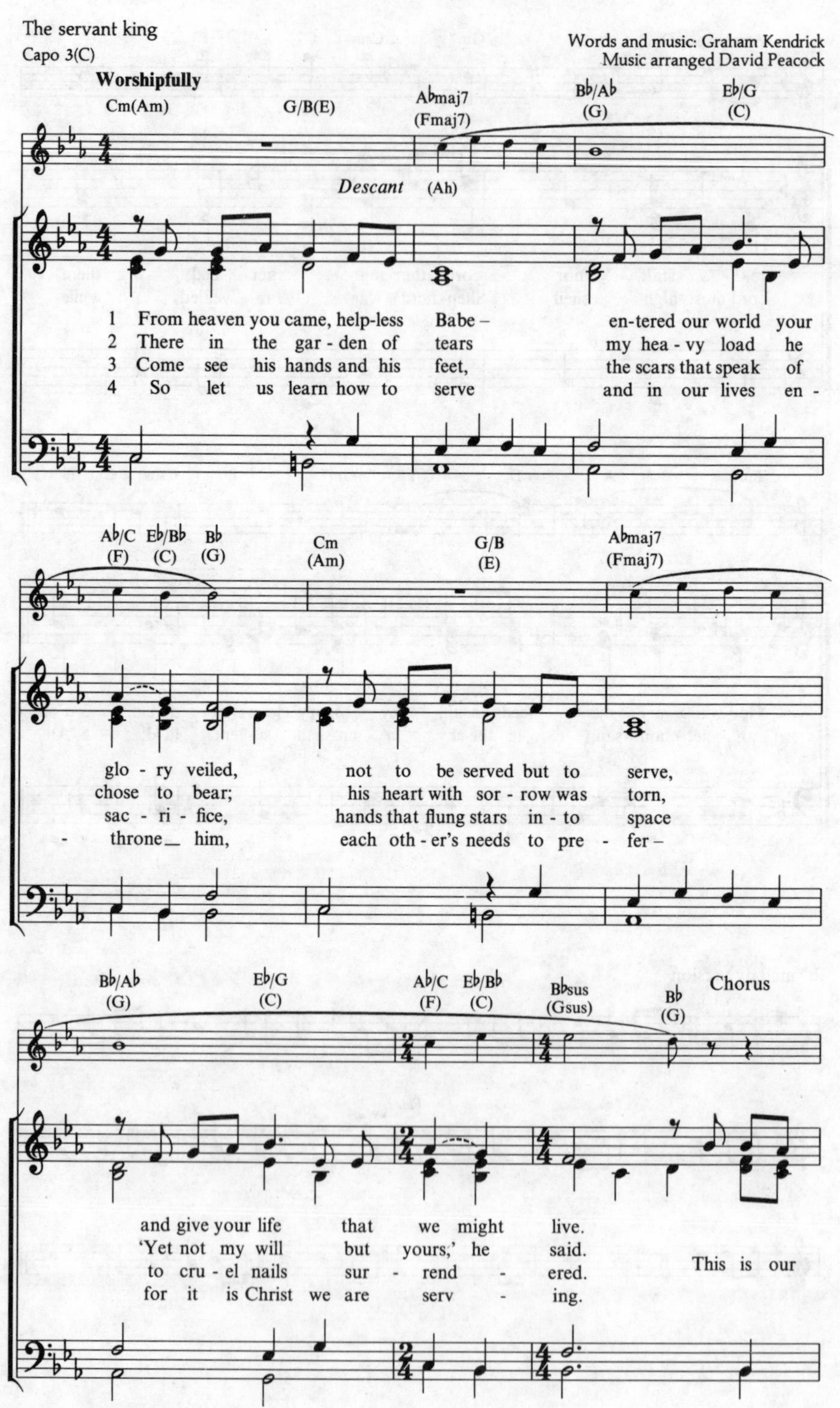
The servant king
Capo 3(C)
Words and music: Graham Kendrick
Music arranged David Peacock
Worshipfully
Cm(Am)
G/B(E)
A♭maj7
(Fmaj7)
B♭/A♭
(G)
E♭/G
(C)
Descant
(Ah)
1 From heaven you came, help-less Babe – en-tered our world your
2 There in the gar-den of tears my hea-vy load he
3 Come see his hands and his feet, the scars that speak of
4 So let us learn how to serve and in our lives en-
A♭/C
(F)
E♭/B♭
(C)
B♭
(G)
Cm
(Am)
G/B
(E)
A♭maj7
(Fmaj7)
glo-ry veiled, not to be served but to serve,
chose to bear; his heart with sor-row was torn,
sac-ri-fice, hands that flung stars in-to space
-throne him, each oth-er's needs to pre-fer –
B♭/A♭
(G)
E♭/G
(C)
A♭/C
(F)
E♭/B♭
(C)
B♭sus
(Gsus)
B♭
(G)
Chorus
and give your life that we might live.
'Yet not my will but yours,' he said.
to cru-el nails sur-rend-ered.
for it is Christ we are serv-ing.
This is our

E♭
(C)
B♭
(G)
Cm
(Am)
Cm/B♭
(Am7)
A♭
(F)
B♭
(G)
Part II This is our God the ser-vant king he calls us now to
God – the ser-vant king, he calls us now to fol - low
E♭
(C)
B♭
(G)
E♭
(C)
E♭/D♭
(C7)
A♭/C
(F)
D
(B)
fol-low him to bring our lives an off - er - ing
him, to bring our lives as a dai-ly of-fer - ing of wor-ship
1.2.3.
4.
E♭
(C)
B♭
(G)
E♭
(C)
Dm7
(Bm7)
G7
(E7)
E♭
(C)
of wor - ship to the ser - vant king. king.
to the ser - vant king. king.

92 From the distant east

Words and music: C R Vaughan
Music arranged David Peacock
Brightly ♩ = 144
Cm
Cm/B♭
Cm/A♭
Cm/G
1 From the dis - tant east and the far-thest west,
(2) cling to the past or the long a - go I will
(3) be a - fraid through the wa-ters deep
Fm
G
Cm
Cm/B♭
bring my peo-ple home:
let my peo-ple re - turn from the
I will make a road and the
do not be a - fraid as you
Cm/A♭
Cm/G
Fm
G
Cm
dis - tant lands -
ri - vers flow, I will bring my peo-ple home.
pass through fire -
Chorus
Cm/B
Cm/B♭
Cm/A
Some-one is shout - ing in the des - ert: Pre -

Ab
Bb
Eb
G7
Cm
Cm/B
- pare a road for the Lord,
make a path straight for him to
Cm/Bb
Cm/A
Ab
Bb
Eb
G7
tra-vel, pre - pare a road for the Lord, turn a-way from your sins!
Cm
Cm/Bb
1.2.
Cm/Ab
Cm/G
3.
Cm/Ab
G7
2 Do not
3 Do not
Turn a-way from your sins,
Cm
Cm/Bb
Cm/Ab
G
Cm
F
Cm
F
G7
Cm
Turn a-way from your sins!

93 From the Father's throne on high

Monkland

Words: Timothy Dudley-Smith
Music: J Antes (1740–1811)
arranged J B Wilkes (1785–1869)

Capo 3(G)

B♭(G) Gm(Em) F(D) B♭(G) E♭(C) Cm(Am) B♭(G)
1 From the Fa - ther's throne on high
2 Dark - ened be the day at noon
3 An - cient powers of sin and death
F(D) B♭(G) F/C(D) C7(A7) F(D)
Christ re - turns to rule and reign.
when the stars of hea - ven fall:
shake to hear the trum - pet blown;
C7(A7) F(D) F7(D7) B♭(G) F(D)
Child of earth, he came to die;
earth and sky and sun and moon –
from the winds' re - mot - est breath
B♭(G) F7/E♭ (D7) B♭/D (G) Fsus (Dsus) F(D) B♭(G)
Judge of all he comes a - gain.
clou - dy dark - ness co - vers all.
God will ga - ther in his own.

4 So behold the promised sign,
sky and sea by tumult riven,
and the King of kings divine
coming in the clouds of heaven.

5 Come then, Lord, in light and power,
at whose word the worlds began;
in the unexpected hour
come in glory, Son of Man.

94 Girls and boys, leave your toys

Words: M Sargent (1895–1967)
in this version Word & Music
Music: Czech traditional melody
arranged David Peacock
Zither Carol
Capo 3(C)
E♭ (C)
E♭/G (C)
A♭ (F) B♭ (G) B♭7 (G7)
1 Girls and boys, leave your toys, make no noise, kneel at his
2 On that day, far a - way, Je - sus lay – an - gels were
3 Shep-herds came at the fame of your name, an - gels their
E♭ (C)
E♭/G (C)
crib and wor-ship him. For this shrine, Child di - vine, is the sign
watch-ing round his head. Ho - ly Child, mo - ther mild, un - de - filed,
guide to Beth - le - hem; in that place, saw your face filled with grace,
A♭ (F) B♭ (G) B♭7 (G7) E♭ (C)
A♭ (F) A♭/C (F) E♭ (C) Fm7 (Dm7) B♭7 (G7)
our Sav-iour's here.
we sing your praise.
stood at your door.
Al-le-lu - ia, the church bells ring, 'Al-le-lu - ia!' the
E♭ (C) Fm7/A♭ (Dm7) G7 (E7) Cm (Am) E♭/G (C) A♭ (F) B♭ (G) B♭7 (G7) E♭ (C)
an - gels sing, al - le - lu - ia from ev - ery-thing – all must draw near!
our hearts we raise.
love ev - er - more.

95 Glad music fills the Christmas sky

(FIRST TUNE)
O Waly, Waly
Words: Michael Perry
Music: English traditional melody
arranged David Peacock
Flowing
C/D G Am7 Bm7 Em7
Part II 5 Then lift your hearts and voi - ces high,
1 Glad mus - ic fills the Christ-mas sky – a hymn of
2 Of ten - der love for God she sings, the cho - sen
3 The an - gel cho - rus of the skies who come to
C G Am D7
sing once a - gain the Christ - mas song:
praise, a song of love; the an - gels
mo - ther of the Son; she knows that
tell us of God's grace have yet to
Bm7 Em Bm/D Em/C♯ Cm6 G/B
for love and praise to Christ be - long –
wor - ship high a - bove and Ma - ry
won - ders have be - gun, and trusts for
know his hu - man face, to watch him

1–4.
5.
Am G Am D7 Gsus G Gsus G
In shouts of joy, and lul - la - by.
sings her lul - la - by. - by.
all the fut - ure brings.
die, to see him rise.

4 Let praise be true and love sincere,
rejoice to greet the saviour's birth;
let peace and honour fill the earth
and mercy reign – for God is here!

5 Then lift your hearts and voices high,
sing once again the Christmas song:
for love and praise to Christ belong –
in shouts of joy, and lullaby.

B♭ melody version

96 Glad music fills the Christmas sky

(SECOND TUNE)

Rockhaven

Words: Michael Perry
Music: Roger Mayor

Flute
G♯m
E7
F♯m/A
A/B
E
mf
mp
1 Glad
(Flute tacet vv.2&4)
F♯m
mus - ic fills the Christ - mas sky a
(2) ten - der love for God she sings, the
(3) an - gel cho - rus of the skies who
E/B
C♯m
F♯
B
hymn of praise, a song of love; the
cho - sen mo - ther of the Son; she
come to tell us of God's grace have

Music: © Roger Mayor / Jubilate Hymns

Words: © Michael Perry / Jubilate Hymns

A
A/C♯
E/B
B7
an - gels___ wor - ship___ high a - bove___ and
knows that___ won - ders___ have be - gun,___ and
yet to___ know___ his___ hu - man face, to
flute plays phrase every time
D
B7/A
A/B
E
1–4.
E7
F♯m/A
mp
Ma - ry___sings her lul - la - by.___
trusts for___all the fu-ture brings.
watch him___die, to see him rise.___
A/B
B
5.
p
poco rall. . . .
2 Of
3 The
4 Let . . .

4 Let praise be true and love sincere,
rejoice to greet the saviour birth;
let peace and honour fill the earth
and mercy reign – for God is here!

5 Then lift your hearts and voices high,
sing once again the Christmas song:
for love and praise to Christ belong –
in shouts of joy, and lullaby.

97 Glory, glory, glory to God

Words and music: Lesley Neal

Lively, disco-feel
Dm
Am
Dm
Glo - ry,
glo - ry,
Am
C
A
C
A
glo-ry to God
and peace on earth
C
A
Dm
Christ the sav-iour is born!
Glo - ry,
Am
Dm
Am
glo - ry,

C
A
C
A
C
glo-ry to God
and peace on earth –
Christ the Lord and

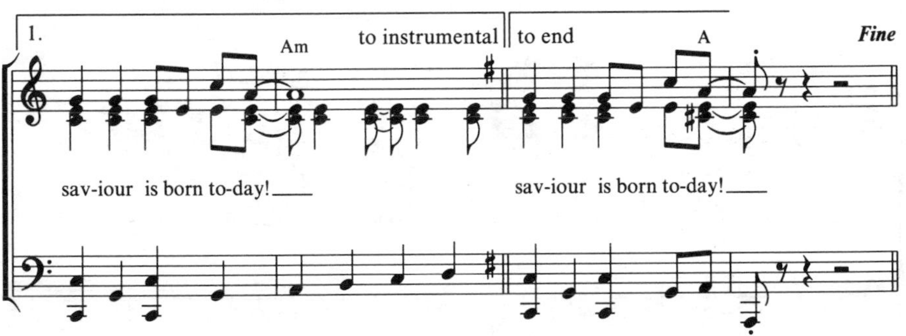
1.
Am
to instrumental
to end
A
Fine
sav-iour is born to-day!
sav-iour is born to-day!

Instrumental
Em
Em7/D
Em/C
B7
Em
Em7/D

1.
Em/C
B
2.
C
Em7/A
A7
D.C.

98 Glory, glory, glory to the King

Glory to the King

Words and music: Tom McLain
Music arranged David Peacock

Joyfully
G/D D A7 D G Asus A
Glo - ry, glo - ry, glo - ry to the King,
G/D D A7 D G G/A D
Fine
glo - ry, glo - ry, glo - ry to the King!
Bm F♯m G G/A D
Who is the king of glo - ry? King Je - sus is his name; he is
Bm F♯m G Em7 Asus A
D.C.
high and lif-ted up a - bove the earth, and his name I will pro - claim:

99 Glory in the highest heaven

Words: Michael Perry
Music: E G Monk (1819–1900)
Angel voices
Capo 2(C)
1 'Glo - ry in the high - est hea - ven, grace and peace on
2 Shep-herds, these glad tid - ings hear - ing, leave their flock and
3 Wise men tra - vel with their trea - sure, frank - in - cense they
4 Christ is born! the sure sal - va - tion for a world of
earth!' to our world a Son is giv - en,
fold, seek the place of Christ's ap-pear - ing –
bring, gold and myrrh in ro - yal mea-sure –
wrong, hope of ev - ery ge - ner - a - tion,
songs at - tend his birth: come with an - gel
Da - vid's town of old: come and ha - sten
this their of - fer - ing: come in ho - mage,
truth a - wait - ed long: come with joy - ful
hosts to name him, then pro-claim him – tell his worth!
to a - dore him, kneel be - fore him and be - hold!
draw - ing near him to re - vere him – migh - ty king!
faith to meet him, glad - ly greet him with a song!

100 Go, tell it on the mountain

Words: in this version Richard Bewes
Music: Traditional melody
arranged Noël Tredinnick

Chorus
G C/G G/B Gdim7 Am7 D7 G7 C D
Go, tell it on the moun - tain, ov-er the hills and ev-ery-where;
Em C G/B D7 G/B Am Bm D7 G (Fine)
go tell it on the moun - tain, that Je - sus Christ is born!
Verse
C D Em B7 Am7 F7 Em7 A7
1 The shep-herds from the hill-side gave wor-ship and a - dored; they
2 The men from east-ern count-ries came la - ter there to bring their
3 A road that Jews and Gen-tiles, both rich and poor have trod – it
4 The learn-èd and the sim - ple come to the man-ger - stall; he
Bm C Bm7 Em7 A G/B A/C♯ D D7
saw the Babe of Beth-l'hem was Je - sus Christ the Lord:
gifts of lo-ving hom - age to Je - sus Christ the King:
led them all to Beth-l'hem, to Christ, the Son of God:
joins us in his fam - ily, the sav - iour of us all!

Optional last Chorus
Ab Db/Eb Ab/C Bdim7 Bbm Eb7 Cm Fm Bbm Eb7
Go, tell it on the moun - tain, ov-er the hills and ev - ery - where;
C7 Db Db/Eb Ab D9b5 Bbm Db/Eb Eb7 Ab
go tell it on the moun - tain, that Je - sus Christ is born!
Bb melody version
Chorus
G D7 G D7
G Am D7 G (Fine)
Verses
G D7 G
A7 D7
Optional last chorus

Simplified chords not compatible with keyboard version

101 God came among us

Words and music: Marilyn Baker
Music arranged David Peacock
Moderate pace ♩ = c.76
C G
1 God came a - mong us, he be - came a man,
2 He came to serve, to show us how much he cared;
3 Death tried to hold him, but it could not suc - ceed;
Dm A7/C♯ Dm7 Dm/C G/B G
be - came a ba - by, though through him the world be - gan.
our joys and sor - rows he so will - ing - ly shared.
he rose a - gain, and now we can be freed.
Am D/F♯ G G/F C/E
He came to earth to bring us peace, but
He came to earth to bring us joy, but
He longs to give e - ter - nal life to
F Dm7 G G7/F
where is that peace to - day? It can be found
where is that joy to - day? It can be found
all who will simp - ly re - ceive, yes to all

C/E
Am
Dm/F
Dm
F/G
G7
by those who will let him di - rect their
by those who let him wash their guilt a -
who will o - pen their hearts and just be -

1.2.
C
G/B
Am
D/F♯
way.
- way.

G7
C/E
F
G
3.
C
- lieve.

102 God has exalted him

Words and music: Austin Martin

Fast and rhythmic
Em Am7 D7
God has ex - alt - ed him to the high - est
G B7 Em Am7
place, gi - ven him the name that is a -
B7 Em Fine E7 Am D7
- bove ev - ery name. And ev-ery knee shall
Gmaj7 Cmaj7 B7(sus) B7 Em E7
bow and ev - ery tongue con - fess that Je-sus
Am D7 Gmaj7 Em7 C6 F♯7 B7sus B7
Christ is Lord to the glo - ry of God the Fa - ther.

103 God has spoken

Words: Willard Jabusch
Music: Israeli folk melody
arranged Norman Warren
descant Angela Reith

Hebrew style
Chorus
Am
Descant
E
God has spo - ken to his peo - ple Al - le - lu - ia,
God has spo - ken to his peo - ple Al - le - lu - ia,
E7
Am
Fine
and his words are words of wis - dom. al - le - lu - ia!
and his words are words of wis - dom. al - le - lu - ia!
Verses
E
E7
Am
E
1 O - pen your ears, O Christ-ian peo - ple, o - pen your ears and hear good news;
2 They who have ears to hear his mes-sage, they who have ears, then let them hear;
3 Is - rael__comes to greet the sav - iour, Ju - dah is glad to see his day;
E
E7
Am
Dm7
E7
D.C.
o - pen your hearts, O roy - al priest-hood, God has come to__ you,
they who would learn the way of wis - dom, let them hear God's word,
from east and west the peo-ples tra - vel, he will show the__ way,

104 God of glory

Capo 2(C)

Words and music: Dave Fellingham

Brightly with strength and feeling
D(C)
Em(Dm)
F♯m(Em)
Bm(Am)
God of glo - ry, we ex - alt your name,
Gmaj7(Fmaj7)
C♯7(B7)
F♯m(Em)
A7/E(G7/D)
you who reign in maj-es - ty; we
D(C)
G(F)
C7(B♭7)
lift our hearts to you and we will wor - ship, praise and
D(C)
Em(Dm)
A7(G7)
D(C)
G(F)
D(C)
mag-ni-fy your ho - ly name. In power res -

Descant
Bm(Am)
F♯m(Em)
In power res - plen - dent you reign in glo - ry;
- plend - ent you reign in glo - ry; e - ter - nal
Em(Dm)
A(G)
e - ter - nal King, you reign for ev - er:
King, you reign for ev - er: your word is
Bm(Am)
F♯m(Em)
your word is migh - ty, re - leas - ing cap - tives,
migh - ty, re - leas - ing cap - tives, your love is
Em(Dm)
A7(G7)
D(C)
G(F)
D(C)
your love is gra - cious – you are my God.
gra - cious – you are my God.

105 God of God, the uncreated

Corde natus
Capo 2(D)
Words: after Prudentius (348–c413)
J M Neale (1818–1866) and H W Baker (1821–1877)
in this version Jubilate Hymns
Music: from Piae Cantiones, (1582)
arranged David Peacock
Not too slow
E (D) C♯m (Bm) Amaj7 (G) B7 (A7) E (D)
1 God of God, the un - cre - a - ted
2 He is here, whom gen - er - a - tions
3 Hap - py is that day for ev - er
C♯m (Bm) Amaj7 (G) Bsus (Asus) B (A)
love, be - fore the world be - gan;
sought through - out the a - ges long;
when, by God the Spir - it's grace,
A (G) E (D) F♯m7 (Em7) B7 (A7) C♯m (Bm)
Christ the source and Christ the end - ing,
prom - ised by the an - cient pro - phets,
low - ly Ma - ry, vir - gin moth - er,
A (G) F♯m7 (Em7) B7 (A7) Esus (Dsus) E (D)
Son of God and Son of Man,
just - ice for a world of wrong,
bore the sav - iour of our race.

C♯m
(Bm)
Amaj7
(G)
E(D)
Amaj7(G)
Lord of all the things that have
God's sal - va - tion for the faith - - -
Man and child, the world's re - deem - - -
Bsus
(Asus)
B
(A)
E
(D)
A
(G)
F♯m7
(Em7)
Bsus
(Asus)
B
(A)
been, mas - ter of th'e - ter - nal plan,
- ful: him we praise in end - less song
- er now dis - plays his sa - cred face
E
(D)
C♯m
(Bm)
Amaj7
(G)
Bsus
(Asus)
B7
(A7)
E
(D)
ev - er - more and ev - er - more.

4 Praise him, heaven of heavens,
praise him, angels in the height;
priests and prophets, bow before him,
saints who longed to see this sight.
Let no human voice be silent,
in his glory hearts unite
evermore and evermore.

5 Christ be praised with God the Father,
and the Holy Spirit, praised!
hymns of worship, high thanksgiving
echo through a world amazed:
Honour, majesty, dominion!
songs of victory be raised
evermore and evermore.

106 God is our strength and refuge

Dambusters March

Words: from Psalm 46
Richard Bewes
Music: Eric Coates (1886–1958)
arranged Noël Tredinnick

Stately

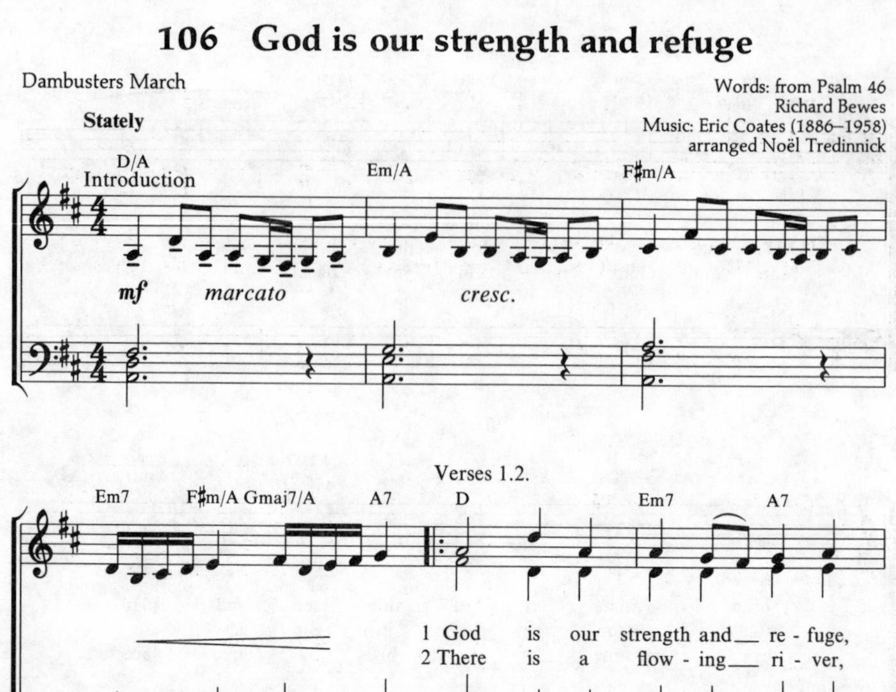

D/A
Introduction
Em/A
F♯m/A
mf
marcato
cresc.
Em7
F♯m/A Gmaj7/A
A7
Verses 1.2.
D
Em7
A7
1 God is our strength and — re - fuge,
2 There is a flow - ing — ri - ver,

D
F♯m
Gmaj7
Em6/G C♯dim/G
D/F♯
Bm
our pre - sent help in — trou - ble; and we there - fore
with - in God's ho - ly — ci - ty; God is in the

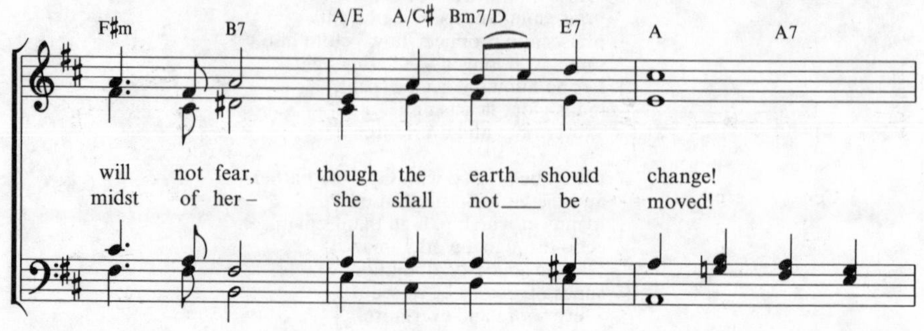

F♯m
B7
A/E
A/C♯
Bm7/D
E7
A
A7
will not fear, though the earth — should change!
midst of her – she shall not — be moved!

D/F♯ Bm7 Em7 A7 Dmaj7 Gmaj7 Gmaj7/C♯ F♯7
Though moun-tains shake and trem-ble, though swirl-ing floods are rag - ing,
God's help is swift - ly giv - en, thrones van - ish at his pres-ence –
Bm D♯dim7/A Em/G B7/F♯ Em G Gmaj7/A A7
1.
D A7/G D/F♯ A7/E
God the Lord of hosts is with us ev - er - more!
God the Lord of hosts is with us ev - er -
2.
D B♭ B♭7
more!
rit.
Verse 3 slower
E♭ Fm7 A♭/B♭ B♭7 E♭maj7 A♭maj7 B♭7/A♭
3 Come, see the works of our ma - ker, learn of his deeds all - power-ful:

G7
Cm
Gm7
Csus
C7
B♭
Gm7
Cm7
F7
B♭
B♭7
wars will cease a - cross the world when he shat-ters the spear!

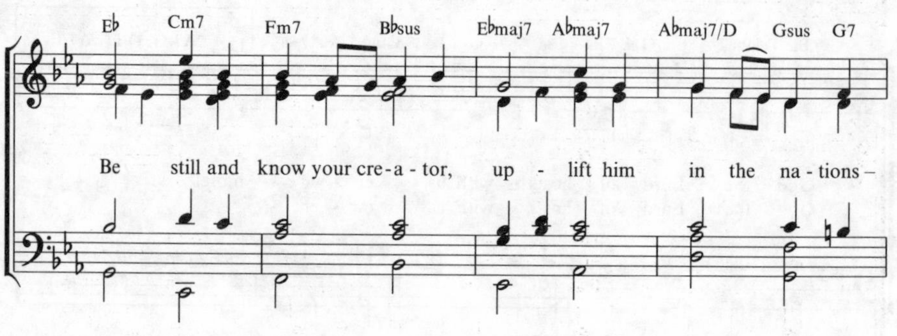
E♭
Cm7
Fm7
B♭sus
E♭maj7
A♭maj7
A♭maj7/D
Gsus
G7
Be still and know your cre-a-tor, up - lift him in the na-tions –

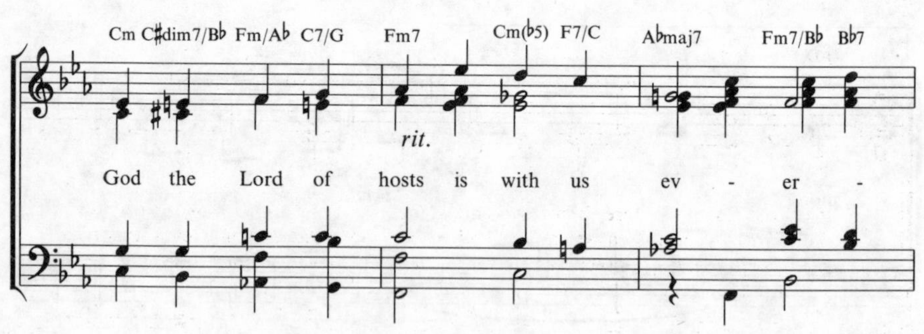
Cm
C♯dim7/B♭
Fm/A♭
C7/G
Fm7
Cm(♭5)
F7/C
A♭maj7
Fm7/B♭
B♭7
rit.
God the Lord of hosts is with us ev - er -

E♭/B♭
N.C.
E♭
- more!
a tempo

107 Good Christians all, rejoice

In dulci jubilo

Words: from *In dulci jubilo* (fourteenth century)
J M Neale (1818–1866)
Music: Fourteenth century German carol melody
arranged J Stainer (1840–1901)
based on a harmony by R L Pearsall (1795–1856)

Capo 5(C)

1 Good Christ-ians all, re - joice with heart and soul and voice!
2 Good Christ-ians all, re - joice with heart and soul and voice!
3 Good Christ-ians all, re - joice with heart and soul and voice!
lis - ten now to what we say, Je - sus Christ is born to-day;
hear the news of end - less bliss, Je - sus Christ was born for this:
now you need not fear the grave; Je - sus Christ was born to save:
ox and ass be - fore him bow and he is in the man - ger now:
he has o - pened hea - ven's door and we are blessed for ev - er-more!
come at his most gra - cious call to find sal - va - tion, one and all:
Christ is born to - day; Christ is born to - day!
Christ was born for this; Christ was born for this.
Christ was born to save; Christ was born to save!

108 God rest you merry

Words: traditional (eighteenth century)
in this version Jubilate Hymns
Music: English traditional melody
arranged Noël Tredinnick

Lively
Dm A7 Dm C Dm Gm
1 God rest you mer - ry, gent - le - men, let no - thing you dis -
2 At Beth - le - hem in Ju - dah the ho - ly babe was
3 From God our heaven - ly Fa - ther a ho - ly an - gel
Asus A7 Dm A7 Dm C G Gm
- may! for Je - sus Christ our sa - viour was born on Christ-mas
born; they laid him in a man - ger on this most hap - py
came; the shep-herds saw the glo - ry and heard the voice pro -
A7 D7 Gm C A7 Dm G7
Day, to save us all from Sa - tan's power when we were gone a -
morn: at which his moth - er Ma - ry did neith - er fear nor
- claim that Christ was born in Beth - le - hem – and Je - sus is his
Chorus
Gm Dm C F Gm Dm A7 Dm G7
- stray:
scorn: O___ tid - ings of com - fort and joy, com-fort and
name:

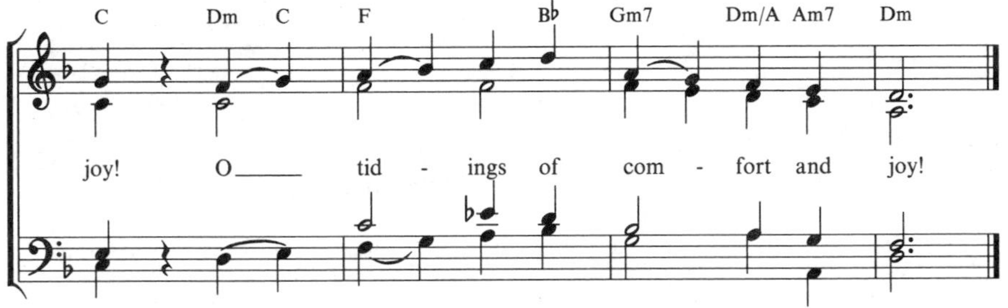
C
Dm
C
F
B♭
Gm7
Dm/A
Am7
Dm
joy! O___ tid - ings of com - fort and joy!

4 Fear not, then said the angel,
let nothing cause you fright;
to you is born a saviour
in David's town tonight,
to free all those who trust in him
from Satan's power and might:
O tidings of comfort and joy . . .

5 The shepherds at these tidings
rejoiced in heart and mind,
and on the darkened hillside
they left their flocks behind,
and went to Bethlehem straightway
this holy child to find:
O tidings of comfort and joy . . .

6 And when to Bethlehem they came
where Christ the infant lay:
they found him in a manger
where oxen fed on hay,
and there beside her newborn child
his mother knelt to pray:
O tidings of comfort and joy . . .

7 Now to the Lord sing praises,
all people in this place!
With Christian love and fellowship
each other now embrace,
and let this Christmas festival
all bitterness displace:
O tidings of comfort and joy . . .

B♭ melody version

1.
2.
Chorus

109 Good King Wenceslas

Tempus adest floridum

Words: J M Neale (1818–1866)
in this version Word & Music
Music: English carol melody
arranged David Peacock

G D7 C G C Am D7
Glockenspiel
1 Good king Wen - ces - las looked out on the Feast of
2 'Hith - er, page, and stand by me! If you know it,
3 'Bring me food, and bring me wine, bring me pine logs
Gsus G D7 C G
Ste - phen, when the snow lay round a - bout,
tell - ing: yon - der poor man – who is he,
hi - ther: you and I will see him dine,
C Am D7 Gsus G Bm7 Em7
deep, and crisp, and e - ven: bright - ly shone the
where and what his dwell - ing?' 'Sir, he lives a
when we take them thi - ther.' Page and mon - arch

Am G C D7 G
moon that night, though the frost was cru - el,
good way hence, un - der - neath the moun - tain;
forth they went, forth they went to - ge - ther,
C Am6 Em Dsus D
when a poor man came in sight,
right a - gainst the for - est fence
through the wild wind's loud la - ment
G G/D D Em C G
gath - ering win - ter fu - el.
by Saint Ag - nes' foun - tain.'
and the bit - ter wea - ther.

4 PAGE
'Sir, the night is darker now,
  and the wind grows stronger;
fails my heart – I know not how,
  I can go no longer.'
KING
'Mark my footsteps well, my page,
  follow in them boldly:
you shall find the winter's rage
  chills your blood less coldly.'

5 ALL
In his master's steps he trod
  where the snow lay even,
strong to do the will of God
  in the hope of heaven:
therefore, Christians all, be sure,
  grace and wealth possessing,
you that now will bless the poor
  shall yourselves find blessing.

Alternative four-part setting may be found at number 335

110 Greetings, Christian friends

Finehaven

Capo 3(Em)

Words: Mollie Knight
and in this version Word & Music
Music: David Peacock

Lively 'Hebrew' style

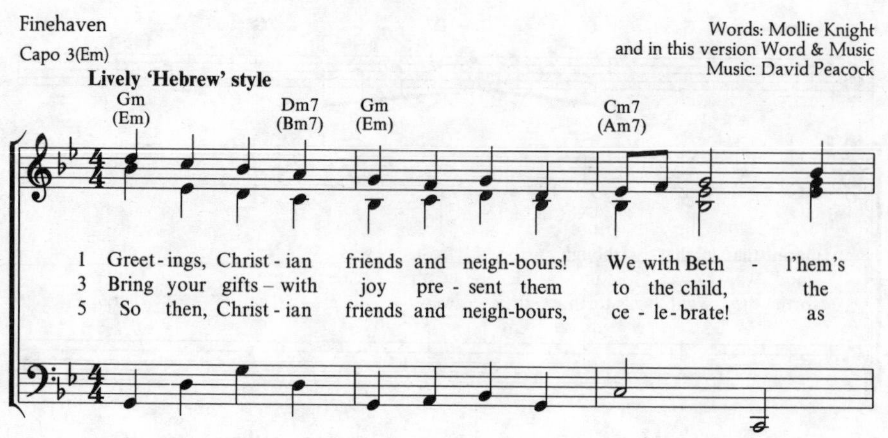

Gm (Em) Dm7 (Bm7) Gm (Em) Cm7 (Am7)
1 Greet-ings, Christ-ian friends and neigh-bours! We with Beth - l'hem's
3 Bring your gifts – with joy pre - sent them to the child, the
5 So then, Christ-ian friends and neigh-bours, ce - le-brate! as

D7 (B7) Gm (Em) Dm7 (Am7) Gm (Em)
shep-herds say 'Wel-come to the ba - by Je - sus,
ho - ly One; give your lives in love and ser - vice
well you may; sing to greet our sav - iour Je - sus

Cm7 (Am7) *last time to* **Coda** D7 (B7) Gm (Em)
born this hap - py Christ - mas Day!'
to God's true and on - ly Son.
born this hap - py

Cm
(Am)
D7
(B7)
Gm
(Em)
Cm
(Am)
D7
(B7)
2 Thank the Fa - ther for his mer - cy, for the gift of
4 Hap - py those who mark this sea - son mind - ful of the
Gm/B♭
(Em)
D7/A
(B7)
Gm
(Em)
Fm7
(Dm7)
B♭7
(G7)
E♭
(C)
Cm
(Am)
peace on earth, for the glor - ious hope of hea - ven
world's great need; hap - py all who love our sav - iour,
Cm/A
(Am)
F♯dim/E♭
(D♯dim)
D7
(B7)
brought to us through Je - sus' birth.
serv - ing him in word and deed.
CODA
D7
(B7)
Gm
(Em)
Christ - mas Day.

111 Good Christian people, rise and sing

Sussex Carol

Capo 5(C)

Words: traditional
in this version Word & Music
Music: English traditional melody
arranged Norman Warren

F (C)
B♭/F (F)
Fmaj7 (Cmaj7)
Gm7/F (Dm7)
F (C)
Gm7/F (Dm7)
1 Good Christ - ian peo - ple, rise and sing to greet the news the
2 Re - joice and be no long - er sad, for Christ is born to
3 Now in our dark - ness shines the light which made the an - gels
F (C)
B♭/F (F)
C7/F (G7)
F (C)
B♭/D (F)
Am/C (Em)
Gm/B♭ (Dm)
F/A (C)
Gm (Dm)
an - gels bring; good Christ-ian peo - ple, rise and sing to greet the news the
make us glad; re - joice and be no long - er sad, for Christ is born to
sing that night; now in our dark-ness shines the light which made the an - gels
F/C (C)
C7 (G7)
F (C)
C (G)
Gm/B♭ (Dm)
Am (Em)
Gm/B♭ (Dm)
C7 (G7)
an - gels bring: news of great joy for all the earth,
make us glad: his power will drive a - way our sin,
sing that night. Glo - ry to God! good-will and peace
Fmaj7/A (Cmaj7)
Gm7 (Dm7)
Am (Em)
B♭ (F)
C7 (G7)
F (C)
news of our ho - ly sav - iour's birth!
his low - ly birth our love shall win.
be to us all, and ne - ver cease!

112 Happy day of great rejoicing

Ode to Joy

Words: Mollie Knight
Music: Ludwig van Beethoven (1770–1827)

Capo 5(C)
F (C) Gm7/F (Dm7) F (C) Dm7 (Am7) F (C) C (G) F (C) C (G) F (C) F/C (C) C (G)
1 Hap-py day of great re - joic-ing! We pro-claim a sav-iour's birth,
2 Prince of peace, God's Word in - car-nate, with the poor i - den - ti - fied;
3 Hear the mes - sage of sal - va - tion Je - sus brings to ev - ery race,
F (C) Gm7/F (Dm7) F (C) Dm7 (Am7) F (C) C (G) F (C) C (G) F (C) Csus (Gsus) C (G) F (C)
for a child lies in a man- ger – Je - sus Christ is born on earth.
all his ri - ches and his glo - ry for love's sake are laid a - side.
see the in - fant who em - bod - ies God's great glo - ry and his grace.
C (G) F/C (C) Dm7/C (Am7) C7 (G7) F/C (C) Dm7/C (Am7) C (G) A7/C♯ (E7) Dm (Am) G (D) Csus (Gsus) C (G)
Glad-ly come, in wor - ship kneel-ing by the cra - dle of the Son;
Je - sus comes to his cre - a - tion, lov - ing sav-iour, God's dear Son:
Pur - est light will reach dark pla - ces through the love of Christ the Son:
F (C) E♭ (B♭) B♭/D (F) F (C) Gm (Dm) B♭ (F) F/A (C) C7/G (G7) F (C) Csus (Gsus) C (G) F (C)
sing with joy, ring out your prai - ses, 'Wel-come to the ho - ly One!'

113 Hail to the Lord's anointed

Words: J Montgomery (1771–1854)
Music: J Crüger (1598–1662)
descant David Peacock
Crüger
Capo 3(D)
F (D) B♭ (G) F/A (D/F♯) B♭ (G) F (D) Csus (Asus) C (A) F (D)
1 Hail to the Lord's a - noint - ed, great
2 He comes with com - fort spee - dy to
3 He shall come down like show - ers up -
F/A (D/F♯) Dm (Bm) Csus (Asus) C (A) F (D) B♭ (G) F/A (D/F♯) B♭ (G) F (D)
Da - vid's great - er son! Hail, in the time ap -
those who suf - fer wrong; to save the poor and
- on the fruit - ful earth; and love, joy, hope, like
Csus (Asus) C (A) F (D) F/A (D/F♯) Dm (Bm) Csus (Asus) C (A) F (D)
- point - ed his reign on earth be - gun! He
nee - dy and help the weak be strong: to
flow - ers spring in his path to birth: be -
B♭/D (G/B) F (D) C (A) Dm (Bm) Asus (F♯sus) A (F♯) Dm (Bm) F (D)
comes to break op - press - ion, to
give them songs for sigh - ing, their
- fore him on the moun - tains shall

Descant: © David Peacock / Jubilate Hymns

C (A) Gm/B♭ (Em/G) A (F♯) Dm (Bm) A (F♯) F (D) C (A) F (D) B♭ (G)
set the cap - tive free, to take a - way trans -
dark - ness turn to light, whose souls, con - demned and
peace, the her - ald, go; and right - eous - ness in
C (A) F (D) F/A (D/F♯) B♭ (G) F (D) Csus (Asus) C (A) F (D)
- gress - ion and rule in e - qui - ty.
dy - ing, are pre - cious in his sight.
foun - tains from hill to val - ley flow.

4 Kings shall bow down before him
and gold and incense bring;
all nations shall adore him,
his praise all people sing:
to him shall prayer unceasing
and daily vows ascend;
his kingdom still increasing,
a kingdom without end.

5 In all the world victorious,
he on his throne shall rest;
from age to age more glorious,
all-blessing and all-blessed:
the tide of time shall never
his covenant remove;
his name shall stand for ever,
his changeless name of love.

Vocal or instrumental descant

5 In all the world vic - tor - ious, he on his throne shall rest; from
age to age more glor - ious, all - bless - ing and all - blessed: the
tide of time shall ne - ver his co - ve - nant re - move; his
name shall stand for ev - er, his change - less name of love.

114 Happy Christmas, everybody

Jubilate, everybody

Words and music: Michael Perry
Music arranged Stephen Coates and others

Capo 3(D)
Lively
C7(A7)
F(D)
C7(A7)
F(D)
1 Hap - py Christ - mas,
2 Hap - py Christ - mas,
3 Hap - py Christ - mas,
Dm7
(Bm7)
Gm7
(Em7)
C7
(A7)
ev - ery - bo - dy! all the world is sing - ing;
ev - ery - bo - dy! join the peo - ple pray - ing;
ev - ery - bo - dy! God's new day is dawn - ing;
F
(D)
Dm7
(Bm7)
come to wor - ship, ev - ery - bo - dy, praise and glo - ry
God is speak - ing, ev - ery - bo - dy– hear what love is
meet the sav - iour, ev - ery - bo - dy– Christ is born this
Gm7
(Em7)
C7
(A7)
Gm
(Em)
C
(A)
B♭/D
(G)
bring - ing:
say - ing: Come to greet the Lord with joy;
morn - ing:

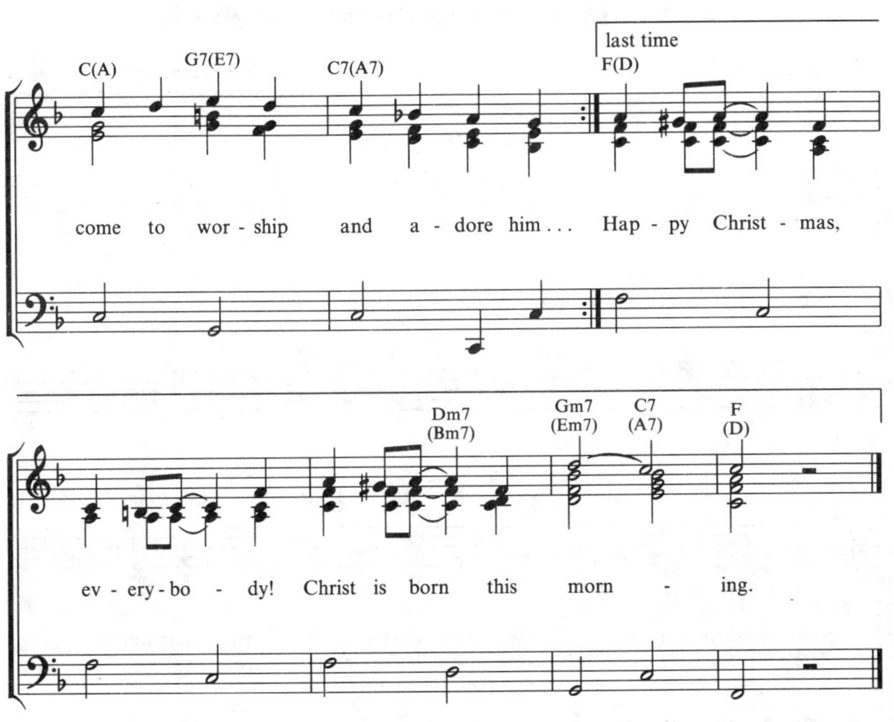
last time
C(A)
G7(E7)
C7(A7)
F(D)
come to wor - ship and a - dore him . . . Hap - py Christ - mas,
Dm7
(Bm7)
Gm7
(Em7)
C7
(A7)
F
(D)
ev - ery - bo - dy! Christ is born this morn - ing.

B♭ melody version

last time

115 Hark! the herald angels sing

Mendelssohn

Words: C Wesley (1707–1788) and others
Music: F Mendelssohn (1809–1847)
arranged with descant Christopher Robinson

G D G G/D D G/B Am/C G/D D G

1 Hark! the her - ald an - gels sing___ glo - ry to the new-born King;
2 Christ, by high - est heaven a - dored, Christ, the ev - er - last - ing Lord:

D7 Em A7 Bm A/C♯ D Gmaj7 A7 D

peace on earth and mer - cy mild,___ God and sin - ners re - con - ciled!
late in time be - hold him come,___ off-spring of a vir - gin's womb;

G D7 G G/D D G D7 G G/D D

Joy - ful all you na - tions rise,___ join the tri - umph of the skies;___
veiled in flesh the God-head see,___ hail th'in - car - nate De - i - ty!___

C Dm6 Am/E E7 Am D7 G G/D D G

with th'an - ge - lic host pro - claim, 'Christ is___ born in Beth - le - hem':
pleased as man with us to dwell, Je - sus___ our Em - man - u - el:

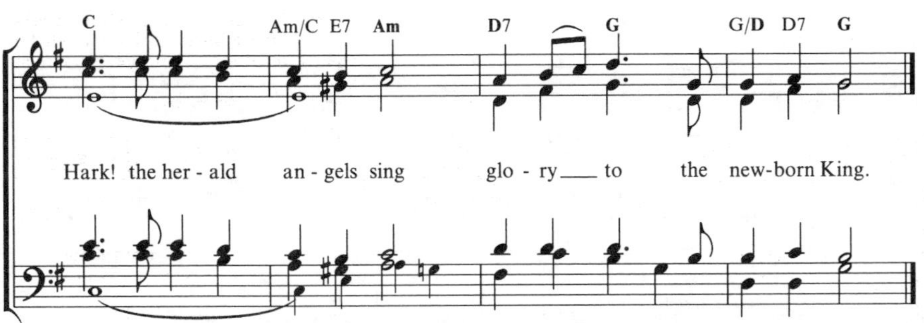
C Am/C E7 Am D7 G G/D D7 G
Hark! the her - ald an - gels sing glo - ry___ to the new-born King.

Descant

G Dsus/C D7/C G Em/C♯ Bm D7 G C G/D D7 G

3 Hail the heaven - born Prince of peace,___ hail the Sun___ of___ right - eous - ness;

3 Hail the heaven - born Prince of peace, hail the Sun of right - eous-ness;

G/D D7/C G/B G/F♯ Em A7 D A7 D Bm D/A A7 D

light and life to all he brings,___ risen with heal - ing in___ his wings:

light and life to all he brings, risen with heal - ing in his wings:

D7 G D7 G G/D D D D7 G G7 C Em G/D D
mild, he lays his glo - ry by, born that we no more may die;
mild, he lays his glo - ry by, born that we no more may die;
E7 Am A7/B Dm/B Am6/E E7 Am7 D D7 G7 C G/D D7 G
born to raise us from the earth, born to give us se - cond birth:
born to raise us from the earth, born to give us se - cond birth:
C Am Am6/D Bm Caug/E E7 Am D D7/C G/B C G/D D7 G
Hark! the her - ald an - gels sing glo - ry to the new - born King.
Hark! the her - ald an - gels sing glo - ry to the new-born King.

116 Have you seen the little Child

Words and music: Mosie Lister
Music arranged David Peacock

Gently ♩ = 96
D
D/F♯
G
Asus
A
1 Have you seen the lit - tle Child
2 Did you hear the an - gels sing,
3 Did you kneel in Beth - le - hem?
4 Have you seen the lit - tle Child

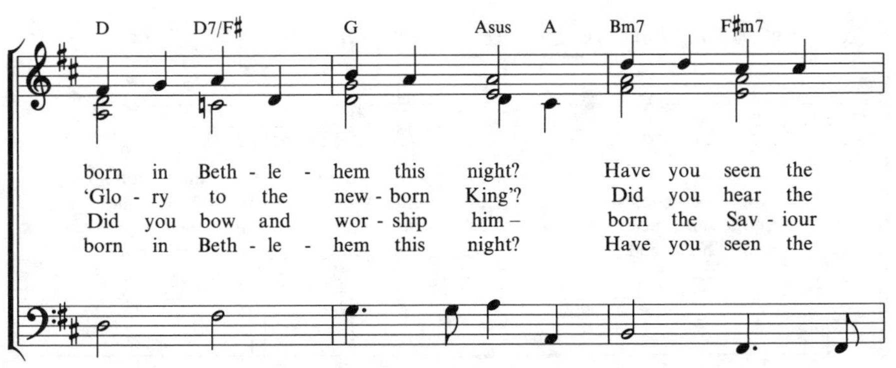
D
D7/F♯
G
Asus
A
Bm7
F♯m7
born in Beth - le - hem this night? Have you seen the
'Glo - ry to the new - born King'? Did you hear the
Did you bow and wor - ship him – born the Sav - iour
born in Beth - le - hem this night? Have you seen the

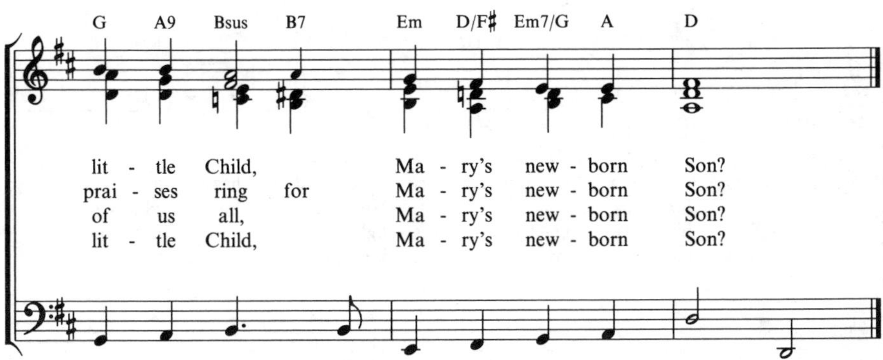
G
A9
Bsus
B7
Em
D/F♯
Em7/G
A
D
lit - tle Child, Ma - ry's new - born Son?
prai - ses ring for Ma - ry's new - born Son?
of us all, Ma - ry's new - born Son?
lit - tle Child, Ma - ry's new - born Son?

117 He is born, our Lord and saviour

Words and music: Jimmy Owens
Music arranged David Peacock

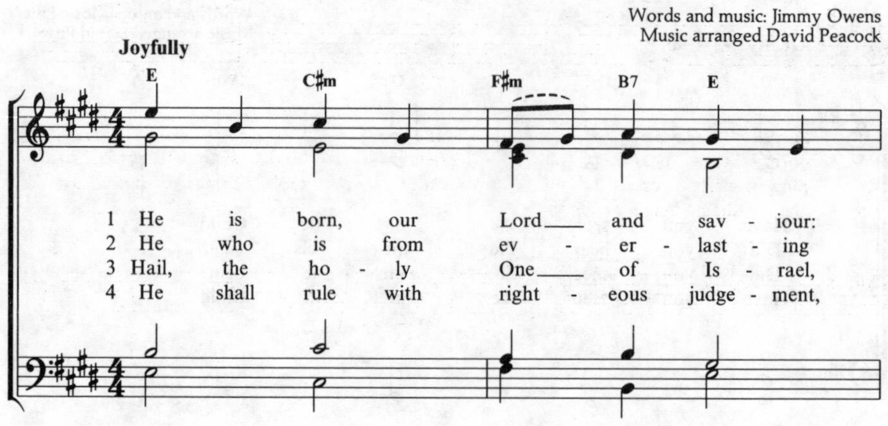

Joyfully
E C♯m F♯m B7 E
1 He is born, our Lord___ and sav - iour:
2 He who is from ev - er - last - ing
3 Hail, the ho - ly One___ of Is - rael,
4 He shall rule with right - eous judge - ment,

B7/D♯ E B7/F♯ E F♯m F♯7 B E C♯m
he is born, our heav-en-ly king: give him hon-our,
now be-comes the in - car - nate Word; he whose name en -
cho - sen heir to Da - vid's throne; hail the bright-ness
and his god - ly rule___ ex - tend; go - ver - nor a -

F♯m B7 E B7/D♯ E B7/F♯ E F♯m B7 E
give___ him glo - ry, earth re - joice and heav - en sing!
- dures___ for ev - er now is born the Son___ of God:
of___ his ri - sing – to his light the gen - tiles come:
- mong the na - tions, his great king-dom has___ no end:

E7
C♯
F♯m
B
Born to be our sanc - tu - ar - y,
born to bear our griefs and sor - rows,
plun - der - er of Sa - tan's king - dom,
he shall reign, the king of glo - ry,

E
A
F♯/A♯
F♯7
B7
E/G♯
C♯m
born to bring us light and peace;
born to ba - nish hate and strife;
down - fall of his ev - il power;
high - er than the kings of earth –
for our sins to
born to bear the
res - cu - er of
al - le - lu - ia,

F♯m
B7
E
E/G♯
A
B7/F♯
E/G♯
C♯m
F♯m
B7
E
bring for - give - ness, from our guilt to bring re - lease.
sin of ma - ny, born to give e - ter - nal life!
all his peo - ple, con - que - ror in death's dark hour!
al - le - lu - ia! praise we now his ho - ly birth!

118 He who made the starry skies

Starry skies
Capo 3(Am)

Words: Unknown
Music: Norman Warren

Fairly slow
Cm(Am)
C(A)
Cm(Am)
C(A)
p
D♭7(B♭7)
Cm7(Am7)
Gm7(Em7)
C(A)
Cm(Am)
1 He who made the star - ry skies sleep - ing in a
2 Jo - seph brings a gar - ment there, Ma - ry wraps her
Fm(Dm)
Gm(Em)
Am(F♯m)
Em7/G(C♯m)
sta - ble lies, ru - ler of the cen - tur - ies:
child so fair, rests him while she sings a prayer:
Gm(Em)
Am(F♯m)
Bm(G♯m)
hum - bly clad king of kings, joy of heaven
f

F♯m(E♭m)
Gm(Em)
Cm(Am)
Gm7(Em7)
1. Cm(Am)
to earth brings, dear a - bove all earth-ly things.
2.
C(A)
Gm7(Em7)
Am(F♯m)
things. 3 While we run this earth - ly race,
f
Bm(G♯m)
F♯m(E♭m)
B(G♯)
then through - out all time and space, may he grant
p
E♭(C)
Gm(Em)
G(E)
us hope and grace.
pp

119 He holds the key

Words and music: Joan Parsons
Music arranged: David Peacock
Lively
Verses
1 He holds the key to sal - va - tion – Je - sus is o - ver all; he is the Lord of cre - a - tion:
2 He is the rock ev - er stan - ding – no - one could break him down; he is the truth ev - er - last - ing:
3 He is a light in the dark - ness, and all shall see his face; he breaks our chains to re - deem us:
4 All power to him who is migh - ty, all praise to him who is God; all glo - ry now and for - ev - er:
Chorus
Al - le - lu - ia, al - le - lu - ia,
al - le - lu - ia, al - le - lu - ia, Lord!

120 Hear the chimes as they ring

Words and music: Georgian Banov and Mark Pendergrass
Music arranged David Peacock

With a lilt

C
F
Part 1 (or Solo)
1 Hear the chimes as they ring, they fore - tell of the
(2) land, ev-ery town, ev - ery home, ev-ery
Part 2 (or Congregation)
1 Hear the chimes as they ring, they fore - tell
2 Ev - ery land, ev-ery town, ev - ery home,

C
King; he is born, let us bring ev - ery
heart: ring it out, sing and shout, dance and
of the King; he is born, let us bring
ev - ery heart: ring it out, sing and shout,

G7
C
gift as we sing to the King.
sing, let it ring to the King.
ev - ery gift as we sing to the King.
dance and sing, let it ring to the King.
Chorus
F G C C/E F G7
Ho - san - na! bring prai - ses to the
C
1.
F G C C/E
King. Al - le - lu - ia!

2.
D7
G
F
G
let your prai - ses ring. (Part 1) 2 Ev-ery Al - le -

C/E
C
Dm
G7
C
- lu - ia! let your prai - ses ring.

B♭ version of chorus

1.
2.

arranged David Peacock

121 Hear how the bells

Easter Song
Words: Timothy Dudley-Smith
Music: Geistliche Kirchengesang, Cologne 1623
arranged David Peacock
Joyfully
glocks or bells vv1,5
1 Hear how the bells of Christ-mas play! Well may they ring for joy and say,
2 Let all the wait-ing earth re - joice, lift ev - ery heart and ev - ery voice, O praise him, al - le - lu - ia; sing now the song to an - gels given, glo -
3 As through the si - lence of the skies shep - herds in won - der heard a - rise, So may we hear a - gain with them songs
God has ful-filled his prom-ised word, born

Bm G Em Am7 Bsus B7 Em Am7 Bm G
is our Sav-iour and our Lord,
-ry to God in high-est heaven! O praise him, O
in the night at Beth-le - hem,
A D Bm E7 A Bm E7 Am B7 Em
praise him, al-le-lu-ia, al-le-lu-ia, al-le-
Em7 Asus A7
1–4.
D G Asus A
5.
D
-lu - ia!
-ia!

4 All nature sang at Jesus' birth,
Hail the Creator come to earth!
O praise him, alleluia;
sun, moon and shining stars above,
tell out the story of his love,
O praise him . . .

5 Hear how the bells of Christmas play!
Well may they ring for joy and say,
O praise him, alleluia;
come now to worship and adore,
Christ is our peace for evermore,
O praise him . . .

122 Hear the skies around

Rajske strune zadonite
Capo 3(C)
Gently
Words: after the Jugoslavian carol
Michael Perry
Music: Jugoslavian melody
arranged David Peacock
Descant (or instrument)
B♭7(G7) E♭(C) Cm7 (Am7)
3 Ban - ish all dis - may, for on Christ - mas Day there's a
1 Hear the skies a - round fill with joy - ful sound, and the
2 'To the earth be peace, fear and sor - row cease!' is the
3 Ban - ish all dis - may, for on Christ-mas Day there's a
A♭ (F) E♭ (C) B♭7 (G7) E♭ (C) B♭ (G7) E♭ (C)
song of praise to sing; ban - ish all dis - may, for on
praise of an - gels ring; Hear the skies a - round fill with
birth-day news they bring. 'To the earth be peace, fear and
song of praise to sing; ban - ish all dis-may, for on
Cm7 (Am7) A♭ (F) E♭ (C) B♭7 (G7) E♭ (C)
Christ - mas Day there's a song of praise to sing; Sing - ing
joy - ful sound, and the praise of an - gels ring;
sor - row cease!' is the birth-day news they bring. Sing-ing
Christ-mas Day there's a song of praise to sing;

B♭7 (G7)
E♭ (C)
B♭7 (G7)
'Glo - ry in the high - est,' sing - ing 'Glo - ry to the
'Glo - ry in the high - est,' sing - ing 'Glo - ry to the
E♭sus (Csus)
E♭ (C)
B♭7 (G7)
E♭ (C)
E♭/D (C)
Cm7 (Am7)
King!' Ban - ish all dis - may, for on
King!' Hear the skies a - round fill with
'To the earth be peace, fear and
Ban - ish all dis - may, for on
E♭/B♭ (C)
Cm/A (Am)
G♯m (Fm)
E♭/G (C)
Fm7 (Dm7)
B♭7 (G7)
E♭ (C)
Christ - mas Day there's a song of praise to sing.
joy - ful sound, and the praise of an - gels ring.
sor - row cease!' is the birth - day news they bring.
Christ-mas Day there's a song of praise to sing.

123 Holy child

(FIRST TUNE)

Holy child

Words: Timothy Dudley-Smith
Music: Michael Baughen
arranged David Iliff

Tenderly
G
C
Am
1 Ho - ly child, how still you lie! safe the
3 Ho - ly child, what gift of grace from the
5 Ho - ly child, so far from home, all the
7 Ho - ly child, how still you lie! safe the

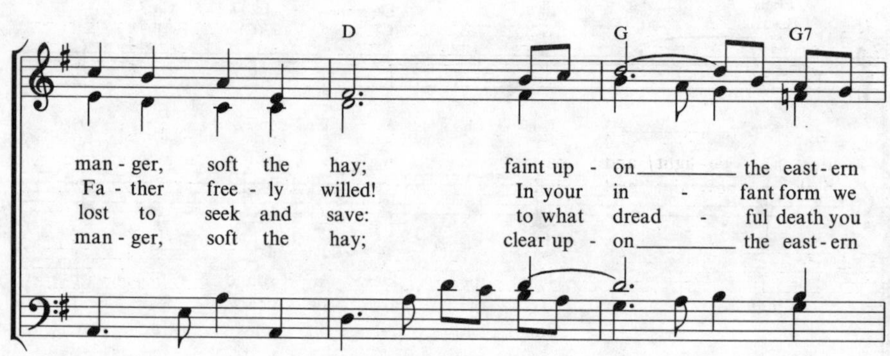
D
G
G7
man - ger, soft the hay; faint up - on the east - ern
Fa - ther free - ly willed! In your in - fant form we
lost to seek and save: to what dread - ful death you
man - ger, soft the hay; clear up - on the east - ern

C
G/D
Dsus
D7
G
Fine
sky breaks the dawn of Christ - mas Day.
trace all God's pro - mi - ses ful - filled.
come, to what dark and si - lent grave!
sky breaks the dawn of Christ - mas Day.

G7
C
Am
D7
2 Ho - ly child, whose birth - day brings shep-herds
4 Ho - ly child, whose hu - man years span like
6 Ho - ly child, be - fore whose name powers of

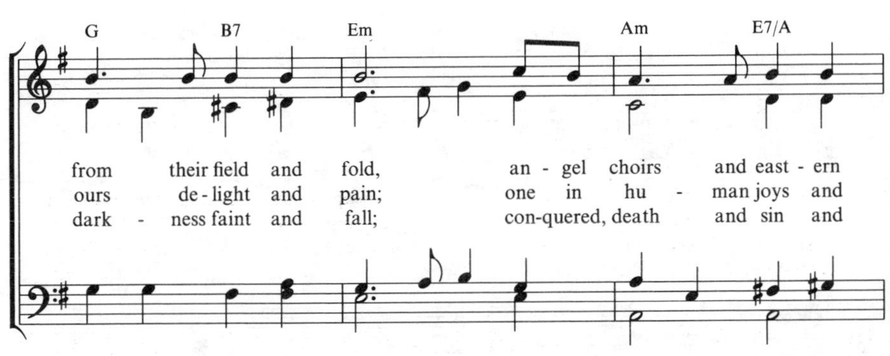
G
B7
Em
Am
E7/A
from their field and fold, an - gel choirs and east - ern
ours de - light and pain; one in hu - man joys and
dark - ness faint and fall; con-quered, death and sin and

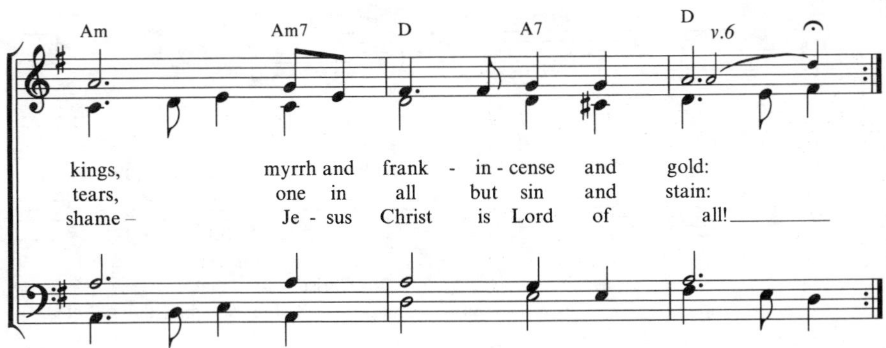
Am
Am7
D
A7
D
v.6
kings, myrrh and frank - in - cense and gold:
tears, one in all but sin and stain:
shame – Je - sus Christ is Lord of all!

124 Holy child

(SECOND TUNE)
Fairmile
Capo 1(G)
Flowing and sustained
Words: Timothy Dudley-Smith
Music: David Peacock
A♭ (G) E♭sus (Dsus) A♭ (G) E♭sus (Dsus)
A♭ (G) A♭+ (G+) D♭/A♭ (C) A♭maj7 (Gmaj7) B♭m (Am) E♭ (D)
1 Ho - ly child, how still you lie!
2 Ho - ly child, whose birth - day brings
3 Ho - ly child, what gift of grace
D♭ (C) A♭ (G) B♭m (Am) E♭sus (Dsus) E♭7 (D7)
safe the man - ger, soft the hay;
shep - herds from their field and fold,
from the Fa - ther free - ly willed!
A♭ (G) A♭+ (G+) D♭/A♭ (C) A♭ (G) Fm (Em) C7 (B7) Fm (Em) D♭ (C) C (B) Fm (Em)
faint up - on the east - ern sky breaks the dawn of
an - gel choirs and east - ern kings, myrrh and frank - in -
In your in - fant form we trace all God's pro - mi -

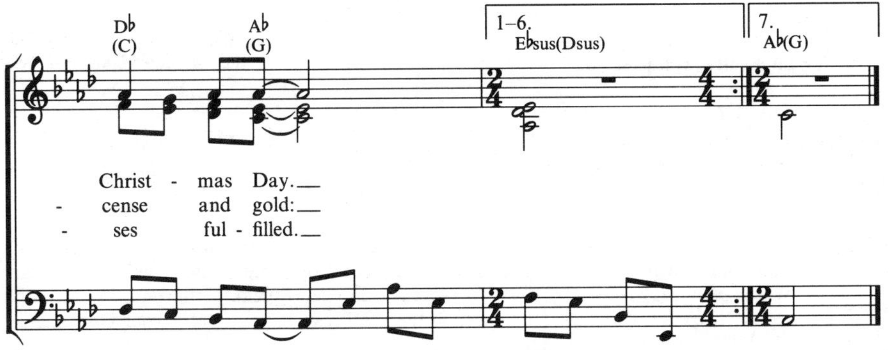
Db
(C)
Ab
(G)
1–6.
Ebsus(Dsus)
7.
Ab(G)
Christ - mas Day.
- cense and gold:
- ses ful - filled.

4 Holy child, whose human years
span like ours delight and pain;
one in human joys and tears,
one in all but sin and stain:

5 Holy child, so far from home,
all the lost to seek and save:
to what dreadful death you come,
to what dark and silent grave!

6 Holy child, before whose name
powers of darkness faint and fall;
conquered, death and sin and shame –
Jesus Christ is Lord of all!

7 Holy child, how still you lie!
safe the manger, soft the hay;
clear upon the eastern sky
breaks the dawn of Christmas Day.

B♭ melody version

125 How lovely on the mountains

From Isaiah 52
Words and music: Leonard E Smith Jnr
Music arranged David Peacock

Capo 1(A)

Triumphantly, with pace

B♭ (A)
E♭ (D)
F7 (E7)
E♭/B♭ (D)
B♭ (A)
1 How love - ly on the moun-tains are the feet of him
2 You watch-men lift your voi - ces joy - ful - ly as one,
3 Waste pla - ces of Je - ru - sa - lem break forth with joy
4 Ends of the earth, see the sal - va - tion of your God

G (F♯)
Cm (Bm)
F7 (E7)
B♭ (A)
F7 (E7)
who brings good news, good news,
shout for your king, your king;
we are re - deemed, re - deemed;
Je - sus is Lord, is Lord!

B♭7 (A7)
E♭ (D)
F7 (E7)
E♭/B♭ (D)
B♭ (A)
pro-claim-ing peace, an - nounc-ing news of hap - pi-ness:
see eye to eye the Lord re - stor - ing Zi - on:
the Lord has saved and com - for - ted his peo - ple:
Be - fore the na - tions he has bared his ho - ly arm:

G
(F♯)
Cm
(Bm)
F7
(E7)
B♭
(A)
E♭/B♭
(D)
our God reigns,
our God reigns!
(vv.2.3.4.)
your God reigns,
your God reigns!

B♭7
(A7)
E♭
(D)
Cm
(Bm)
F7
(E7)
B♭
(A)
Our God reigns,
our God reigns,
Your God reigns,
your God reigns,

Gm
(F♯m)
B♭7
(A7)
E♭
(D)
Cm7
(Bm7)
F7
(E7)
B♭
(A)
E♭/B♭
(D)
B♭
(A)
our God reigns,
our God reigns!
your God reigns,
your God reigns!

126 Holy, holy Lord

Words and music: Philip Warren

Gently
D
G/D
A7/D
D
G/D
A/D
p Ho - ly, ho - ly Lord,
D
G
A7/D
D
G/D
A/D
ho - ly, ho - ly Lord,
B♭
Em7/A
A7
D
G/D
A7/D
God of power and love.
1–3.
Bm
Em7
A7
Dmaj7
f 1 Heaven and earth are full of your glo - ry, ho -
mf 2 Born for us in Beth - le - hem, the
p 3 Sleep - ing there a - mong the hay, the

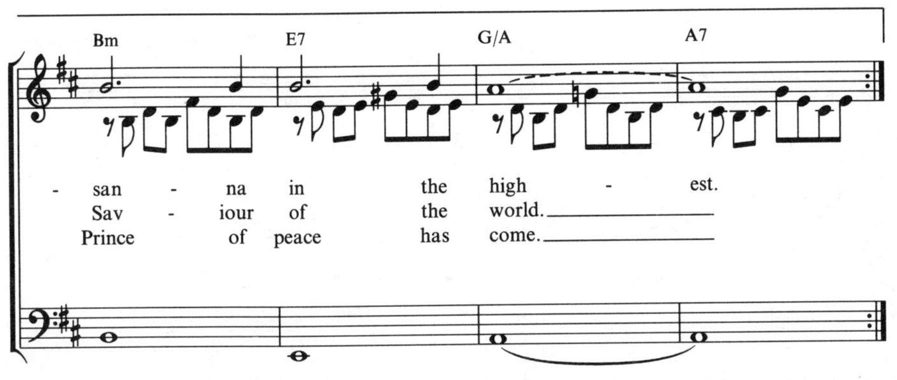
Bm
E7
G/A
A7
- san - na in the high - est.
Sav - iour of the world.
Prince of peace has come.

4.
Bm
Descant
Em7
A7
f 4 Heaven and earth are full of your
f 4 Heaven and earth are full of your

Dmaj7
Bm
E7
glo - ry, ho - san - na in the
glo - ry, ho - san - na in the

G/A
A7
D
high - est,
high - est,
mp
Ho - ly,
G/D
A7/D
D
G/D
A7/D
Ho - ly,
ho - ly
ho - ly
Lord,
p
D
G
D
Lord,
ho - ly,
Lord!
ho - ly,
ho - ly
Lord!

127 Hush you, my baby

Upton Vale
Capo 3(C)
Words: Timothy Dudley-Smith
Music: David Peacock
Gently
1 Hush you, my ba - by, the night wind is cold, the lambs from the hill - side are safe in the fold: sleep with the star - light and wake with the morn – the Lord of all glo - ry a ba - by is born.
2 Hush you, my ba - by, so soon to be grown, watch - ing by moon-light on moun-tains a - lone, toil - ing and trav- 'ling – so sleep while you can, till the Lord of all glo - ry is seen as a man.
3 Hush you, my ba - by, the years will not stay, the cross on the hill - top the end of the way; dim through the dark - ness, in grief and in gloom, the Lord of all glo - ry lies cold in the tomb.

4 Hush you, my baby,
the Father on high
in power and dominion
the darkness puts by;
bright from the shadows,
the seal and the stone,
  the Lord of all glory
returns to his own.

5 Hush you, my baby,
the sky turns to gold,
the lambs on the hillside
are loose from the fold;
fast fades the midnight
and new springs the morn,
  the Lord of all glory
a Saviour is born.

128 Hush, do not cry

Coventry Carol
Capo 3(Em)
Words: R Croo (1534)
in this version Word & Music
Music: English melody
arranged David Peacock
Instrument
Fine
Hush, do not cry, my lit - tle ti - ny child: Lul - la - by, lul - la - by!
1 O bro - thers, tell what ill be - fell
2 O sis - ters too, what may we do
3 He - rod the king, in his rag - ing,
4 Then woe is me, poor child, to see

Gm (Em) D7 (B7) Gm (Em) Cm (Am) D7 (B7) G (E) B♭ (G)
Beth - le - hem's town this day; let
and save from death to - day this
gave his com - mand this day: his
this sad and sor - ry day; from
F (D) Gm (Em) Dm (Bm) Gm (Em) F (D) E♭ C)
grief re - cite these in - fants'
poor young thing to whom we
men of might in his own
your part - ing we say nor
D.C.
D7 (B7) Gm (Em) D7 (B7) Gm (Em) Cm (Am) Dsus (Bsus) D (B) G (E)
plight, sor - row and sore dis - may.
sing: 'Lul - la - by, lul - la - lay'?
sight all lit - tle boys to slay.
sing, 'Lul - la - by, lul - la - lay.'

The repeated refrain may be omitted

129 Hush, little baby

Skye Boat Song

Words: Michael Perry
Music: Scottish traditional melody
arranged David Peacock

Flowing
Instruments
G
Am/G
D7
Hush, lit - tle ba - by; peace, lit - tle boy
G
C
G/B
D7/A
G
slum - ber-ing in the hay; dream while we ca - rol
Am/G
D7
G
C
G
Fine
ti - dings of joy, Je - sus of Christ - mas Day.

Em
Am
Em/B
B7
1 An-gels will tell news of good cheer, glo-ry will light the
2 Jo-seph will guard, Ma-ry will smile, hold-ing in sweet em-
3 Wise men from far, soon they will come, wor-ship and gifts they
Em
Am
Em
sky; shep-herds will kneel
-brace hea-ven's true Lord,
bring: in-cense for prayer,
Am
Em/B
B7
Em
D7
D.C.
won-der-ing here, wor-ship-ping God most high.
here for a while, Je-sus, God's gift of grace.
myrrh for a tomb, gold to re-veal a king.

130 I will come and bow down

Words and music: Martin Nystrom
Music arranged David Peacock

Worshipfully
G/A
Descant
D
Bm
Em7
I will come and bow down at your feet, Lord
I will come and bow down at your feet, Lord
A7
F♯m
B7
Je - sus; in you pre - sence is ful - ness of
Je - sus; in you pre - sence is ful - ness of
Em
A7
Bm
joy. There is no - thing, there is
joy. There is no - thing, there is

C♯/B
F♯m
B7
no - one to com - pare with you: I take
no - one to com - pare with you: I take
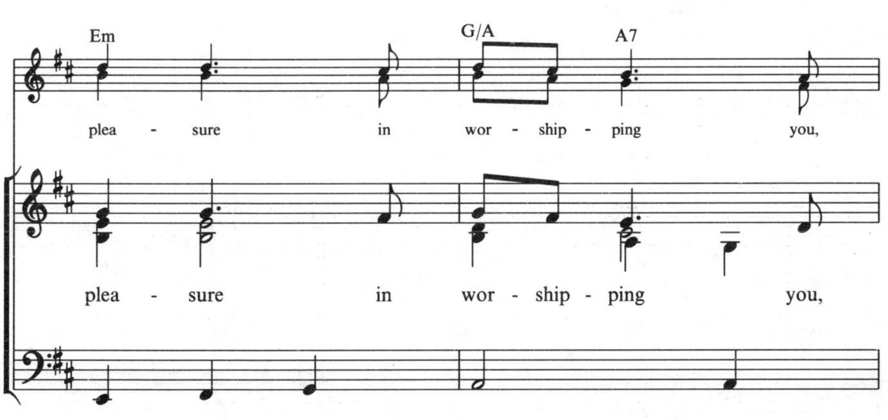
Em
G/A
A7
plea - sure in wor - ship - ping you,
plea - sure in wor - ship - ping you,
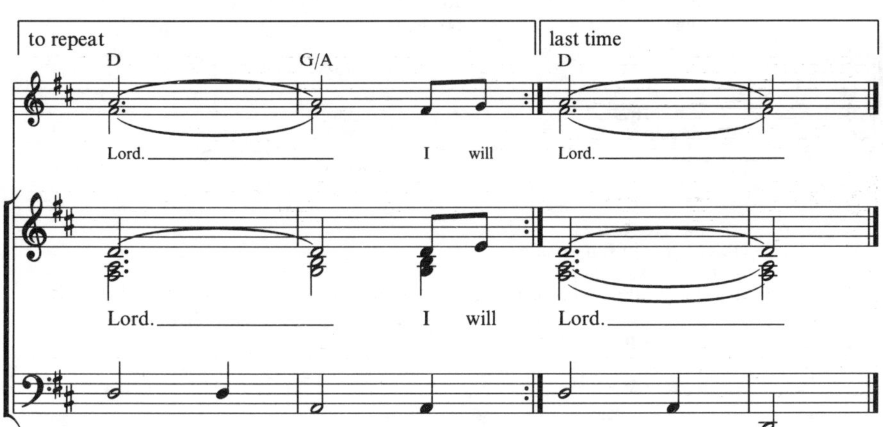
to repeat
last time
D
G/A
D
Lord. I will Lord.
Lord. I will Lord.

131 I wonder as I wander

Words: Appalachian carol
in this version Word & Music
Music: Appalachian traditional melody
arranged Michael Paget

Tenderly
Intro. and link
Am
Am9
Am7
Bm7/A
Am
Am9
Keyboard and/or choir [choir to vocalise to 'ooh' sound]
* Verse
Am
Am6
G/A
Am
Am9
1 I won - der as I wan - der, out
2 When Je - sus was born – it was
3 If Je - sus had want - ed for
4 I won - der as I wan - der, out
Am7
Bm7/A
Am7
Dm7
un - der the sky, why Je - sus the sav - iour came
in a cow's stall – came an - gels and shep - herds and
a - ny one thing – a star in the sky, or a
un - der the sky, why Je - sus the sav - iour came

* Verse may be performed as
either 1 Unison or solo
or 2 Solo and two-part choir, S.A.
or 3 Solo and four-part choir (optional a cappella)
The treble stave provides solo and S.A.; the bass stave T.B. parts.
Choir or group to vocalise 'Ah' sound.

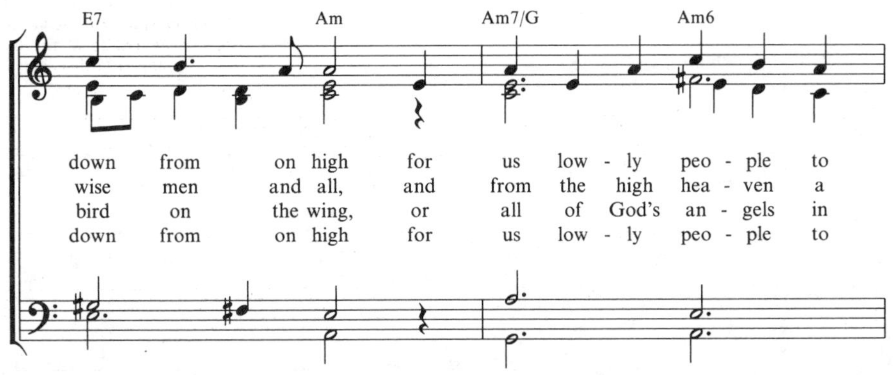
E7
Am
Am7/G
Am6
down from on high for us low - ly peo - ple to
wise men and all, and from the high hea - ven a
bird on the wing, or all of God's an - gels in
down from on high for us low - ly peo - ple to

Full choir (words)
Unison or four-part
C/G
A7
F
Am7
suf - fer and die – I won - der as I
star's light did fall, the won - der - ful
hea - ven to sing – he sure - ly could
suf - fer and die – I won - der as I

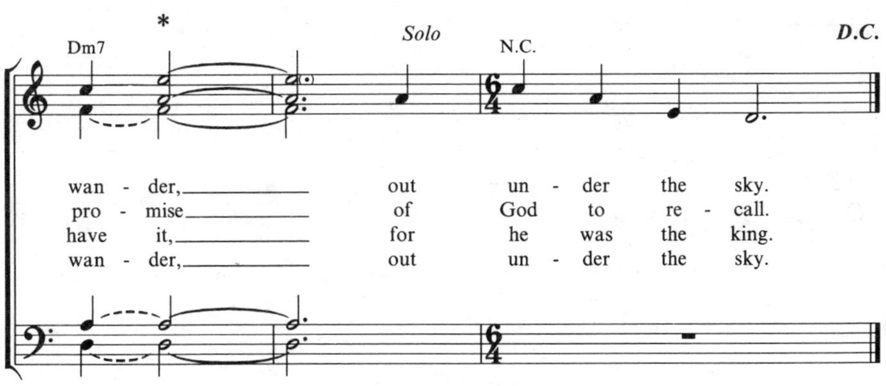
*
Solo
D.C.
Dm7
N.C.
wan - der, out un - der the sky.
pro - mise of God to re - call.
have it, for he was the king.
wan - der, out un - der the sky.

* A is for altos when in unison

132 If I'd been there

Star bright
Words: Elizabeth Bennett
Music: Colin Evans
Moderate tempo
G
Cmaj7
G
mf
Cmaj7
D7
G
Bm
C
G
1 If I'd been there in Beth - le-hem, if
(2) I'd been an as - tro - lo-ger, a
C
D7
G
C
Bm
I had seen that star, would I write a book a -
pro - phet or a king, would I find my-self dis -
più f

Em
Am
D7
- bout it; would I go that far? And
- turbed by such a gen - tle thing? If
mf
G
Bm
C
G
C
D7
if I'd been a tra - vel - ler, and you said 'Fol - low me!'
you, dear Je - sus, had a chance to turn and run a - way,
G
C
Bm
Em
would I go to where you led,
would you stay to live that life,
più f
Am
Dsus
D7
and take you ser - ious - ly?
and still be here to - day?

Chorus
G
Am
G
C
D7
Star bright, gleam-ing white, thoughts I have of
f
mf
G
Bm
Am
B7
Em
you to - night; star bright, gleam-ing white, shine
f
C
G
Em
Dsus
D7
1.
G
Cmaj7
on us all this Christ - mas night!
mf
G
Cmaj7
D7
2.
G
2 If
night!

133 In the beginning

From John 1
Words and music: Russell Hodgson
Music arranged David Peacock

Thoughtfully

Em
Verse 2
Bm/E
C
Bm7
2 So the Word be - came flesh and came to dwell a -
1 In the be - gin - ning, the Word al - rea - dy
Em
Bm/E
- mong us; we have seen his glo - ry, such
was; the Word dwelt with God, the
C
D
Bm
C
Em
glo - ry as be - fits the Fa-ther's Son. No one has ev - er
Word and God were one; in him was

D Bm Em
seen God, but the Son has made him known: and the
life, the life was the light of men; and the
Am/C Bm7 Em
light shines in the dark - ness.
light shines in the dark - ness.
Chorus
Em C D Bm Em
The light of Christ has come in - to the world, the
C Bm7 Em C D
light of Christ is here; the light of Christ has

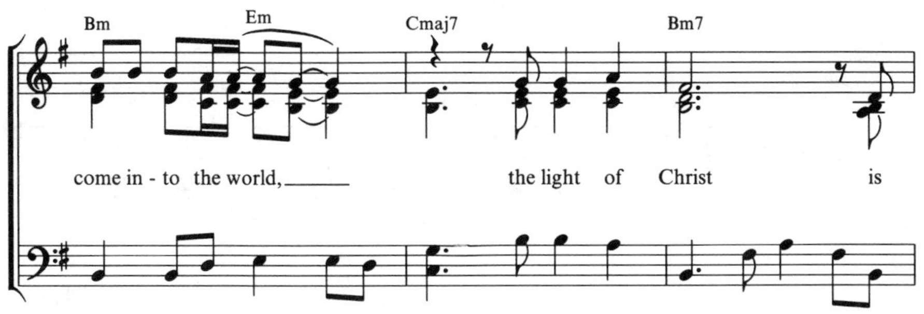
Bm
Em
Cmaj7
Bm7
come in - to the world,
the light of Christ is

Fine
Em
C
D
Em
here!
3 He is our mes - si - ah,

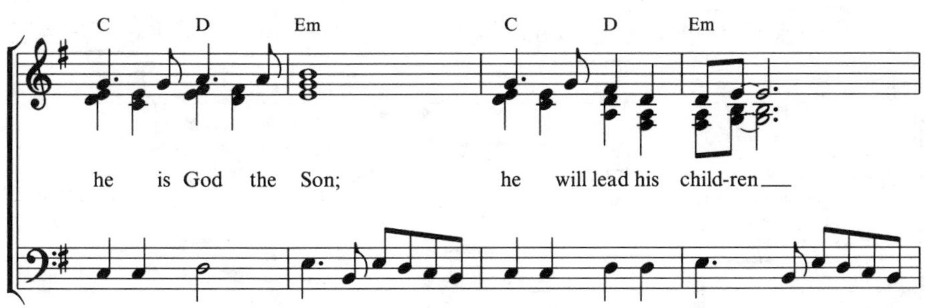
C
D
Em
C
D
Em
he is God the Son;
he will lead his child-ren

D.𝄋 al Fine
C
D
Bm
Em
on and on and on and on.
The

134 In a stable

Words: Michael Perry
Music: Spanish carol melody
arranged Tom Cunningham
Esta noche
Capo 3(D)
Joyfully
F (D)
C7 (A7)
Dm (Bm)
Am (F♯m)
Gm7 (Em7)
D (B)
Chorus
F7 (D7)
1 In a stable, in a manger, lies a baby – our true saviour: hear the carol that we sing you, and the tidings that we bring you.
2 There the virgin mother Mary tends her infant – oh so gently; and the beauty of the Godhead shines around him – her belovèd. There's a
3 Let the mighty faint and tremble at the triumph of the humble; and the guilty leave their sighing where the sinner's hope is lying.

B♭
(G)
F
(D)
F7
(D7)
B♭
(G)
Gm7
(Em7)
light in the hea-vens this morn-ing and a song for the an-gels to
C
(A)
F7
(D7)
B♭
(G)
F/A
(D)
sing; in a sta - ble, in a man-ger, lies a
Gm7
(Em7)
C7
(A7)
1.2.
F(D)
3.
F(D)
ba - by our true sav-iour. sav-iour.
instrumental
ending
B♭/F
(G)
Gm7/F
(Em7)
Gsus/F
(Esus)
F
(D)

135 In the bleak mid-winter

Cranham
Capo 3(D)
Words: C G Rossetti (1830–1894)
Music: G Holst (1874–1934)
F (D) Dm (Bm) Gm/B♭ (Em) Dm (Bm) Gm (Em) C (A)
1 In the bleak mid - win - ter fros - ty wind made moan,
2 Hea - ven can - not hold him, nor earth sus - tain;
3 E - nough for him whom cher - u-bim wor - ship night and day – a
4 What can I give him, poor as I am?
F (D) Dm (Bm) Gm/B♭ (Em) C7 (A7) F (D)
earth stood hard as ir - on, wa - ter like a stone;
heaven and earth shall flee a - way when he comes to reign:
breast - ful of milk, and a man - ger full of hay; e -
If I were a shep - herd I would give a lamb,
B♭ (G) F7 (D7) B♭ (G) Dm (Bm) F/A (D) B♭ (G) C (A)
snow had fall - en, snow on snow, snow on snow,
in the bleak mid - win - ter a sta - ble - place suf - ficed
- nough for him whom an - gels fall down be - fore – the
if I were a wise man I would do my part; yet
F (D) Dm (Bm) Gm/B♭ (Em) C7 (A7) F (D)
in the bleak mid - win - ter long a - go.
God, the Lord al - migh - ty, Je - sus Christ.
wise men and the shep - herds who a - dore!
what I can I give him – give my heart.

136 In the little town

Bethlehem Song

Gently, not too slow

Words: Wiley Beveridge and Glenna McLane
Music: Wiley Beveridge
arranged David Peacock

D
Descant or instrument
3 Wise men, ox and ass, come, join the praise of his
1 In the lit - tle town of Beth - le - hem long a -
2 In the man-ger lay this babe of love through the
3 Wise men, ox and ass, come, join the praise of his
C G/B Am7 G/B C G/B Am G/B
birth;
- go a
night;
birth;
D
child - ren of the light pro - claim the good news to the
lit - tle babe was born to save the world from all
shep-herds came in joy and haste to see God's own
child - ren of the light pro - claim the good news to the

C G/B Am7 G/B C G/B Am D7
earth.
woe.
light.
earth.
G D
Lift your voi - ces, sing 'Al - le - lu',
How the an - gels sang 'Al - le - lu'!
How the shep - herds sang 'Al - le - lu'!
Lift your voi - ces, sing 'Al - le - lu',
G D
sing to Je - sus, sing 'Al - le - lu'!
Sing to Je - sus, sing 'Al - le - lu'!
Sing to Je - sus, sing 'Al - le - lu'!
sing to Je - sus, sing 'Al - le - lu'!

C G/B Am7 G/B C G/B Am7 G/B
D G/D D Am7 D G/D D Am7 D
'Al - le - lu, al - le - lu, al - le - lu'!
'Al - le - lu, al - le - lu, al - le - lu'!
B♭ version of descant
D.C.

137 In the darkness of the night

Words: from Isaiah 9
Michael Perry
Music: Welsh traditional melody
arranged David Peacock

Yr hen gelynnen

Flowing
Em7 Asus A F♯m7 Bsus B Em G/A A
Introduction
con ped.
Verses
D D G/D D
1 In the dark - ness of the night the
2 In the dark - ness of the night a
3 In the dark - ness of the night where
F♯m7 Bm7 Em7 A G Em7 A7
peo - ple walk in sor - row; they have not seen, nor
host of an - gels ga - ther to greet the Won - der -
Ju - dah's hills lie dream-ing, the vir - gin mo - ther
D F♯m7 D/F♯ Em/G Em A D
can they know the light that dawns to - mor-row.
- ful, the Wise, the Ev - er - last - ing Fa - ther.
of the Christ be - holds our world's re - deem-ing.

Chorus
D C/D D7 G E Esus E
For a Child is born to us, to us a Son is

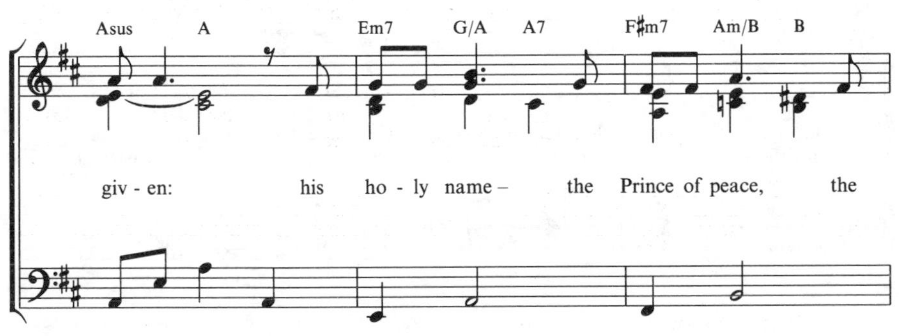
Asus A Em7 G/A A7 F♯m7 Am/B B
giv - en: his ho - ly name – the Prince of peace, the

Em Em/A A 1.2. D 3. D
Migh - ty God of hea - ven. hea - ven.

138 Infant holy

Words: from the Polish
E M G Reed (1885–1933)
Music: Polish carol melody
arranged A E Rusbridge (1917–1969)

G D G G/B C D7 G
1 In-fant ho-ly, in-fant low-ly, for his bed a cat-tle stall;
2 Flocks were sleep-ing, shep-herds keep-ing vi-gil till the morn-ing new,
D7 G D7 G G/B C D7 G
ox-en low-ing, lit-tle know-ing Christ the babe is Lord of all.
saw the glo-ry, heard the sto-ry– tid-ings of a gos-pel true.
C Am D Bm Em Am Dsus D
Swift are wing-ing an-gels sing-ing, no-wells ring-ing, tid-ings bring-ing:
Thus re-joi-cing, free from sor-row, prai-ses voi-cing greet to-mor-row:
G Am D7 Em Bm G/B C G/D D7 G
Christ the babe is Lord of all; Christ the babe is Lord of all!
Christ the babe was born for you; Christ the babe was born for you!

139 Into darkness light has broken

East Acklam
Words: David Mowbray
Music: Francis Jackson
Capo 3(C)
Eb Fm Gm Ab Eb Ab Cm Fm7 Eb/Bb Cm Bb7 Eb
(C) (Dm) (Em) (F) (C) (F) (Am) (Dm7) (C) (Am) (G7) (C)
1 In - to dark-ness light has bro - ken, Christ has been born!
2 For to us a son is gi - ven, Christ has been born!
3 Pro-mised child – we tell the sto - ry – Christ has been born!
Cm D7 Gm Cm/A Gm Cm D7 Cm F Bbsus Bb
(Am) (B7) (Em) (Am) (Em) (Am) (B7) (Am) (D) (Gsus) (G)
out of si - lence God has spo - ken; Christ has been born!
trea-sured gift to earth from hea - ven; Christ has been born!
Son of Da - vid, Is - rael's glo - ry: Christ has been born!
Bbm C7 Fm Eb7 Fm Eb Ab Gsus G
(Gm) (A7) (Dm) (C7) (Dm) (C) (F) (Esus) (E)
Prince of peace, the na-tions greet him, thrones and powers can - not de - feat him:
won-drous coun - sel - lor to guide us, judge when jus - tice is de - nied us,
in this child our God has sought us, wis - dom from on high has taught us,
G7 Cm G7 Cm Fm Eb/Bb Cm Fm/C Ebsus Eb
(E7) (Am) (E7) (Am) (Dm) (C) (Am) (Dm) (Csus) (C)
sing for joy and come to meet him. Christ has been born!
ev - er - last - ing God be - side us. Christ has been born!
hope and heal - ing now has brought us. Christ has been born!

140 It came upon the midnight clear

(FIRST TUNE)

Noël

Capo 3(D)

Words: E H Sears (1810–1876)
in this version Word & Music
Music: English traditional melody
arranged A S Sullivan (1842–1900)
descant: David Peacock

F(D) C(A) F(D) Gm(Em) C7(A7) F(D) C(A) C7(A7)
Descant
4 And still the days are has - tening on – by
1 It came up - on the mid - night clear, that
2 With sor - row brought by sin and strife the
3 And those whose jour - ney now is hard, whose
4 And still the days are has - tening on – by
F(D) B♭(G) F(D) C(A) Dm(Bm)
pro - phets seen of old – to - wards the ful - ness
glo - rious song of old, from an - gels bend - ing
world has suf - fered long and, since the an - gels
hope is burn - ing low, who tread the rock - y
pro - phets seen of old – to - wards the ful - ness
B♭(G) F(D) C(A) F(D) Dm(Bm) F/A(D) F/C(D) C7(A7) F(D) Dm(Bm)
of the time when comes the age, the age fore - told:
near the earth to touch their harps of gold: 'Through
sang, have passed two thou - sand years of wrong; the
path of life with pain - ful steps and slow: O
of the time when comes the age fore - told: then

A7 (F♯7) Dm (Bm) Gm (Em) A7 (F♯7) Dm (Bm) G7/D (E7)
then earth and heaven re -
all the earth, good - will and peace from
na - tions, still at war, hear not the
lis - ten to the news of love which
earth and heaven re - newed shall see the
C (A) Dm (Bm) C/G (A) G7 (E7) C (A) F (D) D7 (B7)
- newed shall see their king; the world
heaven's all - gra - cious king!' The world in so - lemn
love - song which they bring: O hush the noise and
makes the hea - vens ring! O rest be - side the
prince of peace, their king; and all the world re -
Gm (Em) F/A (D) C (A) Dm (Bm) F (D) F/C (D) C7 (A7) F (D)
the song which now the an - gels sing.
still - ness lay to hear the an - gels sing.
cease the strife to hear the an - gels sing!
wea - ry road and hear the an - gels sing!
- peat the song which now the an - gels sing.

141 It came upon the midnight clear

(SECOND TUNE)

Carol

Capo 3(G)

Words: E H Sears (1810–1876)
in this version Word & Music
Music: R S Willis (1819–1900)

Bb (G)
Eb/Bb (C)
Bb (G)
Eb/Bb (C)
Bb (G)
1 It came up - on___ the mid - night clear, that
2 With sor - row brought__ by sin and strife the
3 And those whose jour - ney now is hard, whose
4 And still the days___ are has - tening on – by

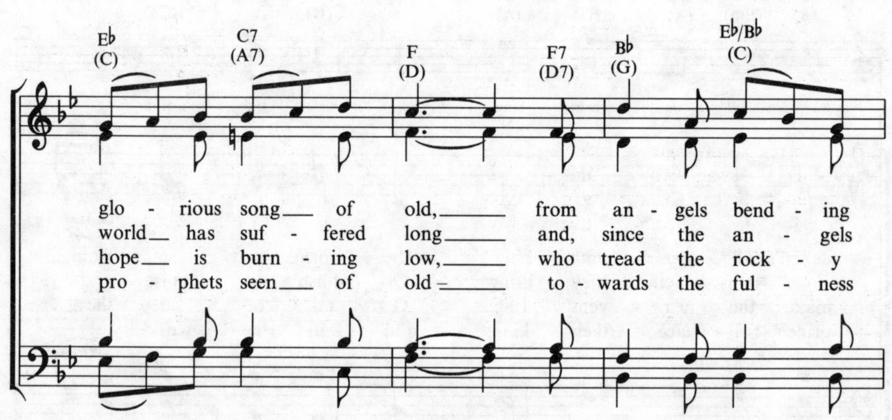

Eb (C)
C7 (A7)
F (D)
F7 (D7)
Bb (G)
Eb/Bb (C)
glo - rious song___ of old,_____ from an - gels bend - ing
world__ has suf - fered long_____ and, since the an - gels
hope__ is burn - ing low,_____ who tread the rock - y
pro - phets seen__ of old –_____ to - wards the ful - ness

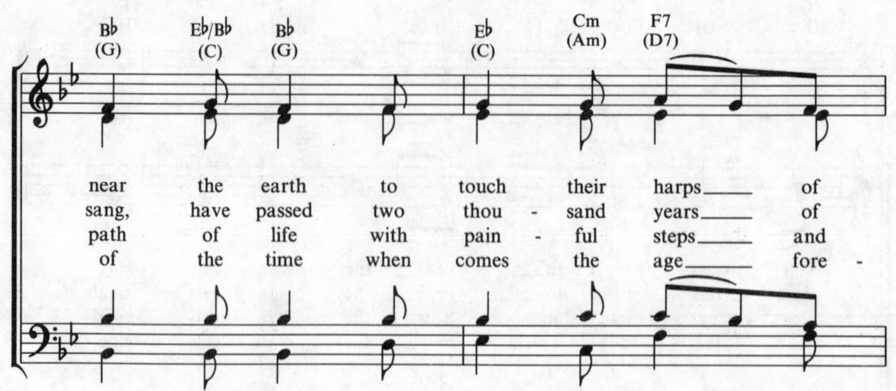

Bb (G)
Eb/Bb (C)
Bb (G)
Eb (C)
Cm (Am)
F7 (D7)
near the earth to touch their harps_____ of
sang, have passed two thou - sand years_____ of
path of life with pain - ful steps_____ and
of the time when comes the age_____ fore -

B♭ (G)
D (B)
D7 (B7)
Gm (Em)
D (B)
Gm (Em)
gold: 'Through all the earth, good - will and peace from
wrong; the na - tions, still at war, hear not the
slow: O lis - ten to the news of love which
- told: then earth and heaven re - newed shall see the

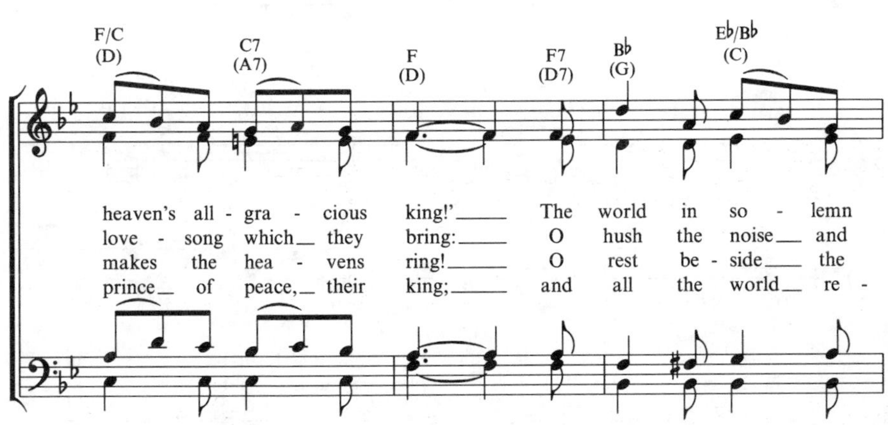
F/C (D)
C7 (A7)
F (D)
F7 (D7)
B♭ (G)
E♭/B♭ (C)
heaven's all - gra - cious king!' The world in so - lemn
love - song which they bring: O hush the noise and
makes the hea - vens ring! O rest be - side the
prince of peace, their king; and all the world re -

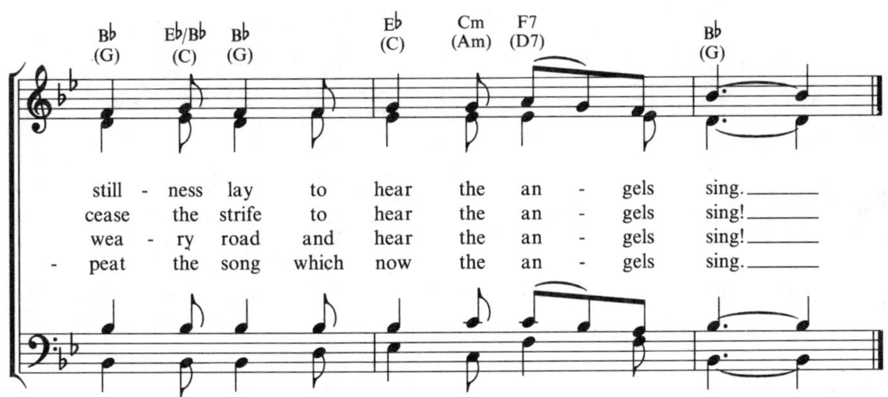
B♭ (G)
E♭/B♭ (C)
B♭ (G)
E♭ (C)
Cm (Am)
F7 (D7)
B♭ (G)
still - ness lay to hear the an - gels sing.
cease the strife to hear the an - gels sing!
wea - ry road and hear the an - gels sing!
- peat the song which now the an - gels sing.

142 It was in Judah's land

Judah's land

Words: in this version Word & Music
Music: Appalachian carol
arranged David Peacock

Capo 3(C)
Gently
Flute obligato
Eb (C) Gm (Em) Cm (Am) Fm (Dm) Bb7 (G7) Eb (C)
1 It was in Ju-dah's land by God's al-migh-ty hand that
2 For by his mo-ther's hand he was wrapped in swath-ing band and
Cm (Am) Gm (Em) Ab (F) Bb7 (G7) Ab/Eb (F) Eb (C) Ab (F) F#dim (D#dim)
Je-sus Christ was born in a sta-ble: in a sta-ble, in a
in a man-ger laid in a sta-ble: in a sta-ble, in a
Eb (C) Cm (Am) Ab (F) Gm7 (Em7) Fm7 (Dm7) Bb7 (G7) Ab/Eb (F) Eb (C)
sta-ble, that Je-sus Christ was born in a sta-ble.
sta-ble, and in a man-ger laid in a sta-ble.

143 Jesus, child of Mary

Hayle
Capo 3(C)

Words and music: Michael Perry
Music arranged Norman Warren

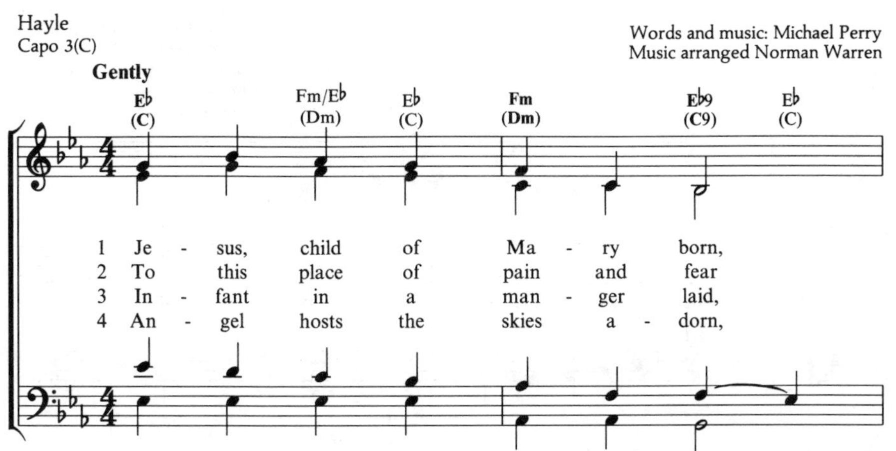
Gently
Eb (C) Fm/Eb (Dm) Eb (C) Fm (Dm) Eb9 (C9) Eb (C)
1 Je - sus, child of Ma - ry born,
2 To this place of pain and fear
3 In - fant in a man - ger laid,
4 An - gel hosts the skies a - dorn,

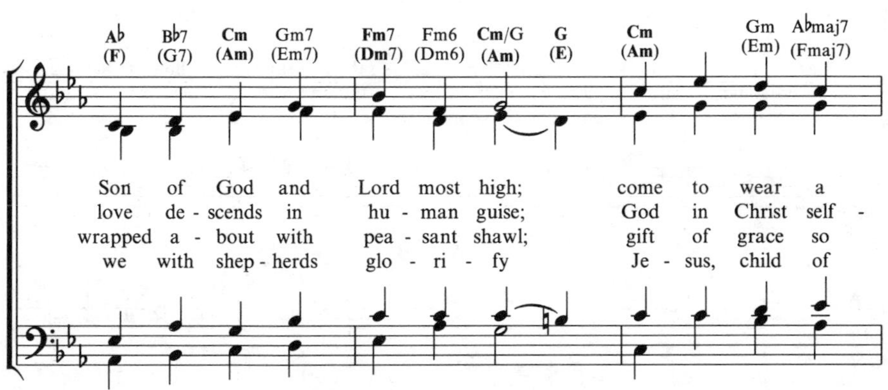
Ab (F) Bb7 (G7) Cm (Am) Gm7 (Em7) Fm7 (Dm7) Fm6 (Dm6) Cm/G (Am) G (E) Cm (Am) Gm (Em) Abmaj7 (Fmaj7)
Son of God and Lord most high; come to wear a
love de - scends in hu - man guise; God in Christ self -
wrapped a - bout with pea - sant shawl; gift of grace so
we with shep - herds glo - ri - fy Je - sus, child of

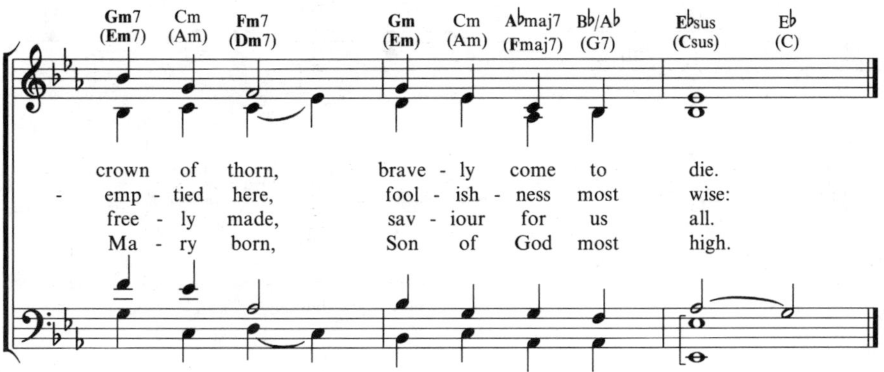
Gm7 (Em7) Cm (Am) Fm7 (Dm7) Gm (Em) Cm (Am) Abmaj7 (Fmaj7) Bb/Ab (G7) Ebsus (Csus) Eb (C)
crown of thorn, brave - ly come to die.
- emp - tied here, fool - ish - ness most wise:
free - ly made, sav - iour for us all.
Ma - ry born, Son of God most high.

144 Jesus comes

Helmsley

Words: after J Cennick (1718–1755)
C Wesley (1707–1788) and M Madan (1726–1790)
in this version Jubilate Hymns
Music: Eighteenth-century English melody,
verse 4 arranged Noël Tredinnick

G Em C G D7
1 Je - sus comes with clouds de - scend - ing – see the
2 Ev - ery eye shall then be - hold him robed in
3 All the wounds of cross and pas - sion still his
G D G Am G/D D G Em C
Lamb for sin - ners slain! thou - sand thou - sand
awe - some ma - jes - ty; those who jeered at
glor - ious bo - dy bears; cause of end - less
G D7 G D G Am
saints at - tend - ing join to sing the glad re -
him and sold him, pierced and nailed him to the
ex - ul - ta - tion to his ran - somed wor - ship -
G/D D G D7 G C G/D D7 G
- frain: Al - le - lu - ia, al - le - lu - ia,
tree, shamed and grie - ving, shamed and grie - ving,
- pers. With what glad - ness, with what glad - ness,

D7 G D Em G D C G/D D7 G
al - le - lu - ia! God ap - pears on earth to reign.
shamed and grie - ving, shall their true Mes - si - ah see.
with what glad - ness, we shall see the Sav - iour's scars!
G Em C Em7 A7 Dsus D7 G
4 Yes, A - men! let all a - dore you
D7 G Dsus D G7 Am A7 G/B D
high on your e - ter - nal throne;
G Em A♯dim Bm Em G/A A7 D7 G
crowns and em - pires fall be - fore you –

D D7/C G Em Am D7 Bm G♯dim
claim the king - dom for your
Asus A D7 G/D Em Am
own. Come, Lord Je - sus; come, Lord
B7 Em G E7 Am E7 A7 B7
Je - sus; come, Lord Je - sus –
Em Asus A D Dm7/B E Am D7 G
ev - er - last - ing God, come down!

145 Jesus Christ our great redeemer

Capo 2(Am)

From Job 19 and Ephesians 1
Words and music: Peter and Diane Fung

Strongly

Bm (Am) G (F) Bm (Am) G (F)
Je - sus Christ our__ great re-deem-er, migh-ty vic - tor and strong de - liv-erer,
Dmaj7 (Cmaj7) Em7 (Dm7) A7 (G7) F♯m (Em) Bm (Am) Em (Dm) F♯7 (E7)
king of kings and Lord of lords, we praise you, praise your name – Al-le -
Bm (Am) A (G) Gmaj7 (Fmaj7) Em (Dm) A7 (G7) Dmaj7 (Cmaj7) F♯7 (E7)
- lu - ia, al-le - lu - ia; King of kings and Lord of lords – Al-le -
Bm (Am) A (G) Gmaj7 (Fmaj7) Em (Dm) A7 (G7) D (C)
- lu - ia, al-le - lu - ia! your vic-tory is as - sured.

146 Jesus Christ the Lord is born

Puer nobis

Words: after German authors
Michael Perry
Music: from *Piae Cantiones*, (1582)
arranged David Iliff,
verse 5 arranged David Peacock

D A7 D Em D/A A7 D A D G A7
1 Je - sus Christ the Lord is born, all the bells are
2 'Go to Beth - le - hem to - day, find your king and
3 Held with - in a cat - tle stall, loved by love ma -
4 Soon shall come the wise men three, rous - ing Her - od's
Bm E7 A D G A7 D Bm
ring - ing! an - gels greet the ho - ly One and
sav - iour: glo - ry be to God on high, to
- ter - nal, see the mas - ter of us all, our
an - ger; mo - ther's hearts shall bro - ken be and
D/A G/A D/A A7 Bm F♯m Em D G D/A A7 D
shep-herds hear them sing - ing, and shep-herds hear them sing - ing.
earth his peace and fa - vour, to earth his peace and fa - vour!'
Lord of lords e - ter - nal, our Lord of lords e - ter - nal.
Ma - ry's son in dan - ger, and Ma - ry's son in dan - ger.

D Em F♯7 Bm A7 D G A7
5 Death from life and life from death, our sal - va - tion's

Dsus D Bm E Amaj7 D G A7 D Bm
sto - ry: let all liv - ing things give breath to

Em A7 Bm Em F♯m Em D Gm E7 A7 Dsus D
Christ-mas songs of glo - ry, to Christ-mas songs of glo - ry!

147 Jesus, hope of every nation

Eversley

From Luke 2 (*The Song of Simeon / Nunc dimittis*)
Words and music: Michael Perry
Music arranged David Peacock

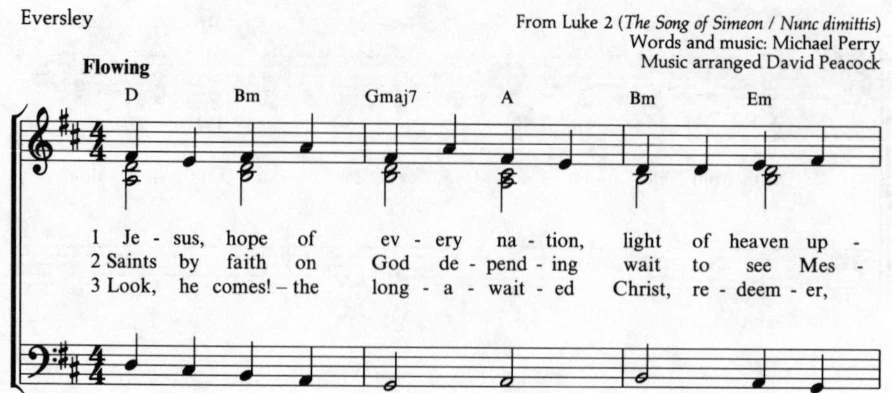

Flowing
D
Bm
Gmaj7
A
Bm
Em
1 Je - sus, hope of ev - ery na - tion, light of heaven up -
2 Saints by faith on God de - pend - ing wait to see Mes -
3 Look, he comes! – the long - a - wait - ed Christ, re - deem - er,

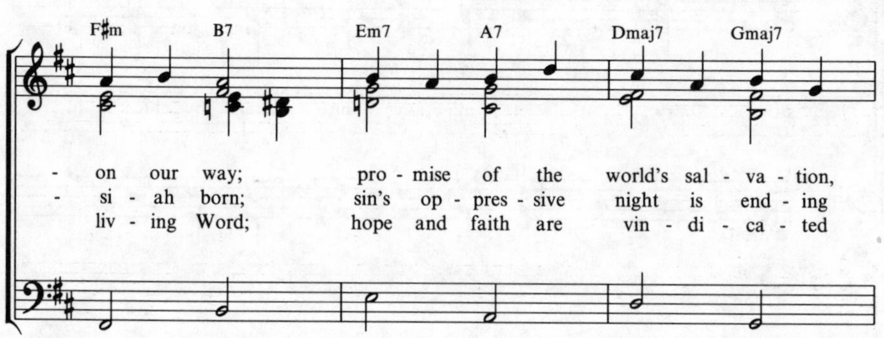

F♯m
B7
Em7
A7
Dmaj7
Gmaj7
- on our way; pro - mise of the world's sal - va - tion,
- si - ah born; sin's op - pres - sive night is end - ing
liv - ing Word; hope and faith are vin - di - ca - ted

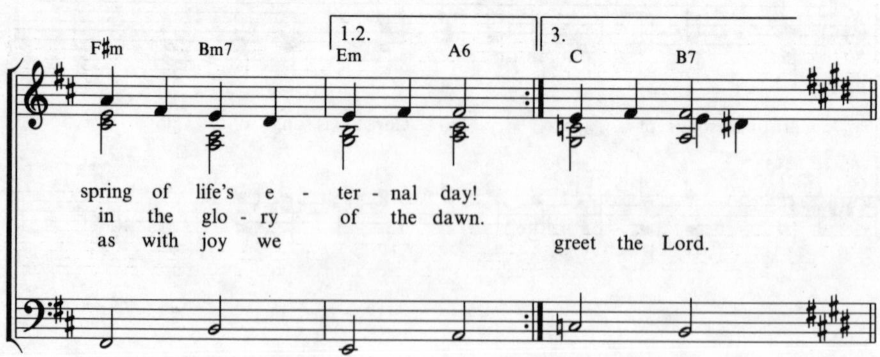

1.2.
3.
F♯m
Bm7
Em
A6
C
B7
spring of life's e - ter - nal day!
in the glo - ry of the dawn.
as with joy we greet the Lord.

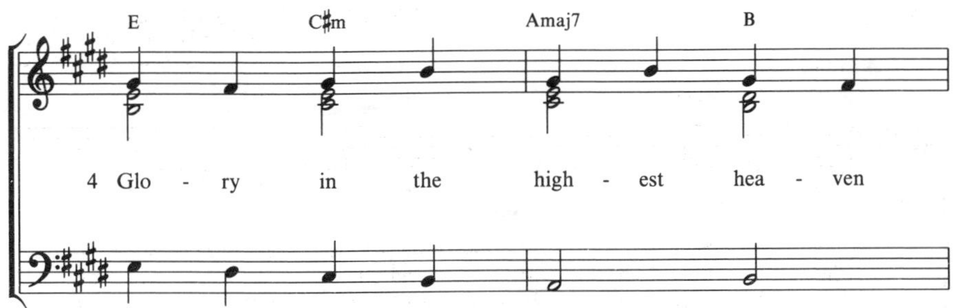
E
C♯m
Amaj7
B
4 Glo - ry in the high - est hea - ven

C♯m
F♯m
G♯m
C♯7
F♯m7
B7
to the Fa - ther, Spi - rit, Son; and on earth let

Emaj7
Amaj7
G♯m7
C♯m7
F♯m/B
B
E
praise be giv - en to our God, the Three - in - one!

Optional soprano descant verse 4

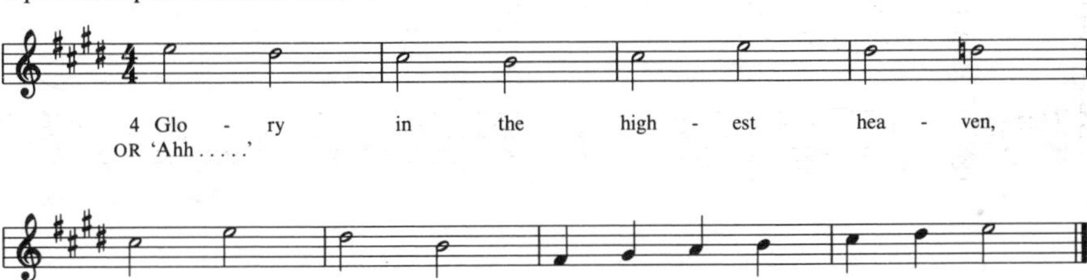
4 Glo - ry in the high - est hea - ven,
OR 'Ahh . . . . .'
praise be giv - en to our God, the Three - in - one!

148 Jesus, Lamb of God

Communion Song 3

Capo 5(G)

Words and music: Paul Inwood

Gently
C(G)
Dm7 (Am7)
Gsus (Dsus)
G (D)
ADVENT
1 Je - sus, Lamb of God and source of life;
2 Je - sus, com - ing near to bring us joy;
3 Je - sus, bring - ing hope to all who fear;
4 Je - sus, Sav - iour her - ald - ed by John:
Am (Em)
Em7 (Bm7)
Dm7 (Am7)
Gsus (Dsus)
G (D)
Je - sus, lov - ing bear - er of our sins:
Je - sus, Son of God, Em - ma - nu - el:
Je - sus, bring - ing strength to all who mourn:
Je - sus, son of Da - vid's house and line:
Chorus
F (C)
C (G)
Dm (Am)
Am (Em)
hear our prayer, have mer - cy, hear our prayer, have mer - cy,
F (C)
C (G)
last chorus
Dm (Am)
Am7 (Em7)
give us your peace. hear our prayer, have mer - cy,

Bb
(F)
F
(C)
Dm6
(Am6)
3
A
(E)
hear our prayer, have mer - cy, give us your peace.

CHRISTMAS

1 Jesus, Lamb of God, the Word made flesh;
Jesus, Son of God come down on earth:
hear our prayer, have mercy,
hear our prayer, have mercy,
give us your peace.

2 Jesus, King of glory, Prince of peace,
Jesus, shining in our darkened world:
hear our prayer . . .

3 Jesus, King of angels, Lord of joy;
Jesus, born to save the world from sin:
hear our prayer . . .

B♭ melody version

Verse
Chorus
3
last chorus
3

149 Jesus, name above all names

Words and music: Naida Hearn
Music arranged David Peacock

Gently
E B/D♯ C♯m B7 E B/D♯ C♯m
Je - sus, name a-bove all names, beau-ti-ful
F♯m F♯m7/A B B7 E/G♯ A E/B B
sav - iour, glo-ri-ous Lord; Em -
E B/D♯ C♯m B7 E B/D♯ C♯m
- ma - nu-el - God is with us! bless-èd re -
to repeat
to end
F♯m F♯m7/A B B7 E A E/B B7 E
- deem - er, liv - ing Word.

150 Jesus, saviour, holy child

Words: Michael Perry
Music: Czech carol melody
arranged David Peacock

Rocking

Unhurried
D Bm/D E7 A Bm E7 A
1 Je - sus, sav - iour, ho - ly child, sleep to - night,
2 From your Fa - ther's home you come to this earth,
3 Now to hea - ven's glo - ry song we re - ply
Em7 A7 D Em7/G A7 D
slum - ber deep till morn - ing light. Lul - la - by, our
by your low - ly man - ger birth: Child of God, our
with a Christ - mas lul - la - by. Hush, the e - ter - nal
Em A7 D D/C G/B D/A Em/G E7/G♯ A7
joy, our treas - ure, all our hope and all our pleas - ure:
na - ture shar - ing; Son of Man, our sor - rows bear - ing;
Lord is sleep - ing close in Ma - ry's ten - der keep - ing:
D Bm E7 A G/B A7/C♯ D Em/G A7 D
at the cra - dle where you lie we will wor - ship – lul - la - by!
rich, yet here a - mong the poor: Christ the Lord, whom we a - dore!
babe on whom the an - gels smiled – Je - sus, sav - iour, ho - ly child.

151 Jesus was born in a stable

Good enough for him

Words and music: Peter Chesters

Slow blues, with an insistent rhythm
Am6 B7 Em C7 B7
Em
1 & 4 Je - sus was born in a sta - ble,
2 Cat - tle a - sleep in the cor - ner,
Am7 Dsus D7 Am6/F♯ B7
there was no room in the inn; he had a stall for a
Jo - seph kept watch from with - in. Can you im - ag - ine the
last time to Coda
Em/G Am B7 1. Em C7 Am6/F♯ B7
cra - dle, that was good e-nough for him.
sor - row? That was good e-nough for

2.
Em
Am7
D7
Gmaj7
G7
3
him.
3 No king-ly robes for his ves - ture,

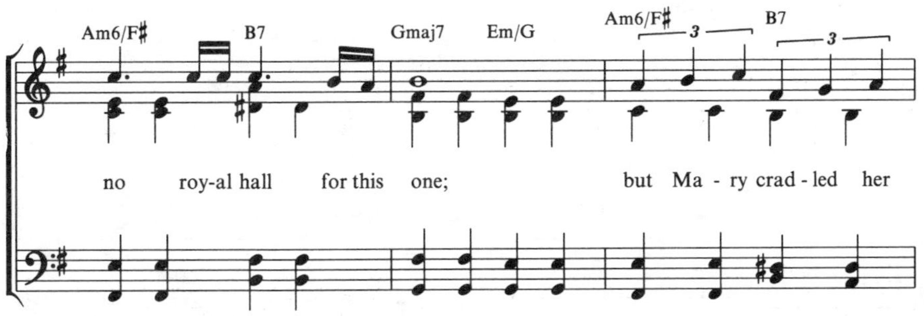
Am6/F♯
B7
Gmaj7
Em/G
Am6/F♯
B7
3
no roy-al hall for this one;
but Ma - ry crad - led her

D.𝄋 al Coda
Em/G
E/G♯
Am
F♯7
B7
3
treas - ure,
for he was God's dear Son.

CODA
Em
C7
Am6/F♯
B7
Am6
B7
Em
him.
And that was good e-nough for him.

152 Journey to Bethlehem

Stony Brook
Words: Michael Perry
Music: Roger Mayor
Lively
G C G
1 Jour - ney to Beth - le - hem, wor - ship your king,
2 Come with your pre - sents of hon - our and love,
3 Come with your sor - row for wrongs you have done,
4 Come with your prai - ses and joy - ful - ly sing,
C Am Am7 D7 B7 E7
wor - ship your king, wor - ship your king;
hon - our and love, hon - our and love;
wrongs you have done, wrongs you have done;
joy - ful - ly sing, joy - ful - ly sing;
Am B7 C
come with your prai - ses and joy - ful - ly sing,
this is the birth - day of hope from a - bove,
find your for - give - ness in God's on - ly Son,
jour - ney to Beth - le - hem, wor - ship your king,

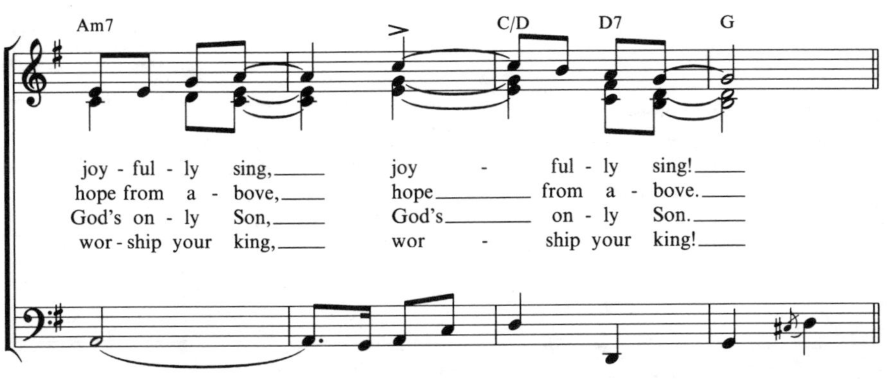
Am7
C/D
D7
G
joy - ful - ly sing, joy - ful - ly sing!
hope from a - bove, hope from a - bove.
God's on - ly Son, God's on - ly Son.
wor - ship your king, wor - ship your king!

1.2.3. Am
G/D
D7
4.
Am
D
G
8va
pp

B♭ melody version

1–3.
4.

153 Joy to the world

Antioch

Words: I Watts (1674–1748)
Music: G F Handel (1685–1759)
arranged L Mason (1792–1872)

D Em D/A A7 D
1 Joy to the world – the Lord has come: let
2 Joy to the earth – the sav - iour reigns: your
3 He rules the world with truth and grace, and
G A D G/D D
earth re-ceive her king, let ev - ery heart pre -
sweet - est songs em - ploy, while fields and streams and
makes the na - tions prove the glo - ries of his
G/D D
- pare him room and heaven and na - ture sing, and
hills and plains re - peat the sound-ing joy, re -
right - eous - ness, the won-ders of his love, the
and heaven and na - ture
re - peat the sound-ing
the won - ders of his
A A7 D G/D D Em D/A A7 D
heaven and na - ture sing, and heaven, and heaven and na - ture sing!
- peat the sound-ing joy, re - peat, re - peat the sound-ing joy.
won - ders of his love, the won - ders, won - ders of his love.
sing, and heaven and na - ture sing, and heaven and na - ture sing!
joy, re - peat the sound-ing joy, re - peat the sound-ing joy.
love, the won - ders of his love, the won - ders of his love.

154 King of kings

Words: Sophie Conty and Naomi Batya
Music: Ancient Hebrew folk song

Lively
Em
B7
Em
King of kings and Lord of — lords, — Glo - ry, al - le - lu - ia;
B7
Em
King of kings and Lord of — lords, — glo - ry, al - le - lu - ia!
*
B7
Em
Je - sus, Prince of peace, — glo - ry, al - le - lu - ia;
B7
Em
Je - sus, Prince of peace, — glo - ry, al - le - lu - ia!

* To sing as a round in two parts,
group 2 should begin singing when group 1 arrives at this point.

155 Kings came riding

Words and music: Joan Lawton

With increasing pace
Dm Am Dm
Chime bars / Descant recorder
1 Kings came rid - ing from the East,
2 Her - od told them: 'Find the babe;
(3) all he wan - ted was his blood,
Am Dm
search - ing for the Prince of peace; then king Her - od,
come and tell me where he's laid: I will go there,
have this in - fant gone for good. Quick - ly rid - ing
A7 Dm A7 Dm
wick - ed man, schemed and plot - ted ev - il plan.
kneel me down, of - fer him my gold - en crown.' 3 But
through the sand, kings left Her - od's des - ert land.

156 Let the desert sing

(FIRST TUNE)
Desert Song
Capo 2(C)
Words: from Isaiah 35
Michael Perry
Music: Norman Warren
Lively
D9(C9) D(C)
1 Let the de - sert sing and the
(2) blind shall see and the
(3) ran - somed walk with their
Dmaj7 (Cmaj7) D7(C7) G(F) Gm6(Fm6)
waste - land flower, for the glo - ry of God in its
deaf shall hear and the lame___ shall leap like the
Lord that day on the per - fect road called the
Em7 (Dm7) A(G) D(C) Bm(Am)
light and power shall be seen on the hills where he
fal - low deer and the voice of the dumb shall___
Sac - red Way, ev - ery tear shall give place to a
1.2.
3.
F♯(E) A7(G7) G/A(F/G) F♯(E) A7(G7) D(E)
comes to save! 2 Then the
shout a - loud. 3 When the song of joy,___ a song of joy!

157 Let the desert sing

(SECOND TUNE)

Let the desert sing

Capo 3(D)

Words: from Isaiah 35
Michael Perry
Music: Tom Cunningham
arranged David Peacock

With a swing
F(D)
B♭/C(G)
F(D)
B♭/C(G)
F (D)
B♭/C (G)
F (D)
B♭/C (G)
F (D)
Dm7 (Bm7)
B♭/C (G)
1 Let the de - sert sing and the waste-land flower,
2 Then the blind shall see and the deaf shall hear
3 When the ran-somed walk with their Lord that day
F (D)
B♭/C (G)
F (D)
Gm7 (Em7)
Dm7 (Bm7)
B♭ (G)
Dm7/A (Bm7)
for the glo-ry of God
and the lame shall leap
on the per - fect road
Gm7 (Em7)
Am (F♯m)
Gm (Em)
Gm7 (Em7)
in its light and power
like the fal - low deer
called the Sa - cred Way,

C (A) | C7/B♭ (A7) | Am7 (F♯m7) | Dm (Bm) | Am/C (F♯m)

shall be seen________ on the hills
and the voice________ of the dumb
ev-ery tear________ shall give place

Gm/B♭ (Em) | F (D) | B♭/C (G) | To end F (D)

where he comes to save!____
shall__shout a-loud.____
to a song of joy!____

B♭ melody version

158 Let all the earth

Words and music: Graham Kendrick
Lively
Introduction
C G/B Am Am/G D/F♯
Gsus G
Verse
C G/B Am Am/G
1 Let all the earth hear his voice, let the peo - ple re -
2 Let all the earth hear his voice, let the prison-ers re -
3 Let all the earth hear his song; sing it loud, sing it
D/F♯ Gsus G C G/B
- joice at the sound of his name; let all the val - leys and
- joice – he is com-ing to save. Sa-tan's dark strong-holds crash
strong – it's the song of his praise. Si - lent no more, we cry
Am Am/G D/F♯ Gsus G
hills burst with joy, and the trees of the field clap their hands.
down as with prayer we sur - round, as the cross we pro - claim.
out – let the world hear the shout: in the earth the Lord reigns.

Chorus

F G E7 Am F G
Just - ice and love he will bring to the world, his king-dom will nev - er

C (E) F G E7 Am
fail; held like a two - ed - ged sword in our hand,

Fmaj7 Gsus G
his word and truth shall pre - vail, shall pre -

C F C G To end C
- vail!

159 Let God arise

Triumphantly

From Psalm 68
Words and music: Graham Kendrick

Chorus
D A6 D D7/F♯ G Bm A7 D
Let God a - rise, and let his en - e - mies be scat - tered, and
Em A7 Em A7 A7/C♯
let those who hate him flee be - fore___ him;___
D G D D7/F♯ G Bm A7 D
let God a - rise, and let his en - e - mies be scat - tered, and
Em A7 A D G/D D
Fine
let those who hate him flee a - way.

Verse
A A7 A D
WOMEN
The right - eous be
MEN
But let the right - eous be glad;
E E7 A F♯
glad, let them ex - ult be - fore God;
let them ex - ult be-fore God, let them re -
F♯ Bm Bm/A E7 E7/G♯ A
O let them re - joice for the king
- joice with glad - ness, build-ing up a high - way for the king.
D.C. al Fine
Asus A Asus A Asus G7 A
in the name of the Lord!
rit.
We go in the name of the Lord: let the shout go up in the name of the Lord!

160 Let praises ring

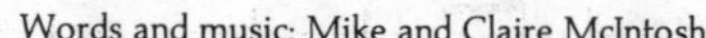
Words and music: Mike and Claire McIntosh

Lively
G
1 Let prai - ses ring, let prai - ses ring,
2 Let prai - ses ring, let prai - ses ring,

Bm
C
C9
lift voi - ces up to love him; lift
bow down in a - dor - at - ion; cry

Bm
C
C/D
G
hearts and hands to touch him! O let prai - ses ring,
out his ex - alt - a - tion – O let prai - ses ring,

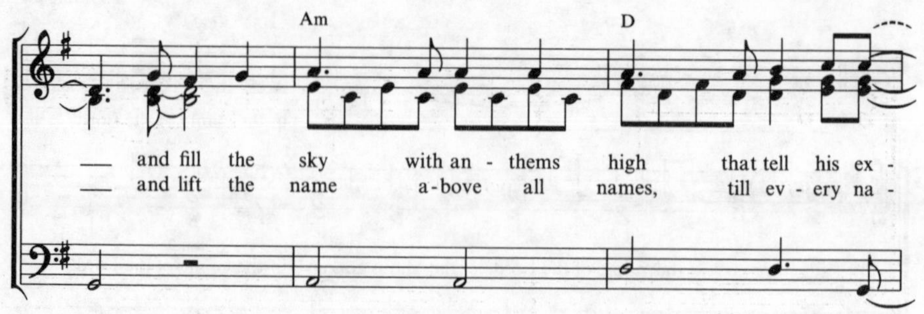
Am
D
and fill the sky with an - thems high that tell his ex -
and lift the name a - bove all names, till ev - ery na -

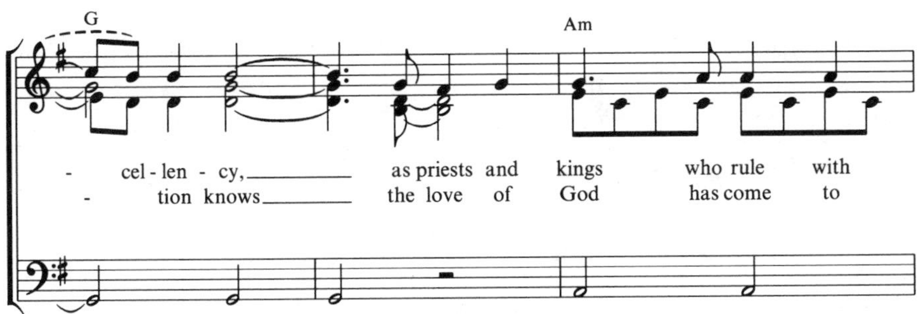
G
Am
- cel - len - cy, as priests and kings who rule with
- tion knows the love of God has come to
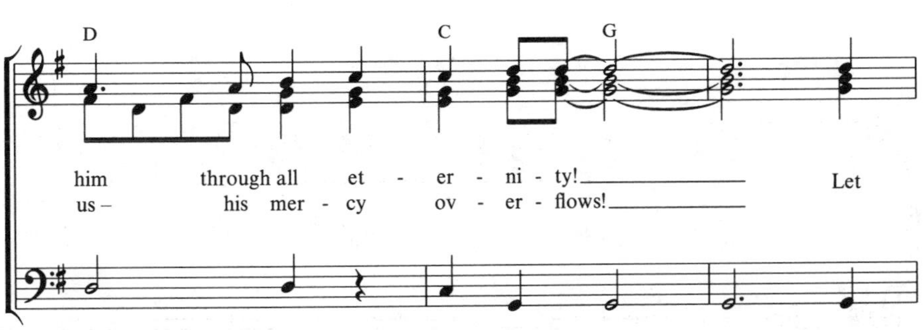
D
C
G
him through all et - er - ni - ty! Let
us – his mer - cy ov - er - flows!
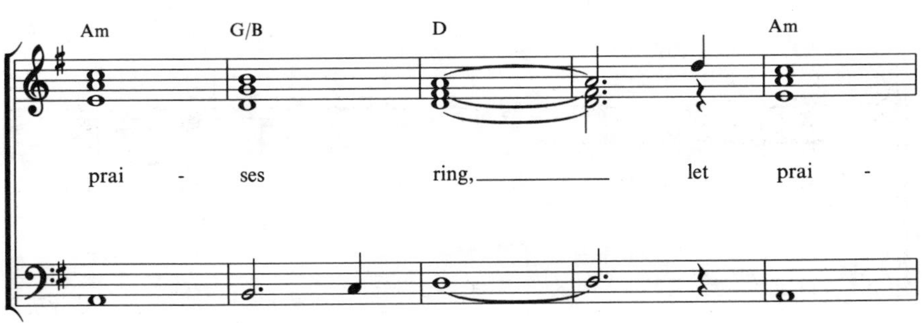
Am
G/B
D
Am
prai - ses ring, let prai -

G/B
D
C
D
G
- ses ring, to our glo - ri - ous King!

161 Lift up your heads

Capo 2(G)

Words and music: Steven Fry

Broadly
A (G) E7/B (D7) A/C♯ (G) D (C) E (D) E7/G♯ Asus (G) A A/G♯
Lift up your heads to the com-ing King;
F♯m (Em) D (C) E/D (D) A/C♯ (G) Bm7sus (Am) A/E (G) Esus (D) E
bow be-fore him and a-dore him, sing
A (G) E7/B (D7) A/C♯ (G) D (C) E (D) E7/G♯ Asus (G) A A/G♯
to his ma - je - sty: let your prai-ses be
F♯m (Em) D (C) E/D (D) A/C♯ (G) Bm (Am7) A/C♯ (G) Esus (Dsus) E (D) A (G)
pure and ho - ly, giv - ing glo - ry to the King of kings.

162 Lift up your heads, O you gates

From Psalm 24
Words and music: Peter Fung

Majestically
WOMEN
MEN
D
D7
G
Gm
D
Lift up your heads, O you gates, —
D7
G
Gm
— and be lif - ted up, you ev - er - last - ing
D
B♭
doors, — that the King of
C
D
Em7/A
D
Em7/A
glo - ry may come in. — Who

MEN
WOMEN
D
Em7/A
is the King of glo - ry? Who is the King of
Who is the King of glo - ry? Who
glo - ry? Who is the King of glo - ry? The
is the King of glo - ry? Who is the King? The
B♭
C
Dsus
1.
Lord of hosts, migh - ty in
Lord of hosts, migh - ty in

2.
3. Slowly in unison
Dsus D Bb C Dsus D D.S.
bat - tle! Who He is the King of glo - ry! Who
bat - tle! He is the King of glo - ry!
Bb C Dsus D Bb C
He is the King of glo - ry: the Lord of
Dsus D Bb C Em7/A D
hosts, he is the King of glo - ry!

163 Lift up your heads

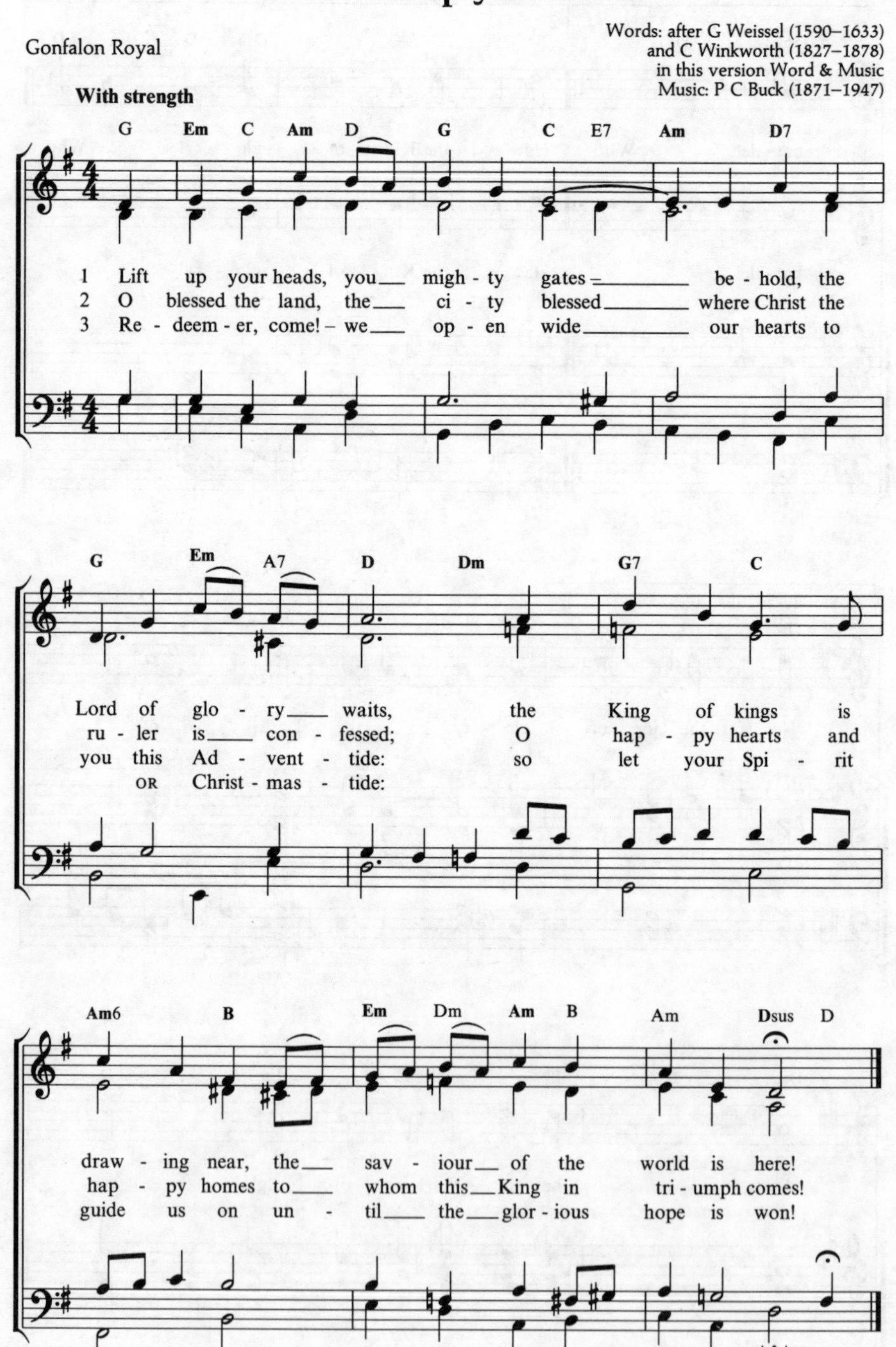
Gonfalon Royal
Words: after G Weissel (1590–1633)
and C Winkworth (1827–1878)
in this version Word & Music
Music: P C Buck (1871–1947)
With strength
G Em C Am D G C E7 Am D7
1 Lift up your heads, you mighty gates – behold, the
2 O blessed the land, the city blessed where Christ the
3 Redeemer, come! – we open wide our hearts to
G Em A7 D Dm G7 C
Lord of glory waits, the King of kings is
ruler is confessed; O happy hearts and
you this Advent tide: so let your Spirit
OR Christmas tide:
Am6 B Em Dm Am B Am Dsus D
drawing near, the saviour of the world is here!
happy homes to whom this King in triumph comes!
guide us on until the glorious hope is won!

164 Lift up your hearts to the Lord

Sound loud the trumpet

From Psalm 98 (*Cantate Domino*)
Words and music: Michael Perry
Music arranged Jubilate Musicians

Capo 3(G)

Majestically
B♭ (G) E♭ (C) B♭ (G) F7/C (D7) B♭ (G) Cm (Am) F7 (D7)
1 Lift up your hearts to the Lord, break in - to songs of
2 Bow down and wor-ship the Lord, greet him who comes to
3 Tell out the word of the Lord, speak of his sav - ing
B♭ (G) F7 (D7) B♭ (G) Gm (Em) Cm (Am) Faug (Daug) Gm (Em) C7 (A7)
joy; let the sea roar, let the hills ring, shout his glo - ri - ous
reign; share his tri-umph, hear his judge-ment, see his mar-vel-lous
power: sure his mer - cy, true his pro - mise, great his won-der-ful
F7 (D7) B♭ (G) F7 (D7) B♭ (G) F7/B♭ (D7) B♭ (G)
name!
works: Harps and horns and trum - pets, sound; praise him, all the
love!
C7 (A7) F7 (D7) B♭ (G) D (B) Gm (Em) D7 (B7) Gm7 (Em7) Cm (Am) F7 (D7) B♭ (G)
world a-round! O sing a new song; O sing a new song!

165 Lift your heart

Marston St Lawrence
Capo 3(C)

Words: Michael Perry
Music: Paul Edwards

Boldly
Cm (Am) Ab (F) Gm (Em) Cm (Am) Ab (F) Fm (Dm)
1 Lift your heart and raise your voice; faith - ful
2 Mor - tals, hear what ang - els say; shep - herds,
3 Here he lies, the Lord of all; na - ture's
4 Lift your hearts and voi - ces high: then shall
Gm (Em) Cm (Am) Fm7 (Dm7) Bb7 (G7) Ab (C) F7 (D7)
peo - ple, come, re - joice: grace and power are shown on
quick - ly make your way, find - ing truth in low - ly
king in cat - tle - stall, God of heaven to earth come
glo - ry fill the sky, Christ shall come and not be
Gm (Em) Cm (Am) Gm (Em) Cm (Am) F7 (D7) Dm7 (Bm7)
earth in the sav - iour's ho - ly
guise, wis - dom to con - found the
down – cross for throne and thorn for
long, earth shall sing the an - gels'
Gsus (Esus) G (E) C (A) Fm (Dm) C (A)
birth.
wise.
crown.
song –
Glo - ri - a!

166 Living under the shadow of his wing

Words and music: David J Hadden and Bob Sylvester

With strength
G
C
1 Liv - ing un - der the sha-dow of his wing we find sec - u - ri - ty; stand-ing in his pre - sence we will bring our wor - ship, wor - ship, wor - ship to the King.
2 Bowed in a - dor - a - tion at his feet we dwell in har-mo-ny, voi - ces joined to - ge - ther that re - peat: 'Wor - thy, wor - thy, wor - thy is the Lamb!'
3 Heart to heart em - bra-cing in his love, we know his pu - ri - ty, rais - ing wor - thy praise to him a - bove: 'Ho - ly, ho - ly, ho - ly is the Lord!'
G
C
Am
D
Bm
Em
Am
D
Gsus
G

167 Light shining in the darkness

Words: Anne Johnson
Music: Paul Herrington and David Stone
arranged David Peacock
Capo 5(C)
Flowing
F (C) Gm7 (Dm7)
Instrument (flute)
1 Light shin-ing in the dark - ness,
2 Love came to dwell a - mong us,
3 Life full of truth and beau - ty,
B♭ (F) Gm7 (Dm7) Gm (Dm) Csus (Gsus) C7 (G7) F (C) Gm7 (Dm7)
light that is the world's true light; light from the be -
love made flesh at Beth - le - hem, love from the be -
life as it was meant to be, life from the be -
Am (Em) Dm7 (Am7) B♭ (F) Gm7 (Dm7) Asus (Esus) A (E)
- gin - ning, now as then, still shin - ing bright.
- gin - ning, our di-vine Cre - a - tor's theme.
- gin - ning, and in - to e - ter - ni - ty.

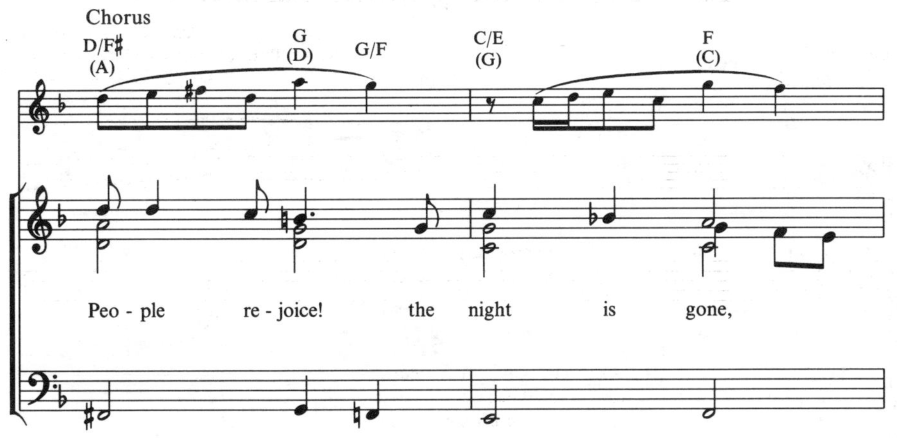
Chorus
D/F♯
(A)
G
(D)
G/F
C/E
(G)
F
(C)
Peo - ple re - joice! the night is gone,

Gm
(Dm)
Csus
(Gsus)
C
(G)
Am7
(Em7)
Gm7
(Dm7)
C7
(G7)
God's re - deem - ing work be - gun in the birth of his

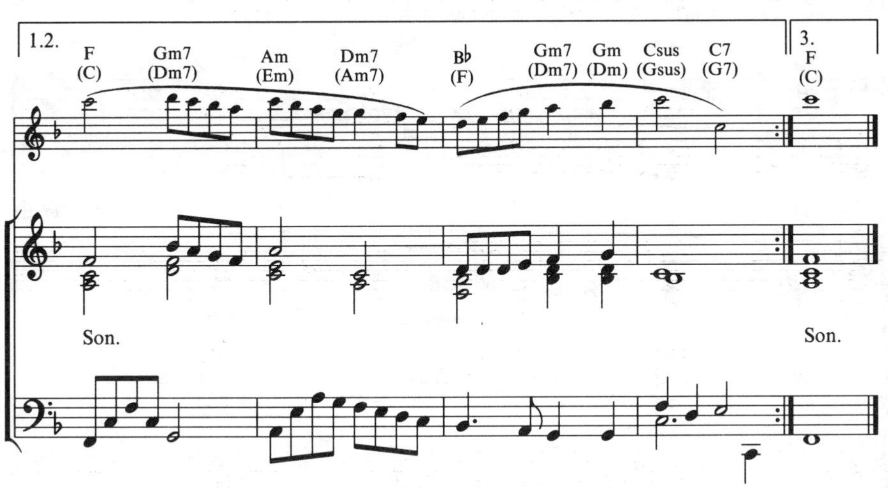
1.2.
F
(C)
Gm7
(Dm7)
Am
(Em)
Dm7
(Am7)
B♭
(F)
Gm7
(Dm7)
Gm
(Dm)
Csus
(Gsus)
C7
(G7)
3.
F
(C)
Son.
Son.

168 Light the candles round the world

Capo 5(C)
Words and music: Unknown
Music arranged David Peacock
Medium paced
Chorus
F (C) Gm/F (Dm) F (C)
Light the candles round the world, pray the
path and show the way, ev - ery
Am (Em) B♭ (F) C (G) C7 (G7) F (C) Gm/F (Dm)
light will ne - ver cease till the na - tions of the
boy and ev - ery girl; make the light as bright as
F (C) F/A (C) B♭ (F)
1.3. Dm (Am) C (G) C7 (G7)
world take each o - ther's hands in peace: light the
day, light the can - dles round the
2.4. Dm (Am) C (G)
last time to Coda
world!

Music arrangement: © David Peacock / Jubilate Hymns

Verses
F
(C)
Gm
(Dm)
Dm
(Am)
Dm/C
1 Make each flame a lov - ing heart, mo - ther,
2 So I tell you this, my love: when you
B♭
(F)
Dm
(Am)
C
(G)
F
(C)
Gm
(Dm)
fa - ther, daugh - ter, son: all it takes is one to
see the light ap - pear it will drive a - way the
Dm
(Am)
Dm/C
Gm/B♭
(Dm)
F/A
(C)
Gm9
(Dm9)
C7
(G7)
D.𝄋
start for the world to be as one. Light the
dark, and there'll be no - thing left to fear. Light the
CODA
F
(C)
B♭/D
(F)
F
(C)
Light the can - dles round the world!

appropriate for children at candlelight services

169 Light a candle in the darkness

Capo 2(G)
Flowing
Words and music: Garth Hewitt
Music arranged David Peacock
Verse
A(G)
C♯m(Bm)
1 Like a flick - er in the dark - ness
2 He did not come in wealth and gran - deur,
3 But he came to heal the wound - ed,
4 And we see him in the hun - gry
5 And I feel his breath up - on me,
F♯m(Em)
D(C)
comes a mo - ther's des - perate cry;
he did not stand with men of power,
and he came to heal the scars
and the home - less ref - u - gee,
and he whis - pers, 'Fol - low me!'
C♯m(Bm)
D(C)
then a ba - by's voice in an - swer
he had no sta - tus to com - mend him,
of a world that's bruised and bro - ken,
in the sick and dy - ing child - ren –
and he grants his fire with - in me,
Bm(Am)
G(F)
brings the com - ing of the light.
he was home - less – he was poor.
where the im - age has been marred.
his hands reach out for you and me.
says, 'Let it shine for all to see!'

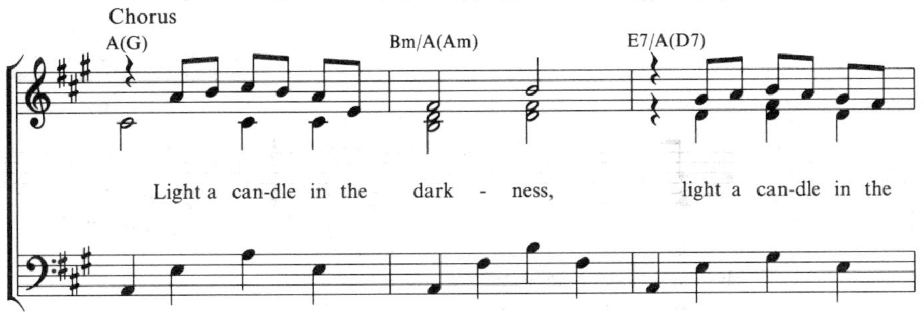
Chorus
A(G)
Bm/A(Am)
E7/A(D7)
Light a can-dle in the dark - ness, light a can-dle in the

A(G)
D(C)
A(G)
Bm/A(Am)
night; let the love of Je - sus light us –

E7(D7)
A(G)
D(C)
light a can - dle in the night!

to verse
to end
G(F)
F♯m7(Em7)
Bm7(Am7)
A(G)

170 Lion of Judah

Words and music: Ted Sandquist

With pace and strength
C
F
C
1 & 4 Li - on of Ju - dah, on the throne,
2 Li - on of Ju - dah, come to earth,
3 Li - on of Ju - dah, come a - gain,
F
G
C
F
G
I shout your name — let it be known
I want to thank you for your birth;
take up your throne – Je - ru - sa - lem;
Dm
G
that you are the King of kings, you
for the liv - ing Word, for your
bring re - lease to this earth! and the
F
C
Em
are the Prince of peace: may your king - dom's
death on the tree, for your res - ur -
con - sum - ma - tion of your king - dom's

F G C G
reign __ ne-ver cease. __ Hail to the king, __
- rec-tion vict-o - ry. __ Al - le - lu - ia, __
reign, __ let it come! __ Ma - ra - na - tha, __

last time to Coda
Gsus G Dm7 G
hail to the king! __
al - le - lu - ia! __
ma - ra - na - tha! __

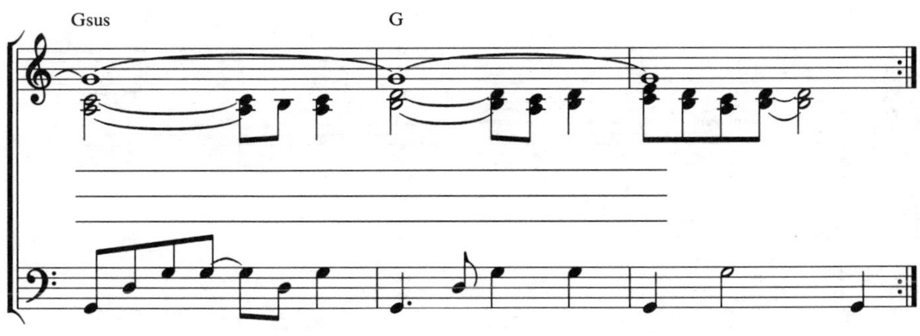
Gsus G

CODA
G7 C Dm7 C G7 C
you are my King! __

171 Little children, wake and listen

Saltash

Capo 5(C)

Words: verse 1 L H Ward, verse 2 Jubilate Hymns
Music: from Plymouth Collection (USA 1855)
arranged Norman Warren
obligato by David Peacock

Light and easy
Instrumental obligato (8ve higher ad lib.)
F(C)
B♭/F(F)
Am/F(Em)
Gm/F(Dm)
1 Lit - tle child - ren, wake and list - en!
2 Shep - herds hur - ry to the sta - ble
F(C)
B♭(F)
F/C(C)
C7(G7)
F(C)
songs are fill - ing all the earth;
by the inn at Beth - le - hem,
B♭(F)
F(C)
B♭(F)
C7(G7)
while the stars in hea - ven glist - en,
run as fast as they are a - ble
F(C)
B♭(F)
Gm7(Dm7)
F/C(C)
C7(G7)
F(C)
hear the news of Je - sus' birth.
to the ba - by born for them.

Am(Em)
B♭(F)
F(C)
F/C(C)
C(G)
Long a - go, to lone - ly mea - dows
Peo - ple find the news a - maz - ing
F(C)
Am(Em)
B♭(F)
Am(Em)
Gm(Dm)
C(G)
an - gels brought the mes - sage down;
as on that first Christ - mas morn:
F(C)
B♭/F(F)
Am/F(Em)
Gm/F(Dm)
still each year through mid - night sha - dows
let us join the shep - herds prais - ing
F(C)
B♭(F)
F/C(C)
C(G)
F(C)
it is heard in ev - ery town.
God, for Christ the king is born!

172 Little donkey

Words and music: Eric Boswell
Music arranged Noël Tredinnick

Medium paced
C F C Dm G7
1 Lit-tle don - key, lit-tle don - key, on a dus - ty road,
2 Been a long time lit-tle don - key, through the win - ter's night –
C F G7 1. C
got to keep on plod-ding on - ward with your pre - cious load:
don't give up now, lit - tle don - key, Beth - le-hem's in
2. C E7 Chorus Am Em F C
sight. Ring out those bells to - night, Beth - le - hem,
Am7 D7 G Am B7 Em Am7 D7 G
Beth - le - hem; fol - low that star to - night, Beth - le - hem,

Dm G7 C F C
Beth - le - hem! 3 Lit-tle don - key, lit-tle don - key, had a hea - vy
Dm G7 C F G7
day – lit-tle don - key, car-ry Ma - ry safe-ly on her
Optional ending
1. 2.
C Am Bm7 E7 C (C7) B♭ F Am Em Dm7 G7
way. way. Lit-tle don - key, car-ry Ma - ry safe-ly on her
C C7 C♯dim7/F Dm F Em Dm7 G7 C
way; lit-tle don - key, car-ry Ma - ry safe-ly on her way.
Optional percussion:
'Clip Clops' (Chinese woodblocks – two pitches)
Two bar phrase throughout

173 Long ago and far away

Caribbean Carol
Words and music: Pamela Verrall
Music arranged David Peacock
Calypso rhythm
G
Am
1 Long a - go and far a - way in
2 Shep - herds on the moun - tain cold a -
3 When they reached the op - en door and
D7
G7
Beth - le - hem, a mo - ther lay her
- woke when an - gel voi - ces told,
saw that love had gone be - fore, they
E7
Am
D
D♯dim
new-born babe up - on the hay. He was the ho - ly
'Go and leave your lambs in fold fol - low the star to
wond-'ring knelt on dir - ty floor, wor-ship - ping ba - by
Em
D7
Am7
D7
Je - sus - child, he was the ho - ly
Beth - le - hem; fol - low the star to
Je - sus there, wor - ship - ping ba - by

Chorus
G
Em
Je - sus.
Beth-le - hem!' Now - ell, now-ell let an - gels sing; now -
Je - sus.

E
Am
G/D
E
- ell, now-ell let church bells ring; now - ell, now-ell let

Am
D7
ev - ery - thing sing al - le - lu - ia to the

1.2.
Gsus
G
3.
Gsus
G
ba - by boy!
ba - by boy!

174 Long, long ago

Words and music: P Shaw (1917–1977)

Fast and rhythmic

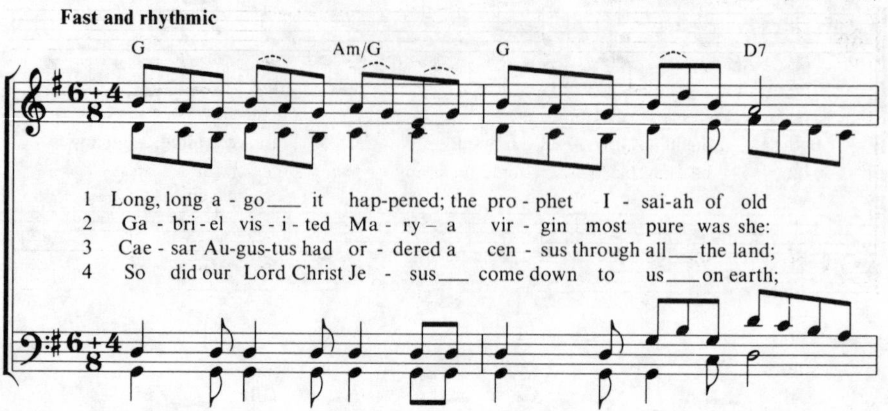
G
Am/G
G
D7
1 Long, long a - go___ it hap-pened; the pro - phet I - sai-ah of old
2 Ga - bri - el vis - i - ted Ma - ry – a vir - gin most pure was she:
3 Cae - sar Au-gus-tus had or - dered a cen - sus through all___the land;
4 So did our Lord Christ Je - sus___ come down to us___on earth;

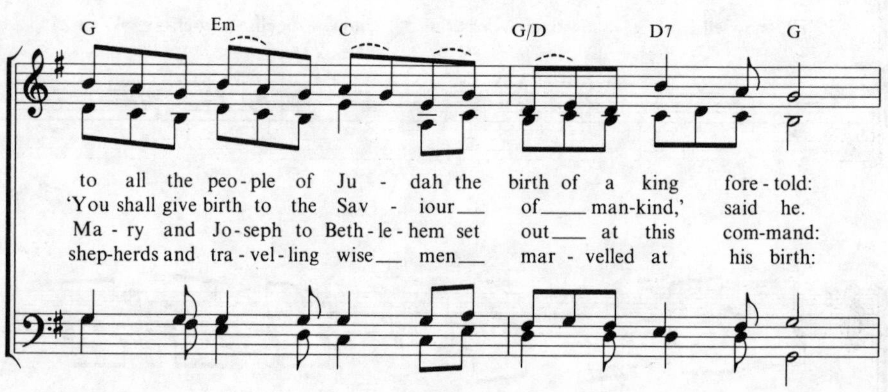
G
Em
C
G/D
D7
G
to all the peo - ple of Ju - dah the birth of a king fore - told:
'You shall give birth to the Sav - iour___ of___man-kind,' said he.
Ma - ry and Jo - seph to Beth - le - hem set out___ at this com-mand:
shep-herds and tra - vel - ling wise___ men___ mar - velled at his birth:

G
Am/G
G
D7
Won - der-ful Coun-sel-lor, Migh-ty God, Lord___and Prince of peace –
'How can this be,'___she ans - wered, ne - ver a man___knew I?'
straight to the inn___they went___ then – 'No room at all,' they were told;
so, at this Christ - mas sea - son,___ cheer-ful - ly do___ we sing

G
Em
C
G/D
D7
G
Fa - ther ev - er - last - ing he should be all of these.
'You have been cho-sen to bear the Son of God most high.'
on - ly the sta-ble was of-fered them to keep them from the cold.
hon-our and praise and glo - ry to Christ our heaven - ly king.
Chorus
G
D7
G
D7
1-3 'Glo-ry to God in the high - est!' thus the an - gels sang;
4 'Glo-ry to God in the high - est,' sing at Christ-mas still,
G
C
Cm
A7
D7
G
Fine
and with Al - le - lu - ias, loud the hea - vens rang.
'and on earth be peace to all peo - ple of good-will!'
1–3. G
C/G
D/G
G
C/G
D/G

175 Long time ago in Bethlehem

(Mary's boy child)

Capo 3(G)

Words and music: Jester Hairston
Music arranged Noël Tredinnick

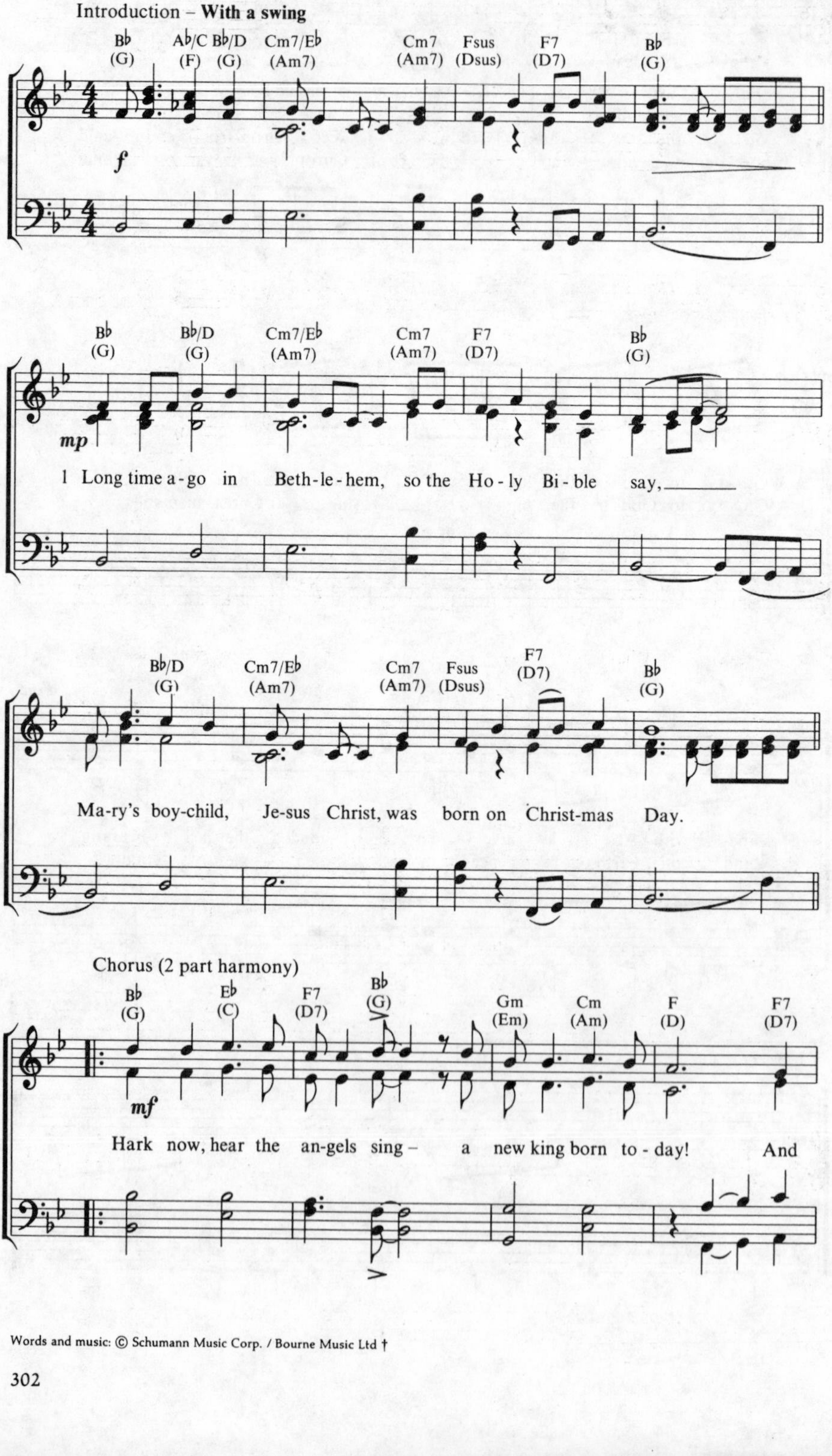

Introduction – **With a swing**

1 Long time a-go in Beth-le-hem, so the Ho-ly Bi-ble say,

Ma-ry's boy-child, Je-sus Christ, was born on Christ-mas Day.

Chorus (2 part harmony)

Hark now, hear the an-gels sing – a new king born to-day! And

B♭ (G) B♭/D (G) Cm7/E♭ (Am7) Cm7 (Am7) Fsus (Dsus) F7 (D7)
we may live for ev - er - more__ be - cause of Christ - mas
B♭ (G) Cm7 (Am7) F7 (D7) Dm7 (Bm7)
Day. Trum - pets sound and an - gels sing -__
f
Gm (Em) C7 (A7) F (D) F7 (D7) B♭ (G) F7/C (D7) B♭/D (G)
list - en to what they say, that we may live for
Cm7/E♭ (Am7) Cm7 (Am7) Fsus (Dsus) F7 (D7) B♭ (G) E♭/F (C)
ev - er - more__ be - cause of Christ - mas Day.
Verses unison
B♭ (G) F7 (D7) B♭ (G) B♭/D(G) Cm7/E♭ (Am7) Cm7 (Am7)
mp
2 While shep-herds watch their flocks by night, them see a
4 By and by__ they find a lit - tle nook____ in a

F7 (D7) B♭ (G) F/A (D) B♭ (G) B♭/D (G)
bright new shin - ing star; them hear a choir
sta - ble all for - lorn, and in a man - ger
Cm7/E♭ (Am7) Cm7 (Am7) Fsus (Dsus) F7 (D7) B♭ (G) F7 (D7)
sing – the mu - sic seems to come from a - far. 3 Now
cold and dark, Ma-ry's lit - tle boy was born.
B♭ (G) B♭/D (G) E♭9 (C9) Cm7 (Am7) F7 (D7)
Jo – seph and his wife Ma - ry come to Beth - le - hem that
5 Long time a - go in Beth - le - hem, so the Ho - ly Bi - ble
B♭ (G) F/A (D) B♭ (G) F7/C (D7) B♭/D (G) E♭9 (C9) Cm7 (Am7)
night; she have no place to bear her child – not a
say, Ma-ry's boy - child, Je - sus Christ, was

vv.3.
vv.5.
Fsus (Dsus) F7 (D7) Bb (G) Eb/F (C) Bb (G) F7 (D7)
sin - gle room was in sight.
born on Christ - mas Day.
Last Chorus (2 part harmony)
Bb (G) Cm7 (Am7) F7 (D7) Dm7 (Bm7) Gm7 (Em7) C7 (A7)
f
Hark now, hear the an-gels sing — a new king born to -
F (D) F7 (D7) Bb (G) Bb/D (G) Cm7/Eb (Am7) Cm7 (Am7)
- day! And we may live for ev - er - more — be -
Fsus (Dsus) F7 (D7) Bb (G) F7 (D7) Bb (G) Eb/G (C) Am (F#m) D/F# (B)
- cause of Christ-mas Day. ff Trum-pets sound and an-gels sing —
Gm (Em) C/E (A) F (D) F7 (D7) Bb (G) F7/C (D7) Bb/D (G)
list - en to what they say, that we may live for

last time to Coda
Optional repeat of last chorus
Cm7/E♭ (Am7) Cm7 (Am7) Fsus (Dsus) F7(D7) B♭(G) F7(D7)
ev - er - more be - cause of Christ - mas Day.
CODA
B♭ (G) B♭sus (Gsus) B♭ (G) A♭/C (F) B♭/D (G) E♭9 (C9) Cm7 (Am7)
Day. Yes, we may live for ev - er - more be -
B♭/F (G) F♯/E (E♭) E♭ (C) F7/C (D7) B♭ (G) B♭ (G7)
cause of Christ - mas Day.
E♭ (C) Cm7 (Am7) Fsus (Dsus) B♭ (G)
Ped.

176 Lord everlasting

Was lebet

Words: David Mowbray
Music: from manuscript by
J H Rheinhardt, Uttigen (1754)

D G A D A/C♯ G/B D A D
1 Lord ev - er - last - ing yet child born in Beth - le - hem,
2 Lord God a - mong us – your strength found in gent - le - ness,
3 Lord of all lords and our prom - ised de - liv - er - er,
4 Lord, tak - ing flight in a re - fu - gee fam - i - ly,
5 Lord, low - ly stoop - ing to raise up your bro - ken - ones –
Em D A7 D E7 F♯m D Bm7 E A
Ma - ry your mo - ther and fav - oured in - deed,
greet - ed by shep - herds in fields with their flock:
wor - shipped by kings bring - ing gifts from a - far:
har - rassed and threat - ened – the poor of the earth:
love at the crib and the cross is the same:
D D7 G D Em A D A A7/G
shar - ing our strug - gle, our grief and un - cert - ain - ty,
call us as ser - vants, and send us as wit - ness - es
guide with your wis - dom all those in auth - or - i - ty,
o - pen our hearts to the out - cast and pris - on - er,
help us with an - gels your great name to glo - ri - fy,
D/F♯ A D G A7 Bm G Em A D
shin - ing as light of the world in its need:
to all our neigh - bours and pla - ces of work.
spar - ing the na - tions from hat - red and war.
bring - ing com - pass - ion and jus - tice to birth.
and with arch - an - gels that love to pro - claim!

177 Look away to Bethlehem

Capo 3(D)

Words and music: Leslie Sturdy

Gently, not fast
F(D)
pp gently
1 Look a - way to Beth - le - hem, seek the star up in the sky;
2 Wan - dering shep - herds saw the star, on that night so long a - go;
3 Let the Christ - mas bells ring out from each stee - ple in the sky;
p
C7(A7)
fol - low where it sends its
left their flocks to find the
let their mu - sic swell un -

F(D)
C7(A7)
sil - ver beam, lis - ten for a lull - a -
ho - ly child sent from hea - ven here be -
- til it blends with the an - gel choirs on
F(D)
- by: find the sta - ble bleak and
- low: prin - ces sought a pal - ace
high: look a - way to Beth - le -
bare, gent - ly op - en up the
fair, bear - ing gifts of un - told
- hem, seek the star up in the

C7(A7)
door, gaze with wond - er at the
worth, but they knelt be-side a
sky, fol - low where it sends its
F(D)
C7(A7)
ho - ly Babe – he whom heaven and earth a -
hum - ble throne when the Lord came to the
sil - ver beam, lis - ten for a lull - a -
F(D)
F7(D7)
B♭(G)
Gm(Em)
- dore.
earth. 'Al - le - lu - ia,' sing the
- by!
ff grandioso

F(D)
Dm(Bm)
Gm7(Em7)
C7(A7)
an - gels, 'Peace on earth, good-will to
F(D)
F7(D7)
B♭(G)
Gm(Em)
men!' 'Al - le - lu - ia,' sing the
3
3
F(D)
Dm(Bm)
Gm(Em)
C7(A7)
1.2.
F(D)
an - gels: 'Look a - way to Beth - le - hem!'
pp
3.
F(D)
Slower
Gm(Em)
C7/A7
F(D)
- hem!' 'Look a - way to Beth - le - hem!'
mp
rit.
ppp

178 Look to the skies

Words and music: Graham Kendrick
Music arranged David Peacock
Triumphantly
F
Dm
1 Look to the skies, there's a ce - le - bra - tion; lift up your heads, join the
2 Won - der - ful Coun - sel - lor, Migh - ty God,___ Fa - ther for ev - er, the
3 Quiet - ly he came as a help - less ba - by – one day in power he will
Gm7
Csus
C
Dm
B♭
an - gel song, for our Cre - a - tor be - comes our sav - iour,
Prince of peace: there'll be no end to your rule of jus - tice,
come a - gain; swift through the skies he will burst with splen - dour
Gm7
Csus
C
F
as a ba - by born! An - gels a - mazed bow in
for it shall in - crease. Light of your face, come to
on the earth to reign. Je - sus, I bow at your
Dm
Gm7
Csus
C
a - do - ra - tion: 'Glo - ry to God in the high - est heaven!' –
pierce our dark - ness; joy of your heart come to chase our gloom;
man - ger low - ly: now in my life let your will be done;

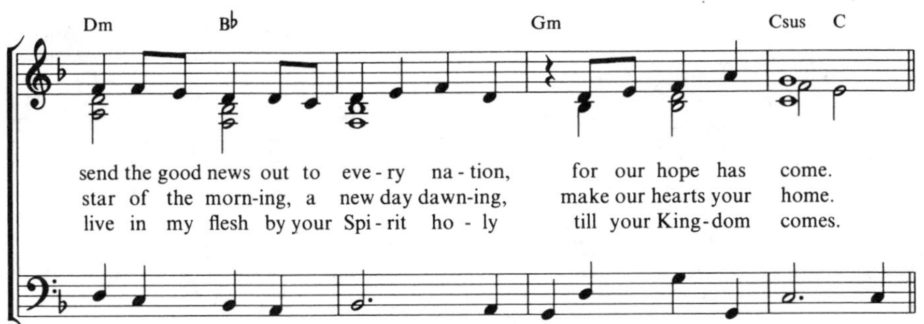
Dm
B♭
Gm
Csus
C
send the good news out to eve - ry na - tion, for our hope has come.
star of the morn-ing, a new day dawn-ing, make our hearts your home.
live in my flesh by your Spi - rit ho - ly till your King-dom comes.

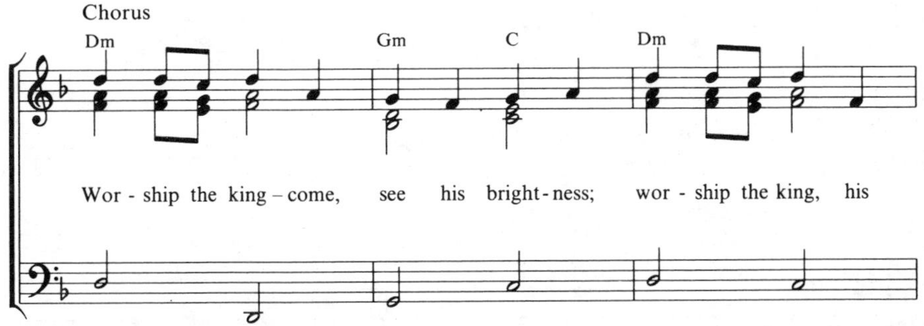
Chorus
Dm
Gm
C
Dm
Wor - ship the king – come, see his bright - ness; wor - ship the king, his

B♭
Csus
C
Dm
B♭
C
won - ders tell: Je - sus our king is born to - day – we

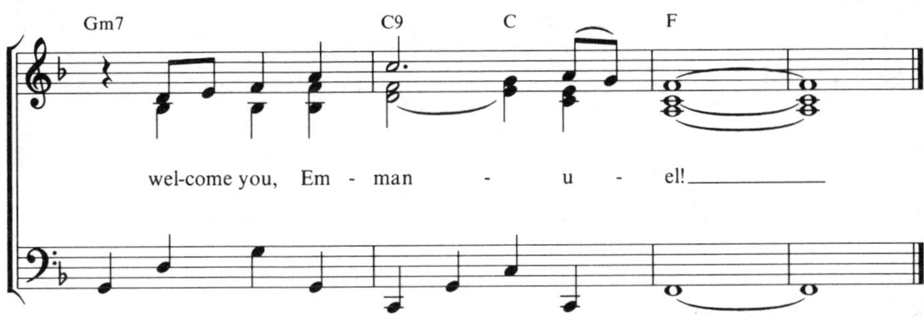
Gm7
C9
C
F
wel-come you, Em - man - u - el!

179 Lord, now let your servant depart

Song of Simeon

Words: from Luke 2 (*The Song of Simeon / Nunc dimittis*)
Music: Andrew Maries
arranged David Peacock

Capo 1(G)

Gentle and flowing
F♯m(Em)
F♯m7(Em7)
B/F♯(A)
Bm/F♯(Am)
p legato
con ped.
F♯m (Em)
C♯m7/F♯ (Bm7)
F♯m (Em)
C♯m7/F♯ (Bm7)
F♯m (Em)
F♯m7 (Em7)
B/F♯ (A)
Bm/F♯ (Am)
Lord, now let your ser - vant de -
for my eyes have seen your sal -
F♯m (Em)
C♯m7/F♯ (Bm7)
F♯m (Em)
1.
C♯m7/F♯ (Bm7)
- part in peace, ac -
- va - tion,
F♯m (Em)
E/F♯ (D)
F♯m (Em)
C♯m (Bm)
- cor - ding to your word:

2.
C♯m/E (Bm)
D (C)
C♯m (Bm)
Bm7 (Am7)
cresc.
which you have pre - pared be - fore the
E (D)
A (G)
f
face of all peo - ple; to be a
F♯m (Em)
Bm (Am)
F♯m (Em)
E (D)
rit.
a tempo
mp
light to light - en the Gen - tiles, and
D (C)
C♯m (Bm)
Bm7 (Am7)
C♯m7 (Bm7)
to be the glo - ry of your peo - ple
F♯m (Em)
E/F♯ (D)
Bm/F♯ (Am)
C♯m7 (Bm)
Is - ra - el.

F♯m (Em) F♯m7 (Em7) B/F♯ (A) Bm/F♯ (Am)
SOLO SOPRANOS Glo - ry
f
Glo - ry to the Father and
F♯m (Em) C♯m7/F♯ (Bm7) F♯m (Em) C♯m7/F♯ (Bm7)
to the Fa - ther and to the
to the Son and
F♯m (Em) E/F♯ (D) F♯m (Em) C♯m (Bm)
Son and to the Ho - ly
to the Ho - ly Spi - rit,

F♯m
(Em)
F♯m7
(Em7)
B/F♯
(A)
Bm/F♯
(Am)
Spi - rit,
as
it
as it was in the be - gin - ning, is
F♯m
(Em)
C♯m7/F♯
(Bm7)
F♯m
(Em)
C♯m7
(Bm7)
was and shall be
rit.
now, and shall be for ev - er,
D
(C)
C♯m7
(Bm7)
F♯m
(Em)
pp
world with - out end. A - men.
slowly
pp
world with - out end. A - men.

180 Lord, now let your servant go his way

Words: from Luke 2
(The Song of Simeon / Nunc dimittis)
J E Seddon (1915–1983)
Music: Norman Warren
Mukono
Capo 3(G)
B♭(G) Gm7(Em7) F7(D7) B♭(G)
1 Lord, now let your ser - vant
2 For my eyes have seen him
3 Light of re - ve - la - tion
Gm7 (Em7) E♭ (C) Dsus (Bsus) D7 (B7)
go his way in peace;
pro - mised from of old –
to the gen - tiles shown,
G (E) C7/B♭ (A7) Am7 (F♯m7) D7 (B7)
your great love has brought me
sav - iour of all peo - ple,
light of Is - rael's glo - ry
E♭ (C) E♭/F F7 (D7) B♭sus (Gsus) B♭ (G)
joy that will not cease:
shep - herd of one fold:
to the world made known.

May also be sung to 'Caswall'

181 Lord, speak softly to my soul

Capo 3(C)
Words and music: Angela Griffiths
Gentle, not too fast
Eb (C) Gm7/D (Em7) Ab/C (F) Bb7 (G7) Ab (F) Eb (C) Eb/D
Cm (Am) Gm6 (Em6) Ab (F) Bb7 (G7) Gm (Em) Fm (Dm) Eb (C) Gm7 (Em7)
Cm (Am) Cm7/Bb (Am7) Fm (Dm) Bb7 (G7) Gm (Em) Fm (Dm) Gm (Em) Ab (F)
Gm (Em) Cm (Am) Fm (Dm) Bb7 (G7) Ebmaj7 (Cmaj7) Ab/Eb (F) Eb (C)
1 Lord, speak soft - ly to my soul; tell me more of that first Christ-mas night when a warm breath of peace cov - ered Beth - le - hem, and the hills came a - live with your light.
2 Lord, speak slow - ly; draw me near, let me share in the joy of your birth: did you know, ev - en then, you would bear my shame – did you weep for the sins of this earth?
3 Lord, speak gent - ly; lead me on, guide me straight to that rough sta - ble door; let me gaze on that low, ho - ly man - ger bed where the royal Son of God slept on straw.
4 Lord, speak clear - ly, teach me now, hear my prayer; let my love ov - er - flow: then my an - them will rise on the pure clear air, as I pledge back the life that I owe.

182 Lord, who left the highest heaven

Highest heaven
Words: Timothy Dudley-Smith
Music: Michael Baughen
arranged David Peacock
Capo 3(D)
Flowing
F (D) Gm (Em) C7 (A7) F (D) B♭ (G) Gm7 (Em7)
1 Lord, who left the high-est heav-en for a home-less hu-man
2 Lord, who sought by cloak of dark-ness re - fuge un - der for-eign
3 Lord, who lived se-cure and set-tled, safe with-in the Fa-ther's
Csus (Asus) C7 (A7) F (D) Gm (Em) C7 (A7) F (D) Cm/E♭ (Am) D (B) D7 (B7)
birth and, a child with-in a sta - ble, came to
skies from the swords of Her-od's sold-iers, rav-aged
plan, and in wis-dom, sta-ture, fa - vour grow-ing
C/G (A) G7 (E7) C (A) C7 (A7) F (D) Cm/E♭ (Am) D7 (B7)
share the life of earth – with your grace and mer - cy
homes, and par - ents' cries – may your grace and mer - cy
up from boy to man – with your grace and mer - cy
Gm (Em) B♭/C (G) C7 (A7) F (D)
bless all who suf - fer home-less - ness.
rest on the home-less and op - pressed.
bless all who strive for ho - li - ness.

4 Lord, who leaving home and kindred,
followed still as duty led,
sky the roof and earth the pillow
for the Prince of glory's head –
with your grace and mercy bless
sacrifice for righteousness.

5 Lord, who in your cross and passion
hung beneath a darkened sky,
yet whose thoughts were for your mother,
and a thief condemned to die –
may your grace and mercy rest
on the helpless and distressed.

6 Lord, who rose to life triumphant
with our whole salvation won,
risen, glorified, ascended,
all the Father's purpose done –
may your grace, all conflict past,
bring your children home at last.

B♭ melody version

183 Lord, you left your throne

Margaret
Words: E Elliott (1836–1897)
in this version Word & Music
Music: T R Matthews (1826–1910)
descant: David Peacock
Descant / instrument obligato
D Bm Em7 A7 Bm Em F♯ Bm A D A D C♯sus C♯7
4 When the heavens shall ring, and the choirs shall sing at your com - ing to vic - to - ry, let your voice call me home say - ing,
1 Lord, you left your throne and your king - ly crown when you came to this earth for me, but in Beth - le - hem's home there was
2 Hea - ven's arch - es rang when the an - gels sang pro - claim - ing your royal de - gree, but to low - ly birth you came
3 You were sent, O Lord, with the liv - ing word that should set your peo - ple free; but with mock - ing scorn and with
4 When the heavens shall ring, and the choirs shall sing at your com - ing to vic - to - ry, let your voice call me home say - ing,

F♯m D/F Esus E7 A Esus E7
'Yes, there is room!' – there is room at your side for
found no - room for your ho - ly na - ti - vi -
here on earth, and in great hu - mi - li -
crown of thorn, they bore you to Cal - va -
'Yes, there is room!' – there is room at your side for
A A7 D
me. Then my heart shall re - joice, Lord
- ty: O come to my heart, Lord
- ty: O come to my heart, Lord
- ry: O come to my heart, Lord
me. Then my heart shall re - joice, Lord
Em7 Em6 D/F♯ E7/B D/A A7 D
Je - sus, when you come and you call for me.
Je - sus; Em - ma - nu - el, come to me.
Je - sus; Re - deem - er, be born in me.
Je - sus, your cross is my on - ly plea.
Je - sus, when you come and you call for me.

184 Lord, you were rich

Bergers

Words: F Houghton (1894–1972)
and in this version Jubilate Hymns
Music: French traditional melody
arranged C H Kitson (1874–1944)

D Gmaj7/D A7/D G/D D Bm/D D Bm G/B
1 Lord, you were rich be - yond all splen - dour,
2 You are our God be - yond all prais - ing,
3 Lord, you are love be - yond all tell - ing,

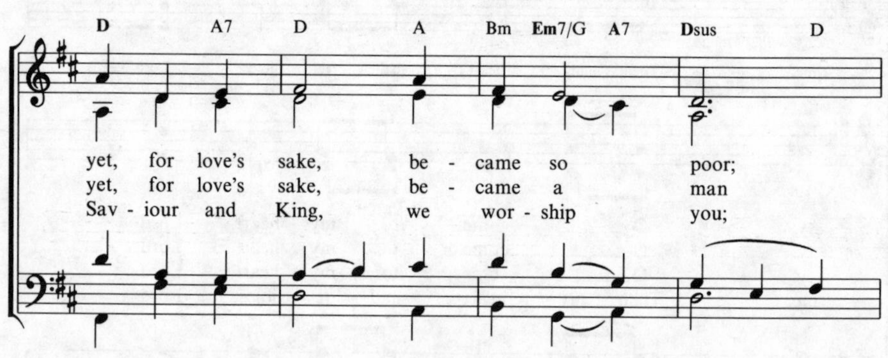

D A7 D A Bm Em7/G A7 Dsus D
yet, for love's sake, be - came so poor;
yet, for love's sake, be - came a man
Sav - iour and King, we wor - ship you;

Dmaj7 G/D D Bm F♯m
leav - ing your throne in glad sur - ren - der,
stoop - ing so low, but sin - ners rais - ing
Em - ma - nu - el, with - in us dwell - ing,

Gmaj7 A7 Bm7 Em7 D G Asus A
sapph - ire - paved courts for sta - ble floor:
hea - ven - wards, by your e - ter - nal plan:
make us and keep us pure and true:

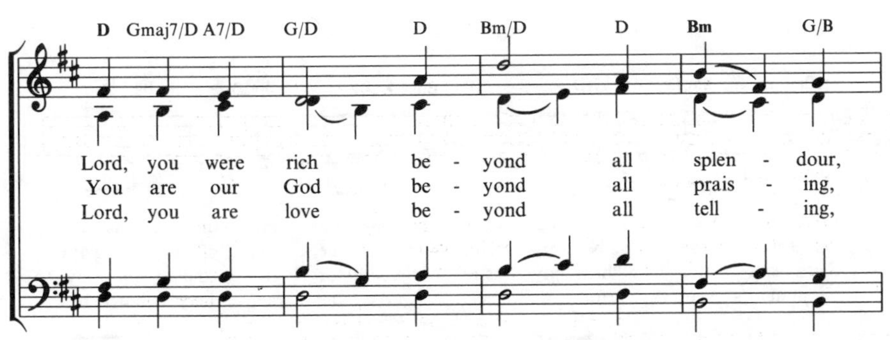
D Gmaj7/D A7/D G/D D Bm/D D Bm G/B
Lord, you were rich be - yond all splen - dour,
You are our God be - yond all prais - ing,
Lord, you are love be - yond all tell - ing,

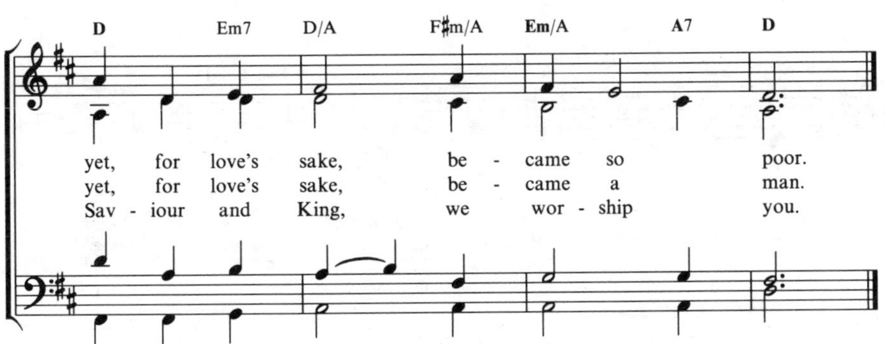
D Em7 D/A F♯m/A Em/A A7 D
yet, for love's sake, be - came so poor.
yet, for love's sake, be - came a man.
Sav - iour and King, we wor - ship you.

For a more piano-based accompaniment see number 351

185 Lowly Jesus, king of glory

Nettleton

Words: Christopher Porteous
Music: American folk hymn melody
arranged David Peacock

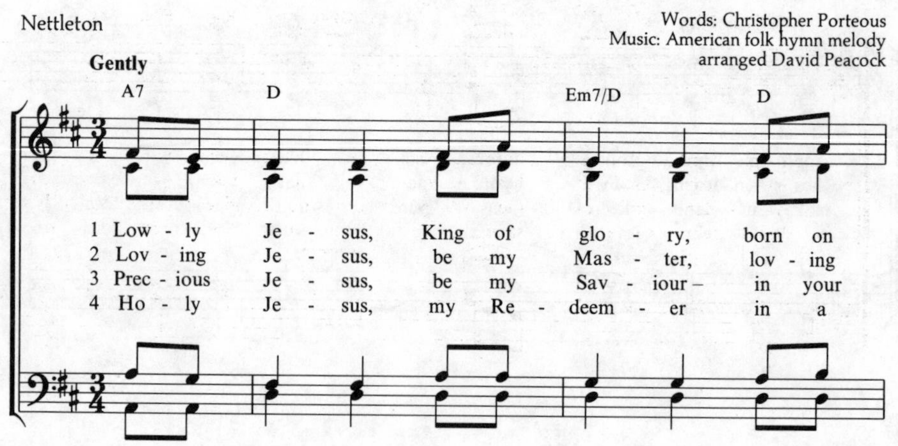
Gently
A7 D Em7/D D
1 Low - ly Je - sus, King of glo - ry, born on
2 Lov - ing Je - sus, be my Mas - ter, lov - ing
3 Prec - ious Je - sus, be my Sav - iour – in your
4 Ho - ly Je - sus, my Re - deem - er in a

Em6/D Bm/D A7/D D F♯7/C♯ Bm Bm7/A
earth a lit - tle child, in your mo - ther's arms a -
Je - sus, be my King; let me come close to your
mer - cy heal my sin; please for - give me for my
man - ger for a bed, ox and ass may bow be -

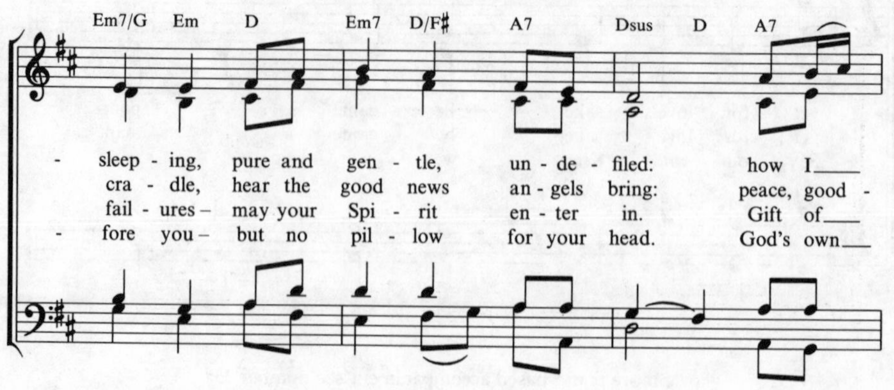
Em7/G Em D Em7 D/F♯ A7 Dsus D A7
- sleep - ing, pure and gen - tle, un - de - filed: how I
cra - dle, hear the good news an - gels bring: peace, good -
fail - ures – may your Spi - rit en - ter in. Gift of
- fore you – but no pil - low for your head. God's own

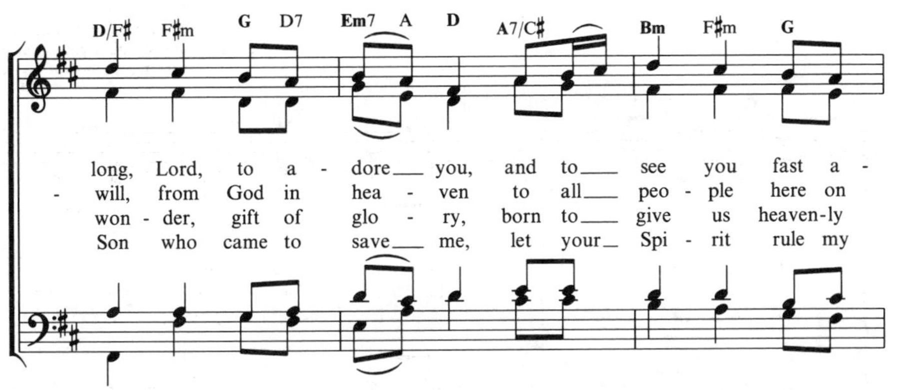
D/F♯ F♯m G D7 Em7 A D A7/C♯ Bm F♯m G
long, Lord, to a - dore__ you, and to__ see you fast a -
- will, from God in hea - ven to all__ peo - ple here on
won - der, gift of glo - ry, born to__ give us heaven-ly
Son who came to save__ me, let your__ Spi - rit rule my

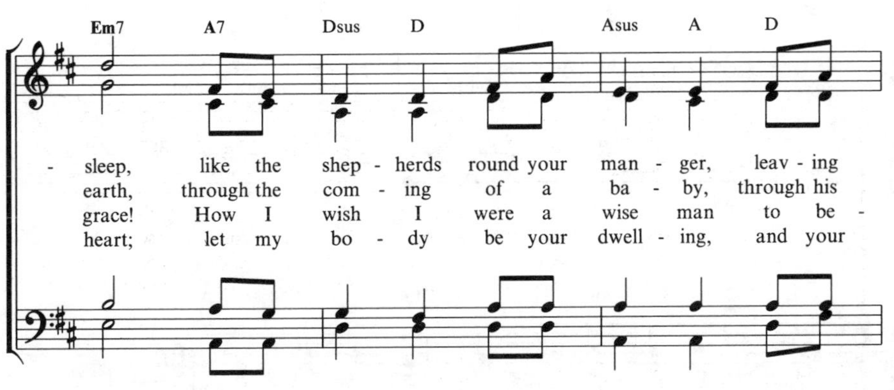
Em7 A7 Dsus D Asus A D
- sleep, like the shep - herds round your man - ger, leav - ing
earth, through the com - ing of a ba - by, through his
grace! How I wish I were a wise man to be -
heart; let my bo - dy be your dwell - ing, and your

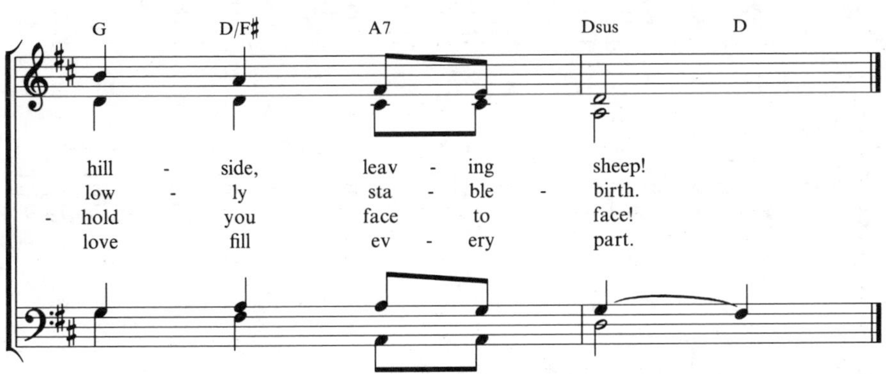
G D/F♯ A7 Dsus D
hill - side, leav - ing sheep!
low - ly sta - ble - birth.
- hold you face to face!
love fill ev - ery part.

186 Love was born at Christmas

Humbly in a manger
Words: from 1 John 4
Geoffrey Rand
Music: Norman Warren
Gently
2 Let
1 Love was born at Christ-mas in such a wond - rous way, for
love be__born this Christ-mas with - in my heart and mind, a
hum - bly__in a man-ger the Christ-child gen - tly lay;
love that knows no lim - it, a love that is div - ine:
love was deep with - in him – a love so filled with light,______ it
love is___now with - in us to guide us on our way,______ for

1.
2.
G7 E/C Am G6/D B7/C G
shone in ___ all its glo - ry and made the whole world bright.
love was born at Christ - mas, God's love on Christ - mas
B E E7 Cmaj7 D/C C Bm E7
Day; for love was born at Christ-mas, God's
Am D7 G C/G G
love on ___ Christ - mas Day. ___
B♭ melody version
3

187 Love came down at Christmas

Sanderling

Capo 3(D)

Tenderly

(FIRST TUNE)

Words: C Rossetti (1830–1894)
and in this version Jubilate Hymns
Music: Andrew Plank
arranged Noël Tredinnick

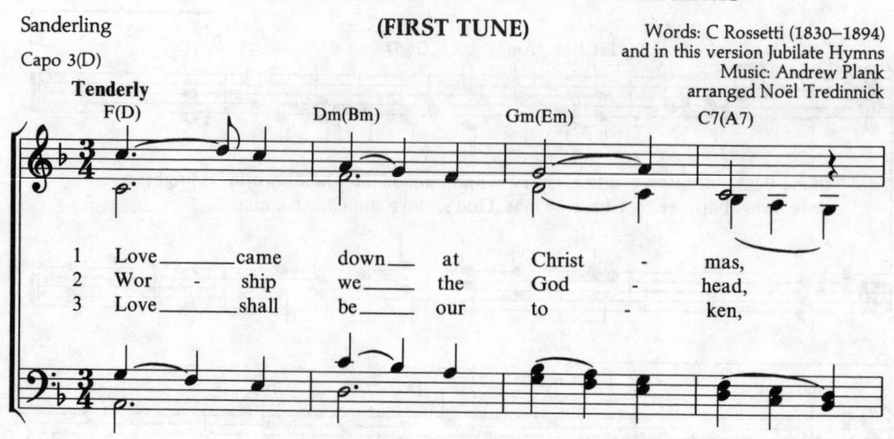

F(D)
Dm(Bm)
Gm(Em)
C7(A7)
1 Love came down at Christ - mas,
2 Wor - ship we the God - head,
3 Love shall be our to - ken,

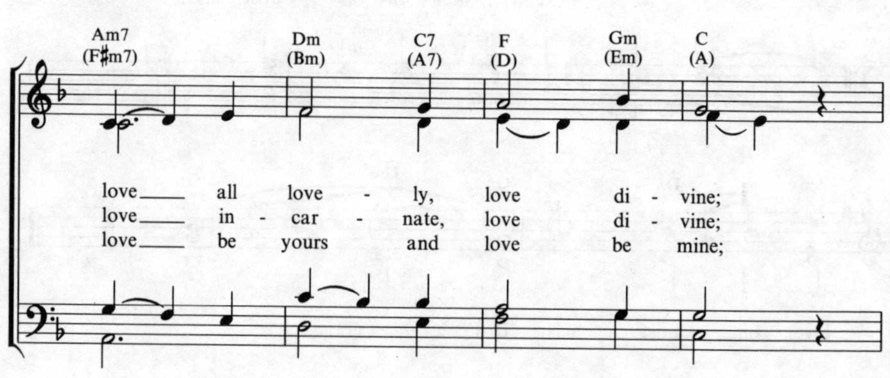

Am7
(F♯m7)
Dm
(Bm)
C7
(A7)
F
(D)
Gm
(Em)
C
(A)
love all love - ly, love di - vine;
love in - car - nate, love di - vine;
love be yours and love be mine;

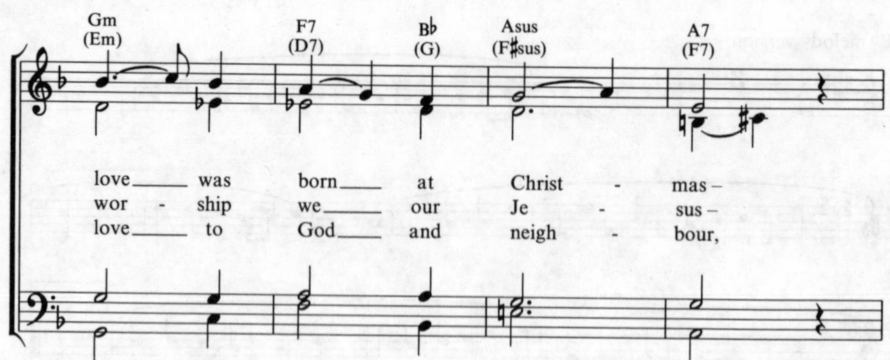

Gm
(Em)
F7
(D7)
B♭
(G)
Asus
(F♯sus)
A7
(F7)
love was born at Christ - mas –
wor - ship we our Je - sus –
love to God and neigh - bour,

Dm
(Bm)
G7
(E7)
F/C
(D)
Dm
(Bm)
Gm7
(Em7)
F♯7
(E♭7)
F
(D)
star___ and ang - els gave___ the sign.
what___ shall be our sa - cred sign?
love___ for prayer and gift___ and sign.
Optional introduction and link
F
(D)
C7
(A7)
F7
(D7)
Dm7
(Bm7)
C
(A)
B♭
(G)
Gm7
(Em7)
C
(A)
D.C.
Last time
F
(D)
B♭ melody version

188 Love came down at Christmas

(SECOND TUNE)

Hermitage

Words: C Rossetti (1830–1894)
in this version Jubilate Hymns
Music: R O Morris (1886–1948)

Bm
G
1 Love came down at Christ - mas,
2 Wor - ship we the God - head,
3 Love shall be our to - ken,
Bm
Em
F♯m
G
Bsus
B
love all love - ly, love di - vine;
love in - car - nate, love di - vine;
love be yours and love be mine;
Am
Em
love was born at Christ - mas –
wor - ship we our Je - sus –
love to God and neigh - bour,
Em7
D/F♯
G
A7
D
star and an - gels gave the sign.
what shall be our sa - cred sign?
love for prayer and gift and sign.

189 Lullaby, little Jesus

Jezus malusienki
Gently but not too slow
Words: after the Polish carol
Michael Perry
Music: Polish melody
arranged David Peacock
Instruments
Am E7 Am E7
1 Lul-la-by, lit-tle Je - sus; there you lie, lit-tle Je - sus –
2 Lul-la-by, lit-tle Je - sus; don't you cry, lit-tle Je - sus:
3 Lul-la-by, lit-tle Je - sus: in the sky, lit-tle Je - sus,
Dm7 G7 C C/E F F/G G7 G/C C
as the winds bite on this cold night – in the hay, lit-tle Je - sus.
come to - mor - row there'll be sor - row and dis-may, lit-tle Je - sus.
there is sing - ing, glo - ry bring - ing to this day, lit-tle Je - sus.
Dm7 G C C/E F F/G7 G7 F/C C
As the winds bite on this cold night: Lul-la-by, lit-tle Je - sus!
Come to - mor - row there'll be sor - row. Lul-la-by, lit-tle Je - sus!
There is sing - ing, glo - ry bring-ing. Lul-la-by, lit-tle Je - sus!

190 Lullaby, baby, lie still and slumber

Lullaby: a child like you

Words: after I Watts (1674–1748)
in this version Michael Paget
Music: Polish carol
arranged Michael Paget

With nobility
D
Em
A
D
Fine
Two flutes * (verse 4 only)
Introduction
(last time)
Fine
Verses
D
Em
A
Keyboard and/or four-part choir
1 & 4 Lul - la - by, ba - by, lie still and
2 Cot - ton and silk are lin - ing your
3 May all our child - ren know him and
D
Em
slum - ber; God's ho - ly an - gels
cra - dle – not like the man - ger where
love him, trust and o - bey him

* if only one flute available, play lower part

A
D
tr
Em
D
guard your bed, heav - en - ly bless - ings
our sav - iour lay; his chos - en birth - place
all their days, then go and dwell for
G6
A7
D
with - out num - ber gent - ly
was a bare sta - ble, and for his
ev - er - more with him, so they may
Em
Em7
A
A7
A7/D
D
tr
fall - ing round your head.
bed - ding, there was on - ly some hay.
see him and sing his praise.

Chorus
F♯m G Em7 A9 G/D D
Je - sus de - scend - ed from hea - ven to this world
Bm G Em7 A D
and he be - came a child for us all;
F♯m G Em7 A9 G/D D Bm Bm7
God's Son de - scend-ed from hea-ven to this world, and he be -
D.C. al fine
1.2.3.
4.
G Em7 A A7 A7/D D
A7/D flute
D
- came a child like you. you.

191 Mary came with meekness

Noël nouvelet

Words: Paul Wigmore
Music: French traditional melody
arranged David Peacock

Bouncy

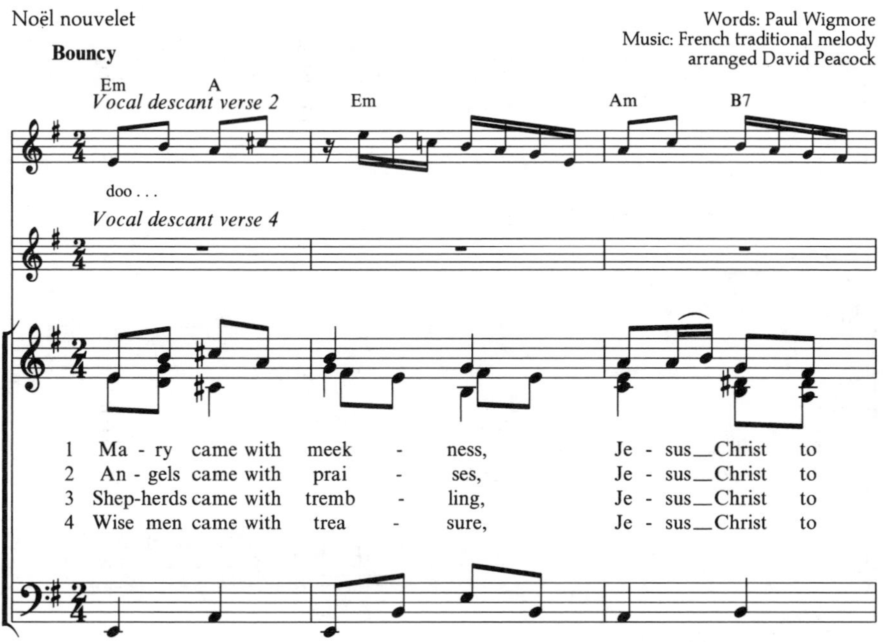
Em A
Vocal descant verse 2
Em
Am B7
doo . . .
Vocal descant verse 4
1 Ma - ry came with meek - ness, Je - sus Christ to
2 An - gels came with prai - ses, Je - sus Christ to
3 Shep-herds came with tremb - ling, Je - sus Christ to
4 Wise men came with trea - sure, Je - sus Christ to

Em A/B Em A Em
doo ba - ba - ba! doo . . .
Je - sus Christ to bless
bear, laid the Lord of glo - ry
name, hea - ven's choirs ex - alt - ing
see; king who, at their bid - ding,
bless – he who shares all bless - ings

Am
B7
Em
B7
Em
do - be - do - be . . .
in a___man - ger there.
him who bears our shame.
would their__shep - herd be.
heaven and__earth pos - sess.
We come re -

B7
Em
B7
come re - joi - cing
Je - sus Christ to love
- joic - ing, Je - sus Christ to love:

Em A Em Am B7
doo . . .
do - be - do - be -
in a man - ger King of hea - ven a -
ba - by in a man - ger – king of heaven a -

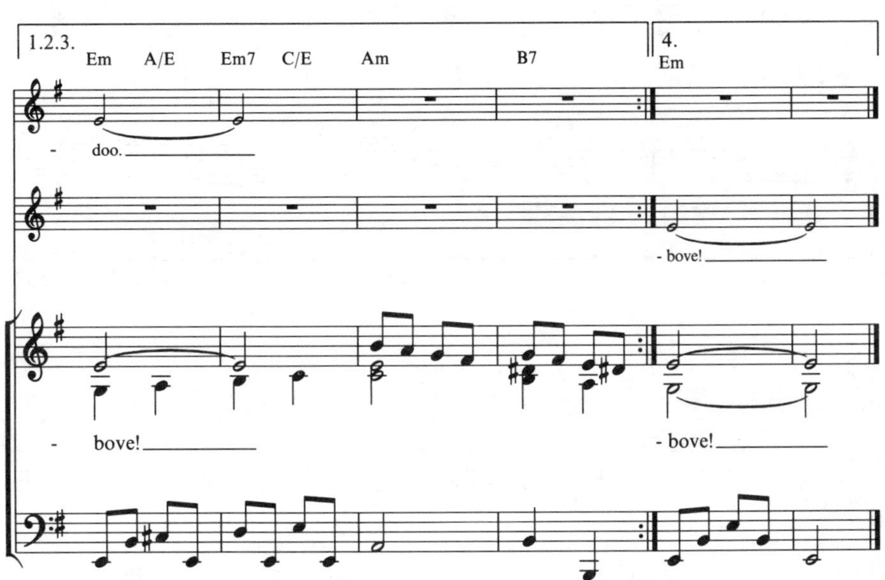
1.2.3.
Em A/E Em7 C/E Am B7
4.
Em
- doo.
- bove!
- bove!
- bove!

192 Mary and Joseph

Manger Dance

Words: Michael Perry
Music: Norman Warren

♩ = 132 **Lively, medieval style**

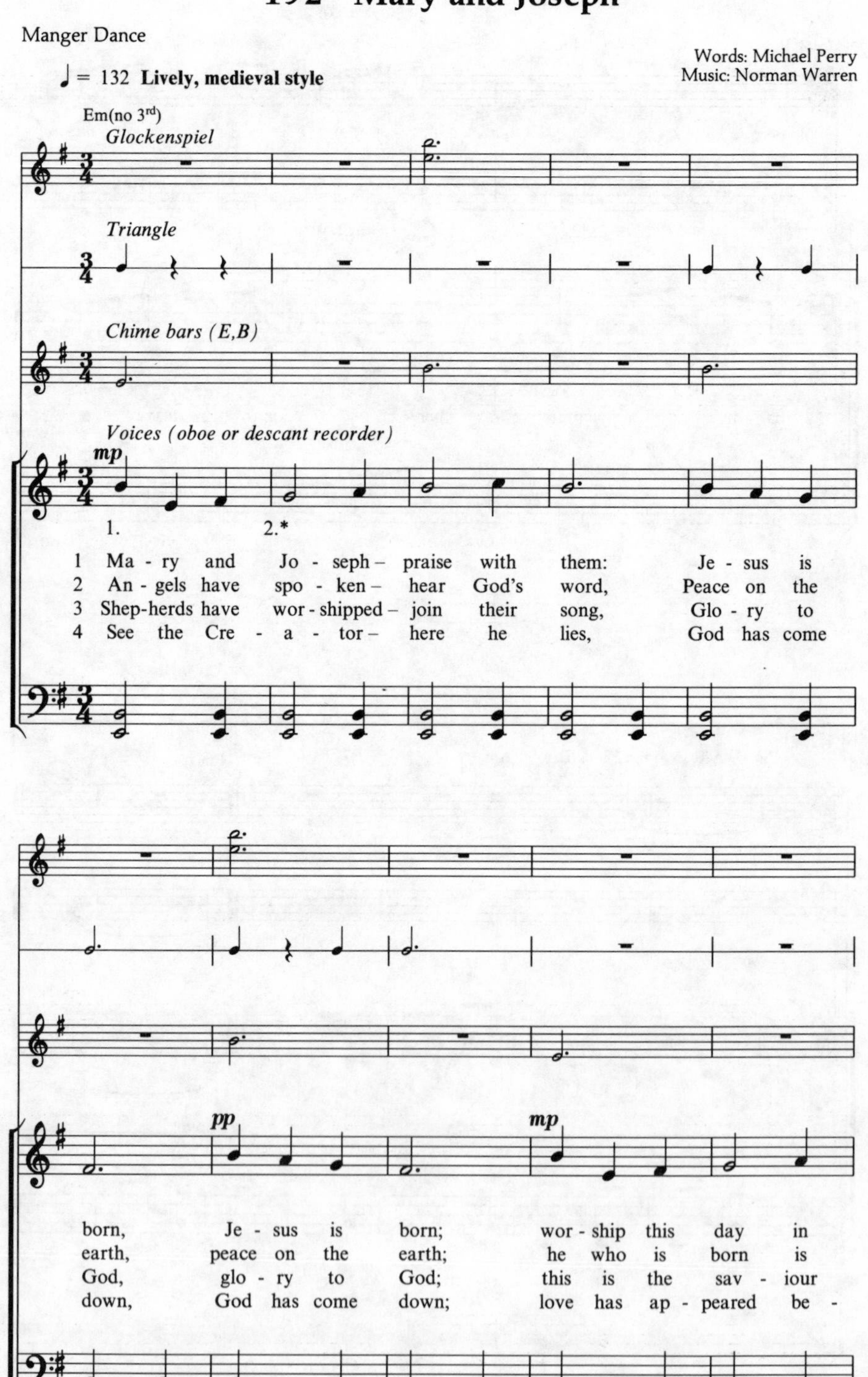
Em(no 3rd)
Glockenspiel
Triangle
Chime bars (E,B)
Voices (oboe or descant recorder)
mp
1.
2.*
1 Ma - ry and Jo - seph – praise with them: Je - sus is
2 An - gels have spo - ken – hear God's word, Peace on the
3 Shep-herds have wor - shipped – join their song, Glo - ry to
4 See the Cre - a - tor – here he lies, God has come
pp
mp
born, Je - sus is born; wor - ship this day in
earth, peace on the earth; he who is born is
God, glo - ry to God; this is the sav - iour
down, God has come down; love has ap - peared be -

* Verse 4 may be sung as a canon, second part entering in bar 2.

Beth - le - hem, Je - sus is born, Je - sus is
Christ the Lord, peace on the earth, peace on the
prom - ised long, glo - ry to God, glo - ry to
- fore our eyes, God has come down, God has come

Last time
born!
earth!
God!
down!

193 Mary had a baby

Words: West Indian spiritual
in this version Word & Music
Music: West Indian traditional melody
arranged David Iliff
Capo 3(D)
With excitement
F(D) Gm7/F (Em7) F(D) Gm7(Em7) C7(A7)
1 Ma - ry had a ba - by, yes, Lord;
QUESTION 2 What did she name him? yes, Lord;
ANSWER 3 Ma - ry named him Je - sus! yes, Lord;
F (D) Gm7/F (Em7) F (D) G7 (E7) Csus (Asus) C (A)
Ma - ry had a ba - by, yes, my Lord;
What did she name him? yes, my Lord;
Ma - ry named him Je - sus! yes, my Lord;
F (D) F7 (D7) B♭ (G) F (D)
Ma - ry had a ba - by, yes, Lord; The
What did she name him? yes, Lord. The
Ma - ry named him Je - sus! yes, Lord. The
C7 (A7) F (D) Dm7 (Bm7) G (E) C7 (A7) F (D)
peo - ple keep a - com - ing for to see her child!
4 QUESTION:
Where was he born?
yes, Lord . . .
5 ANSWER:
Born in a stable!
yes, Lord . . .
6 QUESTION:
Where did she lay him?
yes, Lord . . .
7 ANSWER:
Laid him in a manger!
yes, Lord . . .

194 Mary, listen to the angel

The Annunciation

Words and music: Janet Lunt

Gently but not too slow
Em D/E Em D/E Em
1 Ma - ry,
2 Ma - ry
D Am7 Bm7 Em D/E
lis - ten to the an - gel of the Lord:
an - swered, 'I am the ser - vant of the Lord:
Em D Am7 Bm7
'Hail, O fav - oured one, the Lord is with you!
let it hap-pen to me ac - cord - ing to your word.
Em C G/B
Do not be fright - ened, for
My soul sings out the

Am7
C/D
D
G
he has cho-sen you; you shall have a
great-ness of the Lord; he has done great

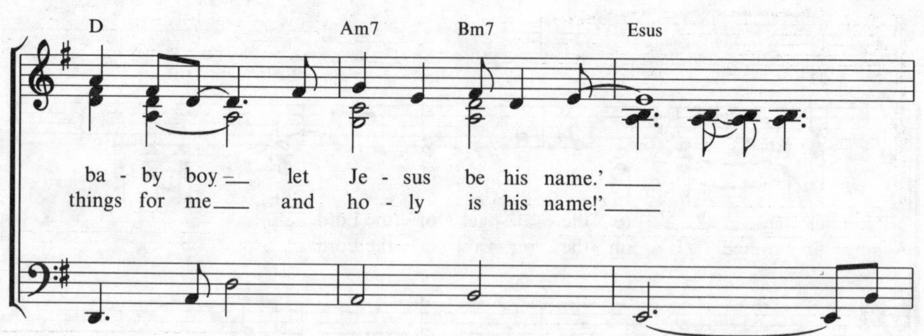
D
Am7
Bm7
Esus
ba - by boy let Je - sus be his name.'
things for me and ho - ly is his name!'

Chorus
Em
C
G/B
He will be great and called the

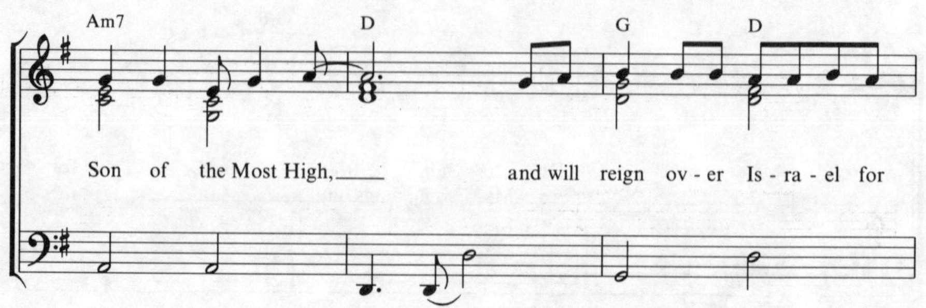
Am7
D
G
D
Son of the Most High, and will reign ov - er Is - ra - el for

Em
A
G
D
Em
A
ev - er: and of his king-dom there will be no end; and of his
G
D7
Em
Bm7
C
Em
king-dom there will be no end.'
Am7
B(no 3rd)
1.
Em
D/E
2.
Em
B♭ melody version of chorus

195 Mary sang a song

(FIRST TUNE)

Mary's Song

From Luke 1 (*Song of Mary / Magnificat*)
Words and music: Michael Perry
Music arranged David Peacock

Lively
Dm
C/D
Dsus
Dm
1 Ma - ry sang a song, a song of love,
2 'God the Lord has done great things for me,
3 'To the hum - ble soul our God is kind,
F
Dm
B♭
Asus
A
mag - ni - fied the migh - ty Lord a - bove;
looked up - on my life's hu - mil - i - ty;
to the proud he brings un - ease of mind:
Dm
C
F
me - lo - dies of praise his name ex - tol
hap - py they shall call me from this day –
who up - lifts the poor, pulls down the strong?
Dm
B♭
Am
Gm7
Am7
Dm
from the ve - ry depths of Ma - ry's soul:
mer - ci - ful is he whom we o - bey.
God a - lone has power to right the wrong!

4 'He who has been Israel's strength and stay
fills the hungry, sends the rich away;
he has shown his promise firm and sure,
faithful to his people evermore.'

5 This was Mary's song as we recall,
mother to the saviour of us all:
magnify his name and sing his praise,
worship and adore him, all your days!

196 Mary sang a song

(SECOND TUNE)

Pavenham

Words: from Luke 1 (*The Song of Mary / Magnificat*)
Michael Perry
Music: Peter Brown

Joyfully
D
F♯7/C♯
1 Ma - ry sang a song, a song of love,
2 'God the Lord has done great things for me,
3 'To the hum - ble soul our God is kind,
Bm
E7
A7
mag - ni - fied the migh - ty Lord a - bove;
looked up - on my life's hum - i - li - ty;
to the proud he brings un-ease of mind:
Bm
Em
A
D
G
Em/C♯
F♯m
B7
me - lo - dies of praise his name ex - tol
hap - py they shall call me from this day
who up - lifts the poor, pulls down the strong?
Em
G
A7
v.5
D
G/D
D
from the ve - ry depths of Ma - ry's soul:
mer - ci - ful is he whom we ob - ey.
God a - lone has power to right the wrong!

4 'He who has been Israel's strength and stay
fills the hungry, sends the rich away;
he has shown his promise firm and sure,
faithful to his people evermore.'

5 This was Mary's song as we recall,
mother to the saviour of us all:
magnify his name and sing his praise,
worship and adore him, all your days!

197 Make way, make way

Words: from Isaiah 61
Graham Kendrick
Music: Graham Kendrick
arranged Christopher Norton

With strength

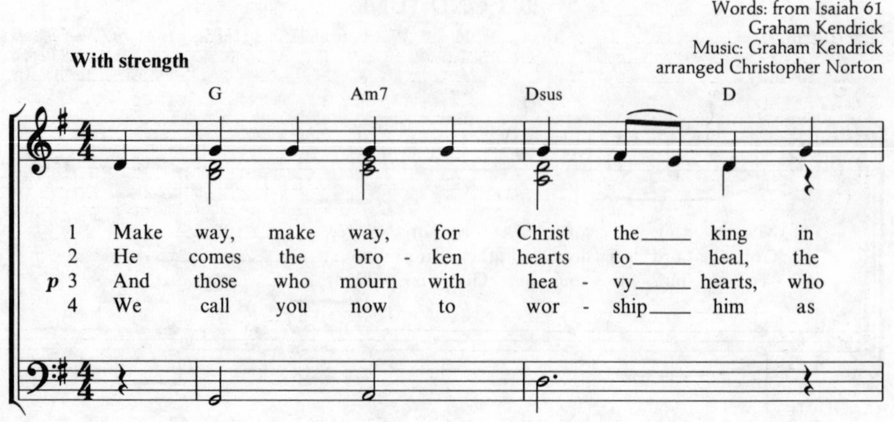

G Am7 Dsus D
1 Make way, make way, for Christ the king in
2 He comes the bro - ken hearts to heal, the
p 3 And those who mourn with hea - vy hearts, who
4 We call you now to wor - ship him as

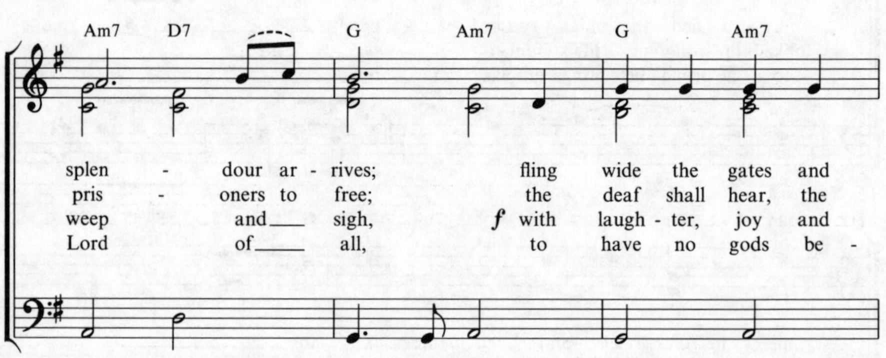

Am7 D7 G Am7 G Am7
splen - dour ar - rives; fling wide the gates and
pris - oners to free; the deaf shall hear, the
weep and sigh, f with laugh - ter, joy and
Lord of all, to have no gods be -

Dsus D Am7 D7 G Chorus
wel - come him in - to your lives.
lame shall dance, the blind shall see.
roy - al crown he'll beau - ti - fy.
- fore him – their thrones must fall!
Make

G
Am7
Dsus
D
Em
D
Part II make way, make way, for the
way, make way, for the King of kings;
Em
D
G
Am7
Dsus
D
King of kings; make way, make way,
make way, make way, and
Em
D7sus
D7
G
C/G
G
let his king - dom in!

Bb melody version

198 Meekness and majesty

This is your God

Words and music: Graham Kendrick
Music arranged Christopher Norton

Thoughtfully
C Am7 Em7 Am7
1 Meek - ness and maj - es - ty, man - hood and de - i - ty,
2 Fath - er's pure ra - di - ance, per - fect in in - no-cence,
3 Wis - dom un - search - a - ble, God the in - vi - si - ble,
C Am7 D9 G7sus G7
in per - fect har - mo - ny – the man who is God:
yet learns o - be - di - ence to death on a cross:
love in - de - struct - i - ble in frail - ty ap - pears:
C C/B♭ F F♯dim
Lord of e - ter - ni - ty dwells in hu - man - i - ty,
suffer - ing to give us life, conquer - ing through sac - ri - fice –
Lord of in - fin - i - ty, stoop - ing so ten - der - ly,
Em7 Am Dm7 C/G G7 C
kneels in hu - mil - i - ty and wash - es our feet.
and, as they cru - ci - fy, prays, 'Fa - ther, for - give'.
lifts our hu - man - i - ty to the heights of his throne.

Chorus
Dm7
F/G G
E7
E/A Am
F
Oh what a my-ste-ry – meek-ness and ma-jes-ty:
F♯dim
C/G
Am
Dm7
G7
bow down and wor - ship, for this is your
B♭
F/A
G7
God, this is your
1.2.
A♭
Gm7
C
G7 F/A G7/B
3.
B♭
God!
God,
F/A
G7
A♭
Gm7
C
this is your God!

199 Mighty in victory

Capo 5(Am)
Hebrew style
Words and music: Mavis Ford
Dm(Am) Gm(Dm)
Migh - ty in vic - tory, glo - rious in ma - je - sty:
A(E) Dm (Am) Dm/C B♭ (F) A7 (E7)
ev - ery eye shall see him when he ap - pears,
Dm (Am) Gm (Dm)
com - ing in the clouds with pow - er and glo - ry.
A (E) Dm (Am) D (A)
Hail to the king! We must be rea - dy,

Gm
(Dm)
Gm/F Gm/E
G7/D
(D7)
C
(G)
watch - ing and pray - ing, serv - ing each o - ther,
F
(C)
Gm
(Dm)
Dm/A
(Am)
A
(E)
Dm
(Am)
build - ing his king - dom; then ev - ery knee shall bow,
Gm
(Dm)
A
(E)
Dm
(Am)
then ev - ery tongue con - fess, Je - sus is Lord!
B♭ melody version
1.
2.

200 My Lord, he is a-coming soon

Capo 2(Dm)

With a slow 'blues' swing: one beat to a bar

Words: Laura Winnen
Music: Jeff Cothran

Chorus
Em(Dm)
Em♯7(Dm♯7)
Em7(Dm7)
Em6(Dm6)
My Lord, he is a - com - ing soon pre -
Am7(Gm7)
Em(Dm)
- pare the way of the Lord; get
Em♯7(Dm♯7)
Em7(Dm7)
Em6(Dm6)
ev - ery-thing rea - dy for that day pre -
Am7(Gm7)
B7(A7)
Em(Dm)
Fine
- pare the way of the Lord!

Am7(Gm7)
Em(Dm)
1 If you're a - sleep, it's time to wake up a -
2 Come, Lord Je - sus, come in - to my heart pre -
Am7(Gm7)
Em(Dm)
Am7(Gm7)
- wake, O sleep - er, a - rise! If you're in the
- pare the way of the king! He is
Em(Dm)
Am(Gm)
dark, it's time to be lit a - wake, O
com - ing, he's com - ing soon: pre - pare the
B(A)
B7(A7)
D.C.
sleep - er, a - rise!
way of the king!

201 My soul glorifies the Lord

From Luke 1 (*Song of Mary / Magnificat*)
Words and music: Simon Humphreys

Gently but with strength
E B/D♯ C♯m A A/B
1 My soul glo - ri - fies the Lord, and my
2 His love ex - tends to those who fear him, from
E F♯m B A/B B7 E B/D♯
spir - it re - joi - ces in my God, my sav - iour; my soul
gen - er - a - tion to gen - er - a - tion; his love ex -
C♯m A A/B E F♯m F♯m/B B
glo - ri - fies the Lord, and my spir - it re - joi - ces in his word:
- tends to those who fear him praise his ho - ly name:
G♯m C♯m F♯m B
for he has been mind - ful of his ser - vant.
he has brought down ru - lers from their thrones,

G♯m C♯m F♯m A/B B G♯m G♯
From now on, all peo-ples will bless me, for ___ the migh - ty ___
but ___ has up - lift - ed the hum-ble; he has filled the hun - gry with
A F♯m7/A A/B B A/B B E/F♯ F♯
one has done ___ great ___ things for me:
good things, and has sent the rich a - way emp - ty.
B B/G♯
1.
C♯m B/D♯ C♯m/E G♯m/E♯ F♯ B/F♯ F♯
Ho - ly, ho - ly, ho - ly is the Lord
2.
C♯m B/D♯ C♯m F♯7 B A/B E/B B
ho - ly is the Lord. ___

202 No room for the saviour

Words and music: Hilda M Day
Words: in this version Word & Music

Capo 5(C)
F (C) B♭ (F) Gm7 (Dm7) C (G) C7 (G7) F (C)
1 No room for the sav - iour at Beth - le - hem's inn,
No room for the Ba - by at Beth - le - hem's inn,
2 O Lord in my heart there's a wel - come for you:
'O Lord, in my heart there's a wel - come for you,'
Dm7 (Am7) G7 (D7) Csus (Gsus) C7 (G7)
on - ly a cat - tle shed; no
on - ly a cat - tle shed; no
glad - ly I now would say, 'Come
glad - ly I now would say, 'Come
F (C) B♭ (F) Gm (Dm7) C (G) Dm (Am)
room on this earth for the dear Son of God,
home on this earth for the dear Son of God,
in, pre - cious sav - iour; my heart and my life
in, bless - ed sav - iour, my heart and my life
G7 (D7) Csus (Gsus) C (G)
no - where to lay his head.
no - where to lay his head.
both shall be yours to - day.
hence - forth would own your sway.

No room for the Baby: original words are set in italics.

C7 (G7) F (C)
On - ly a cross did they give to my Lord,
On - ly a cross did they give to our Lord,
Long have you wait - ed and long knocked in vain
Long have you wait - ed and long knocked in vain
Dm (Am) G (D) G7 (D7) Csus (Gsus) C (G) C7 (G7)
on - ly a bor - rowed tomb. To -
on - ly a bor - rowed tomb. To -
out - side my heart's closed door: so
out - side my heart's closed door: O
F (C) B♭ (F) Gm (Dm) C (G) C♯dim (G♯dim) Dm (Am) F7 (C7)
- day he is seek - ing a place in your heart – will you
- day he is seek - ing a place in your heart, will you
cleanse me from sin, then, my Lord, en - ter in and
cleanse me from sin, then dear Lord en - ter in and
B♭ (F) Gm (Dm) Gm/C C7 (G7) Fsus (Csus) F (C)
still say to him, 'No room'?
still say to him, 'No room'?
live there for ev - er - more!'
dwell there for ev - er - more.'

203 No weapon formed

Words and music: Tom Dowell
Music arranged Gary Wilson

Fast march
Dm Dm(maj7) Dm7 Bdim
No weap-on formed, or ar-my or king, shall be
B♭ Dm7 Gm A
ab-le to stand a-gainst the Lord and his A-noin-ted;
Gm C7 F B♭ Em7 A7
All prin-ci-pal-i-ties and pow-ers shall crum-ble be-fore the
Dm Gm C7 F B♭
Lord, and our hearts shall be re-leased, and
Em7 Gm Asus A7 D.C.
last time
Dm
we shall re-turn to the Lord.

204 Now tell us, gentle Mary

Words: from the French
W B Lindsay and Ruth Heller
Music: French traditional carol
arranged Norman Warren

Capo 3(Em)
Lightly and quickly
Gm (Em) Cm (Am) Gm (Em) D (B) Gm (Em)
1 Now tell us, gen-tle Ma - ry, what did Gab - riel say to you? Now
2 Now tell us, gen-tle Ma - ry, of the birth of Christ that morn; now
C (A) Gm (Em) D (B) Gm (Em)
tell us of the ti - dings that he brought to Ga - li - lee. He
tell us of Christ Je - sus, where it was that he was born. Not
D (B) Gm (Em) Cm6 (Am6) A (F♯) Dsus (Bsus) D (B) Gm (Em)
told me I was fav - oured, that I would be the one God
in a pa - lace glor - ious, not in a silk - en bed, but
Cm6/G (Am6) Gm (Em) C (A) D7 (B7) Gm (Em)
chose to be the mo - ther of Je - sus, his own son.
in a sta - ble hum - ble did Je - sus lay his head.

205 O bless the God of Israel

Words: from Luke 1 (*The Song of Zechariah / Benedictus*)
Michael Perry
Roewen
Music: Roger Mayor
Flowing smoothly
Cmaj7 Dm7/C Em7/C Dm7 Em7 F Dm/F
F/G G7 C/E Am7 Dm7/F G
1 O bless the God of Is - rael who
(2) comes! the Child of Da - vid, the
(3) once were fear and dark - ness, the
F/A Dm7 Gsus G7 C/E Am7
comes to set us free; who vis - its and re -
Son whom God has given; he comes to live a -
sun be - gins to rise – the dawn - ing of for -
G♯dim7 Am Am7 D D7 Gsus Dm A7/E
- deems us, with love for all to see. The
- mong us and raise us up to heaven: be -
- give - ness up - on the sin - ner's eyes. He

Dm C/E F D Gm Cm7 F7
pro - phets spoke of mer - cy, of res - cue and re -
- fore him goes his her - ald – fore - run - ner in the
guides the feet of pil - grims a - long the paths of
B♭ G7/B Csus C/E F G7 G♯dim7
- lease: God shall ful - fil his prom - ise and
way, the proph - et of sal - va - tion, the
peace: O bless our God and Sav - iour, with
D7/A G7
1.2.
C Dm7/C Em7/C Dm7 Em7
bring our peo - ple peace.
har - bin - ger of Day.
songs that nev - er
F Dm/F F/G G7
3.
C
2 He
3 Where
cease!

Can also be sung to 'Morning light'

-4

206 O come, all ye faithful

Words: after J F Wade (1711–1786)
F Oakeley (1802–1880) and others
Music: J F Wade (1711–1786)
arranged mainly by W H Monk (1823–1889)
verses 3, 4 arranged with descant Christopher Robinson

Adeste fideles

G Am7/G D/F♯ G D G C G/D D (Em)
1 O come, all ye faith - ful, joy - ful and tri - um - phant; O
2 God from God, Light from light
Em D A D G D G D/A A7 D
come ye, O come ye to Beth - le - hem;
lo, he ab - hors not the vir - gin's womb!
G Am G Am7 D7/A G D G Em Am D G
come and be - hold him, born the king of an - gels! O
Ve - ry God, be - got - ten, not cre - a - ted.
G D G D7 G D G D7 G D G
come, let us a - dore him, O come, let us a - dore him, O

D7 G D A7 D D7 G/B C G/D D G
come, let us a - dore him, Christ the Lord!
Descant
G Gmaj7 Am7/G D G D Em7 Am7 G/D D7
3 Sing, choirs of an - gels, sing in ex - ul - ta - tion!
4 Yea, Lord, we greet thee, born for our sal - va - tion;
OR, ON CHRISTMAS DAY: born this hap - py morn - ing;
3 Sing, choirs of an - gels, sing in ex - ul - ta - tion!
4 Yea, Lord, we greet thee, born for our sal - va - tion;
OR, ON CHRISTMAS DAY: born this hap - py morn - ing;
G Em7 A6 A7 D Em D/A A7 D D7
Sing, all ye ci - ti - zens of heaven a - bove,
Je - sus, to thee be glo - ry given!
Sing, all ye ci - ti - zens of heaven a - bove,
Je - sus, to thee be glo - ry given!

G7 F7/B Esus E7 Am6 E7 G/A A D G
'Glo - ry to God in the high - est!'
Word of the Fa - ther now in flesh ap - pear - ing. O
'Glo - ry to God in the high - est!'
Word of the Fa - ther now in flesh ap - pear - ing. O
G/D C/G D7/G G/D Bm/D Am/D Bm/D D7 G G7
come, let us a - dore him, let us a - dore him,
come, let us a - dore him, O come, let us a - dore him, O
C Em7 A6 A7 D7/C G Am7 G/D D7 G
let us a - dore him, Christ the Lord!
come, let us a - dore him, Christ the Lord!

207 O come, Christians, wonder

Words: from the Welsh
Michael Perry
Music: Norman Warren
Sarach
Capo 3(Em)
Gently
Gm (Em) Dm7/G (Bm) Gm (Em) Cm/G (Am) Gm (Em)
1 O come, Christ - ians, won - der, be thank - ful, and
2 So lift high your voi - ces, as hea - ven re -
3 Let sis - ter and bro - ther speak peace to each
Cm6/G (Am6) Dsus/G (Bsus) D/F♯ (B) Gm (Em) E♭maj7 (Cmaj7) F (D) A (F♯)
pon - der the birth of our sav - iour and Lord: for
- joi - ces to tell of the babe in the hay: this
o - ther, and bro - ther and sis - ter a - gree: for
Dm (Bm) B♭maj7 (Gmaj7) E♭ (C) D7 (B7)
we who were sigh - ing, and sin - ning, and dy - ing, in
Je - sus – the ho - ly, the poor, and the low - ly – we
love is our sto - ry – to Je - sus the glo - ry both
Cm (Am) Gm (Em) Cm/A (Am) D7 (B7) Gm (Em) C (A) Gm (Em)
Je - sus are ful - ly re - stored.
praise him and serve him to - day!
now and for ev - er shall be.

208 O come, let us worship and bow down

Capo 5(C)

Words and music: Iain Anderson

Worshipfully
F(C) C/E(G) Dm(Am) B♭(F)
O come let us wor-ship and bow down, let us
F(C) B♭(F) C(G) Gm(Dm)
kneel be - fore the Lord our king. let us whis - per his
last time to Coda
1.
C(G) A7(E7) Dm(Am) Gm(Dm)
name, – won - der - ful name, – Je - sus our Lord and
2.
C(G) Gm(Dm) F/C(C) C(G) F(C) F7(C7)
king. O Je - sus our Lord and king.

B♭(F)
C(G)
F(C)
F7(C7)
For he is Lord of all the earth, his

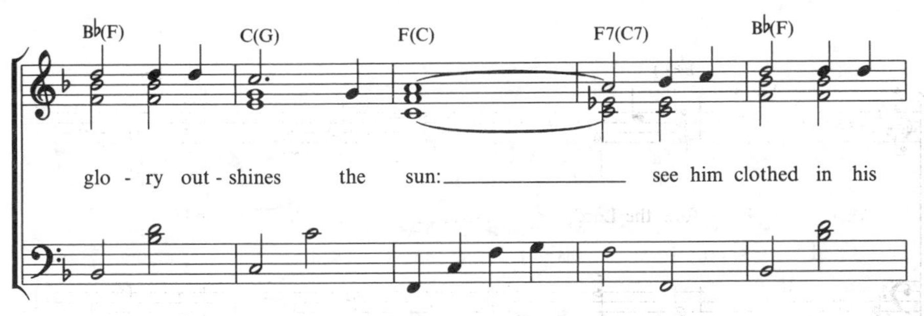
B♭(F)
C(G)
F(C)
F7(C7)
B♭(F)
glo - ry out - shines the sun: see him clothed in his

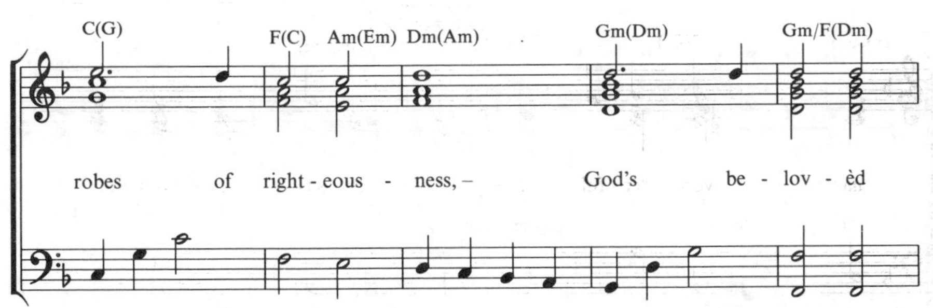
C(G)
F(C) Am(Em) Dm(Am)
Gm(Dm)
Gm/F(Dm)
robes of right - eous - ness, – God's be - lov - èd

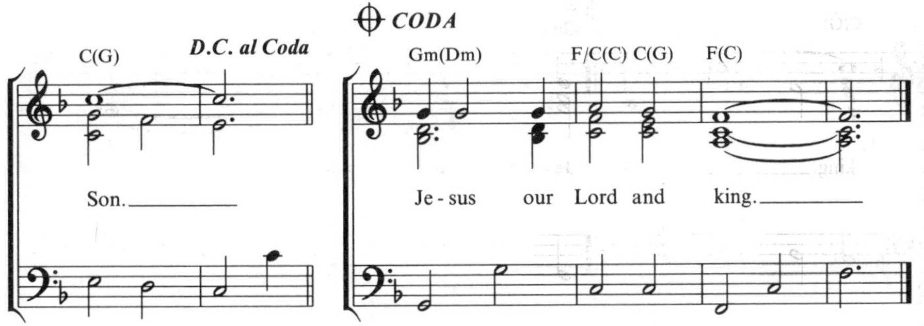
C(G)
D.C. al Coda
CODA
Gm(Dm)
F/C(C) C(G)
F(C)
Son.
Je - sus our Lord and king.

209 O come, O come, Emmanuel

Veni Emmanuel

Words: from the Latin (thirteenth century)
J M Neale (1818–1866) and others,
in this version Jubilate Hymns
Music: from a fifteenth century plainsong melody
arranged Noël Tredinnick

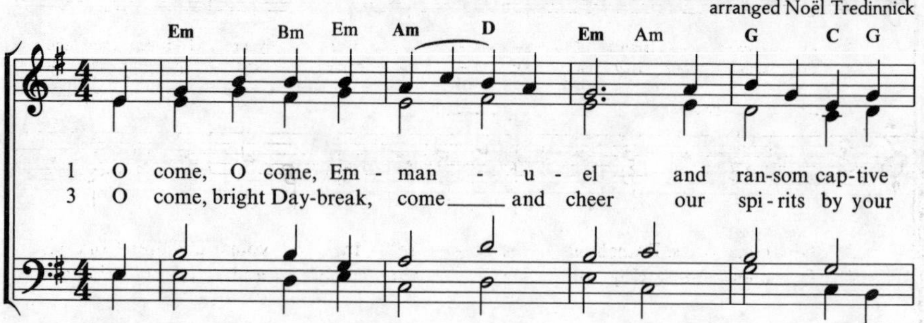

Em Bm Em Am D Em Am G C G
1 O come, O come, Em - man - u - el and ran-som cap-tive
3 O come, bright Day-break, come and cheer our spi-rits by your

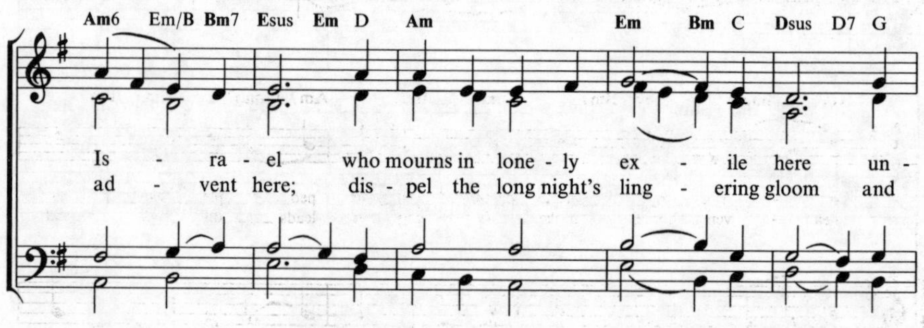

Am6 Em/B Bm7 Esus Em D Am Em Bm C Dsus D7 G
Is - ra - el who mourns in lone - ly ex - ile here un -
ad - vent here; dis - pel the long night's ling - ering gloom and

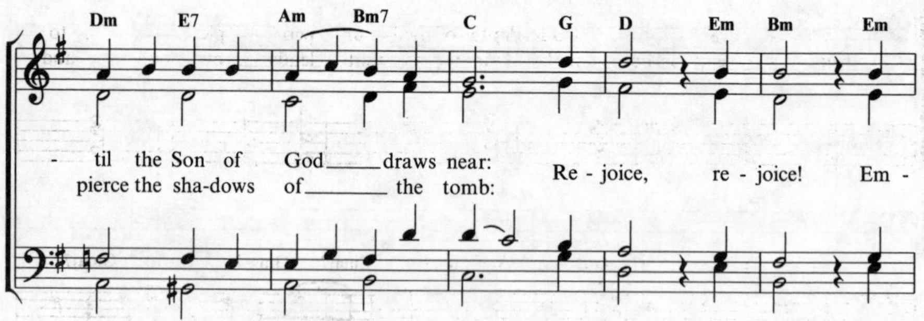

Dm E7 Am Bm7 C G D Em Bm Em
- til the Son of God draws near: Re - joice, re - joice! Em -
pierce the sha-dows of the tomb:

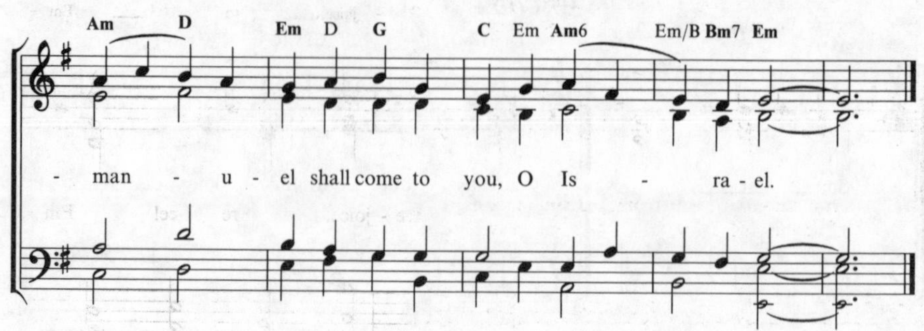

Am D Em D G C Em Am6 Em/B Bm7 Em
- man - u - el shall come to you, O Is - ra - el.

Accompaniment for verses 2 & 4
Cmaj7 Bm7 Am7 Gmaj7 Am7 Bm7 Cmaj7 Bm7
Optional descant
2 O come, true Branch of Jes - se, free your child - ren from this
4 O come, strong Key of Da - vid, come and op - en wide our
mp sostenuto
2 O come, true Branch of Jes - se, free your child-ren from this
4 O come, strong Key of Da - vid, come and op - en wide our
Am7 Gmaj7 Am7 Bm7 Cmaj7 Bm7 Am7 Gmaj7 Am7 Bm7
ty - ran - ny; from depths of hell your peo - ple save to
hea - venly home; make safe the way that leads on high, and
ty - ran - ny; from depths of hell your peo - ple save to
hea - venly home; make safe the way that leads on high, and
Cmaj7 Bm7 Am7 Gmaj7 Am7 Bm7 Cmaj7 Gmaj7 Am7 Gmaj7
rise vic - tor - ious from the grave:
close the path to mi - se - ry:
Re - joice, re - joice! Em -
mf
rise vic - tor - ious from the grave:
close the path to mi - se - ry:
Re - joice, re - joice! Em -

Am7
Bm7
Cmaj7
Bm7
Am7
Gmaj7
Bm7
E
- man - u - el shall come to you, O Is - ra - el.
- man - u - el shall come to you, O Is - ra - el.
Accompaniment for verse 5
Em
E
Am
B7
Em
D7
Optional descant (2 parts)
f
5 O come great Lord of might who
f
grandioso
5 O come, O come, great Lord of might who
G
Am7
Bm
Em
D
Am
B7
long a - go on Sin - ai's height gave all your tribes the
long a - go on Sin - ai's height gave all your tribes the

Em A7 D Em7 Am E7/G♯ Am B7
an - cient law, in cloud and ma - jes - ty and
an - cient law, in cloud and ma - jes - ty and
C G7/F E♭ G♯m Am7 Bm7
ff
awe: Re-joice, re-joice! Re-joice, re-joice! Em - man - u -
ff resoluto
awe: Re - joice, re - joice! Em - man - u -
C7 F7 Em7 D7 Bm7 E
- el shall come, O Is - ra - el.
poco rit.
- el shall come to you, O Is - ra - el.

210 O come all you children

Ihr Kinderlein kommet

Words: from the German
Paul Wigmore
Music: J A P Schulz (1747–1800)
arranged David Peacock

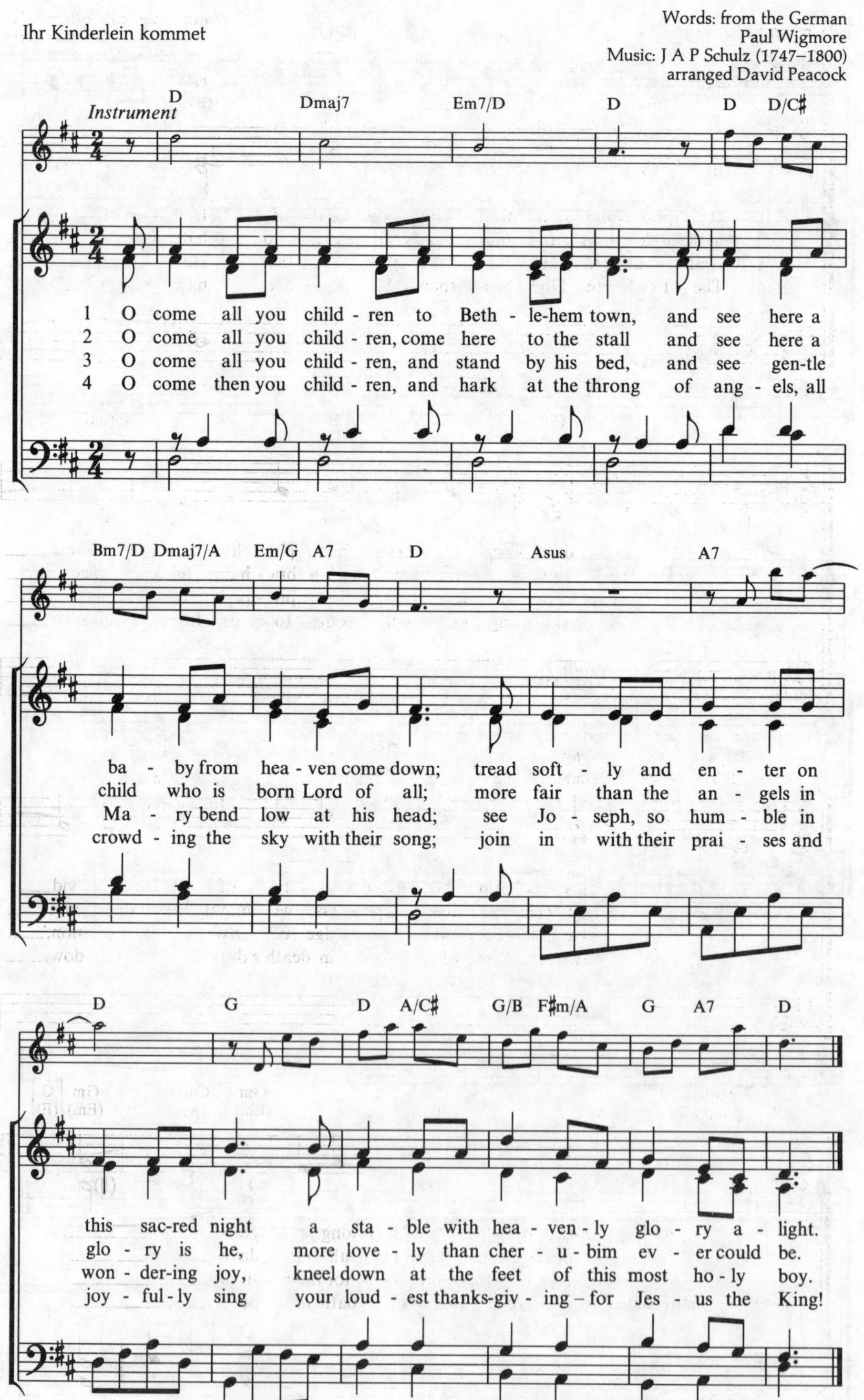
Instrument
D
Dmaj7
Em7/D
D
D D/C♯
1 O come all you child - ren to Beth - le-hem town, and see here a
2 O come all you child - ren, come here to the stall and see here a
3 O come all you child - ren, and stand by his bed, and see gen-tle
4 O come then you child - ren, and hark at the throng of ang - els, all
Bm7/D Dmaj7/A Em/G A7 D Asus A7
ba - by from hea - ven come down; tread soft - ly and en - ter on
child who is born Lord of all; more fair than the an - gels in
Ma - ry bend low at his head; see Jo - seph, so hum - ble in
crowd - ing the sky with their song; join in with their prai - ses and
D G D A/C♯ G/B F♯m/A G A7 D
this sac-red night a sta - ble with hea - ven-ly glo - ry a - light.
glo - ry is he, more love - ly than cher - u - bim ev - er could be.
won - der-ing joy, kneel down at the feet of this most ho - ly boy.
joy - ful - ly sing your loud - est thanks-giv - ing – for Jes - us the King!

211 O praise the Lord

Crown Lane
Capo 3(Em)
Words: from Luke 1 (*Benedictus*)
Michael Perry
Music: Norman Warren
Flowing
Gm (Em) Cm (Am) D (B)
1 O praise the Lord, the migh - ty God of Is - rael,
2 Sal - va - tion from the hands of those who hate us!
3 And you will be the pro - phet of the High - est,
4 The Lord our God has shown his ten - der mer - cy,
D7 (B7) Cm (Am) F (D) B♭maj7 (Gmaj7)
re - deem - er of his peo - ple he has come;
His cov - en - ant with A - bra - ham ful - filled!
to go be - fore him and pre - pare his way;
his shin - ing sun will come to us from heaven
D7/A (B7) Cm6/G (Am6) Dm/F (Bm) E♭maj7 (Cmaj7)
he rais - es up the dyn - as - ty of Da - vid
He res - cues us that, fear - less, we might serve him
to give his peo - ple know-ledge of sal - va - tion,
to dawn on those who live in death's dark sha - dow,
B♭m6/D♭ (Gm6) C (A) Dm7 (Bm7) Gm (Em) Cm/G (Am) Gm (Em) [G (E)]
as prom-ised by his pro-phets long a - go.
in hon - our and in good-ness all our days.
the bless - ing of for - give - ness for their sins.
and guide our foot-steps in the path of peace.

212 O leave your sheep

Words: from the French
John Rutter and in this version Word & Music
Music: French traditional melody
arranged David Peacock
Quittez Pasteurs
Capo 3(C)
Lively
Instrument
E♭ (C) B♭ (G) E♭ (C) B♭ (G) Cm (Am) B♭ (G) E♭ (C) A♭ (F)
1 O leave your sheep, where ewes with lambs are
2 For Love lies there with - in a low - ly
3 You wise men three ar - rayed in roy - al
4 O Spi - rit blessed, the source of life e -
B♭ (G) E♭ (C) B♭ (G) Cm (Am) B♭7 (G7) E♭ (C) B♭ (G) Cm (Am)
feed - ing; you shep - herds, hear our mes-sage of good
man - ger – the in - fant poor whom an - gel hosts a -
splen - dour, true hom - age pay: your king is born to -
- ter - nal, our souls in - spire with your ce - les - tial
B♭sus (Gsus) B♭ (G) E♭/B♭ (C) B♭ (G) B♭7 (G7) E♭ (C) B♭7 (G7)
cheer. No long - er weep; the an - gel tid - ings
- dore! Such per - fect care has saved us all from
- day! The star you see its ra - diance must sur -
fire! We make our guest the Christ, the Lord su -

E♭ (C) B♭ (G) E♭ (C) B♭ (G) E♭ (C) B♭ (G) Cm (Am) B♭sus (Gsus) B♭ (G)
heed - ing, to Beth - l'hem haste a - way Our
dan - ger and brought us to the fold. Now
- ren - der be - fore our Sun most bright. Your
- per - nal, and sing the peace on earth God
E♭ (C) B♭ (G) E♭ (C) A♭ (F) Fm (Dm)
Lord, our Lord, our Lord is born this
see, now see God's faith - ful love re -
gifts. your gifts, your gifts are pre - cious
gives, God gives, God gives us by this
1. E♭/B (C) B♭ (G) E♭ (C)
2. E♭/B♭ (C) B♭7 (G7) E♭ (C)
hap - py day. Our hap - py day.
- vealed of old. Now - vealed of old.
in his sight. Your in his sight.
ho - ly birth; God ho - ly birth.

-4

213 O little town of Bethlehem

(FIRST TUNE)
Forest Green
Capo 5(C)
Words: P Brooks (1835–1893)
Music: English traditional melody
arranged R Vaughan Williams (1872–1958)
1 O lit - tle town of Beth - le - hem, how still we see you
2 For Christ is born of Ma - ry and, ga - thered all a -
3 How sil - ent - ly, how sil - ent - ly the won - drous gift is
4 O ho - ly child of Beth - le - hem, de - scend to us we
lie! A - bove your deep and dream-less sleep the sil - ent stars go
- bove while mor - tals sleep, the an - gels keep their watch of won-dering
given! So God im - parts to hu - man hearts the bles - sings of his
pray; cast out our sin and en - ter in, be born in us to -
by: yet in your dark streets shin - ing is ev - er - last - ing
love: O morn-ing stars, to - ge - ther pro - claim the ho - ly
heaven: no ear may hear his com - ing, but in this world of
- day! We hear the Christ-mas an - gels the great glad ti - dings
light; the hopes and fears of all the years are met in you to - night.
birth, and prai - ses sing to God the king, and peace to all the earth.
sin, where meek souls will re - ceive him – still the dear Christ en - ters in.
tell – O come to us, a - bide with us, our Lord Em - man - u - el.

214 O little town of Bethlehem

St Louis

(SECOND TUNE)

Words: P Brooks (1835–1893)
Music: L Redner (1831–1908)

Capo 5(C)

F (C) Gm (Dm) F/C (C) C (G) C7 (G7)
1 O lit - tle town of Beth - le - hem, how still we__ see you
2 For Christ is born of Ma - ry and, gath - ered__ all a -
3 How sil - ent - ly, how sil - ent - ly the wond - rous__ gift is
4 O ho - ly child of Beth - le - hem, des - cend to__ us we
F (C) F7 (C7) D7 (A7) Gsus (Dsus) Gm (Dm) F/C (C) C7 (G7)
lie! A - bove your deep and dream-less sleep the sil - ent__stars go
- bove while mor - tals sleep, the an - gels keep their watch of__won-dering
given! So God im - parts to hu - man hearts the bless - ings__ of his
pray; cast out our sin and en - ter in, be born in__ us to -
F (C) Gm (Dm) G♯dim (D♯dim) A (E) Dm (Am) Gm (Dm)
by: yet in your dark streets shin - ing is ev - er - last - ing
love: O morn - ing stars, to - geth - er pro - claim the ho - ly
heaven: no ear may hear his com - ing, but in this world of
- day! We hear the Chris - tmas an - gels the great glad tid - ings
A (E) F (C) Gm (Dm) F/C (C) G7 (D7) F/C (C) C7 (G7) F (C)
light; the hopes and fears of all the years are met in you to - night.
birth, and prais - es sing to God the king, and peace to all the earth.
sin, where meek souls will re - ceive him – still the dear Christ en - ters in.
tell – O come to us, a - bide with us, our Lord Em - man - u - el.

215 O little town of Bethlehem

(THIRD TUNE)

Christmas Carol

Words: P Brooks (1835–1893)
Music: H Walford Davies (1869–1941)

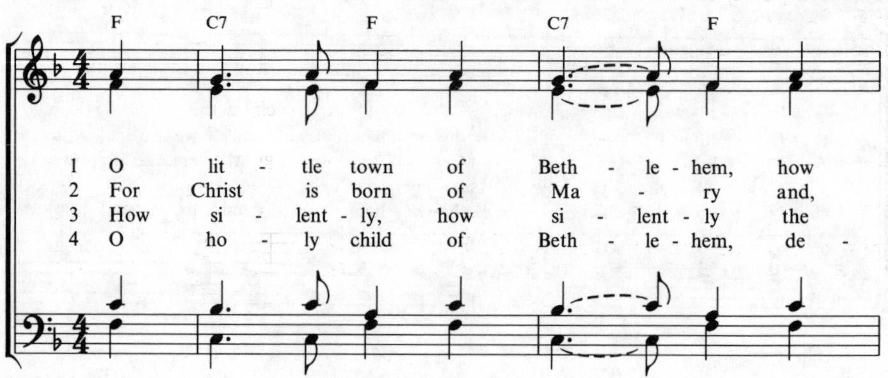
F C7 F C7 F
1 O lit - tle town of Beth - le - hem, how
2 For Christ is born of Ma - ry and,
3 How si - lent - ly, how si - lent - ly the
4 O ho - ly child of Beth - le - hem, de -

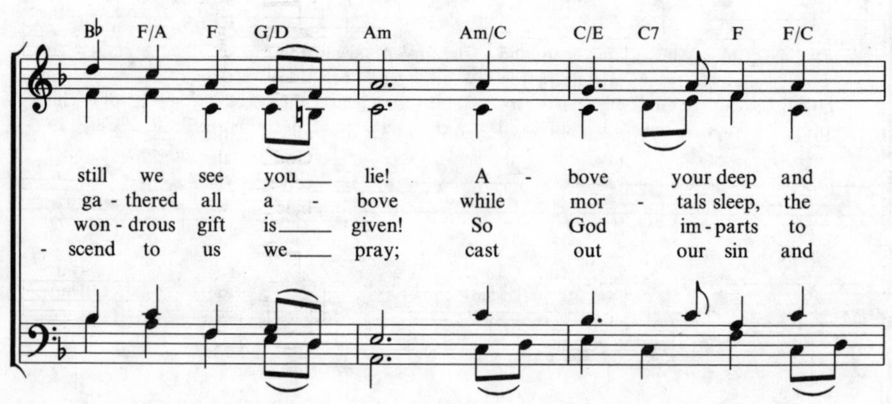
B♭ F/A F G/D Am Am/C C/E C7 F F/C
still we see you___ lie! A - bove your deep and
ga - thered all a - bove while mor - tals sleep, the
won - drous gift is___ given! So God im - parts to
- scend to us we___ pray; cast out our sin and

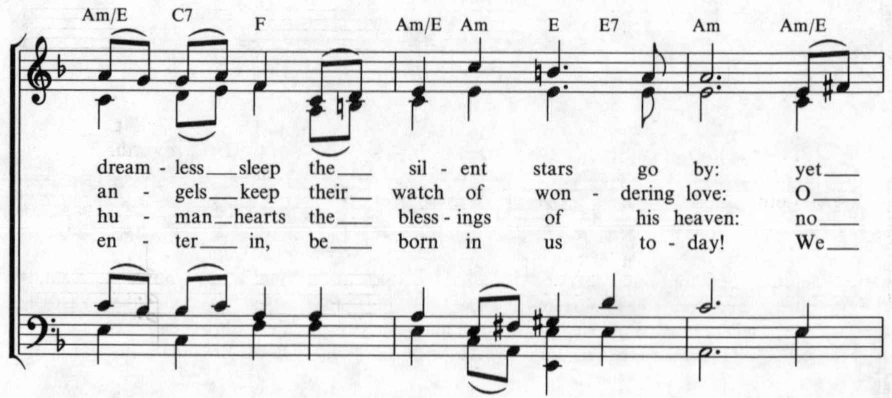
Am/E C7 F Am/E Am E E7 Am Am/E
dream - less___ sleep the___ sil - ent stars go by: yet___
an - gels___ keep their___ watch of won - dering love: O___
hu - man___ hearts the___ bless - ings of his heaven: no___
en - ter___ in, be___ born in us to - day! We___

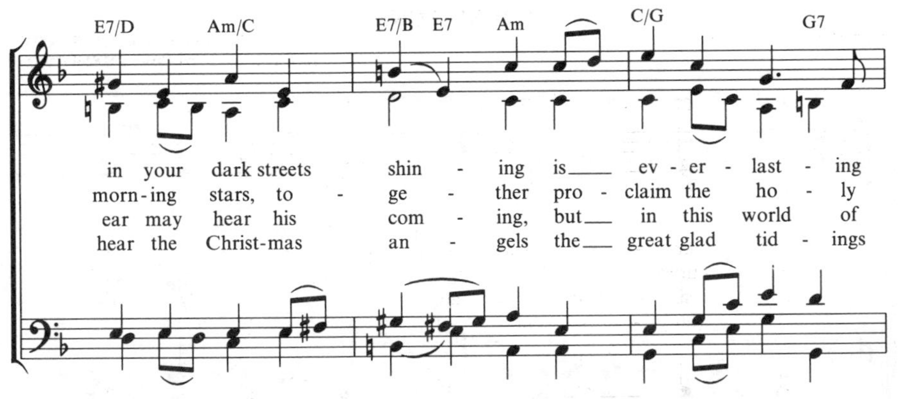
E7/D Am/C E7/B E7 Am C/G G7
in your dark streets shin - ing is ev - er - last - ing
morn-ing stars, to - ge - ther pro - claim the ho - ly
ear may hear his com - ing, but in this world of
hear the Christ-mas an - gels the great glad tid - ings

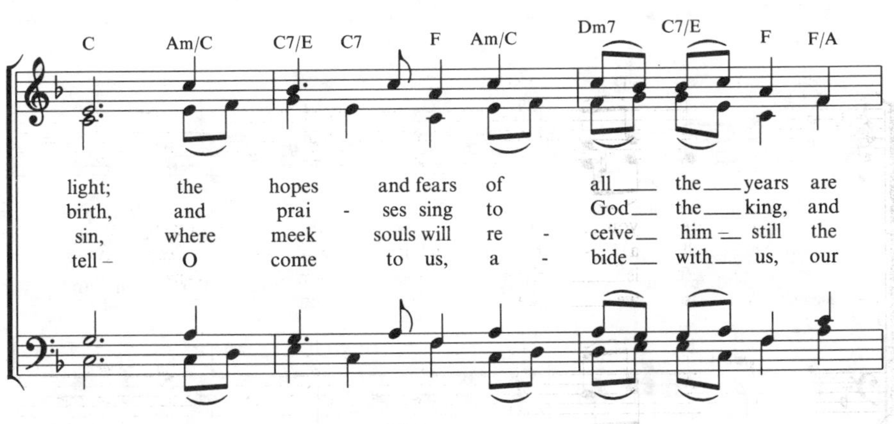
C Am/C C7/E C7 F Am/C Dm7 C7/E F F/A
light; the hopes and fears of all the years are
birth, and prai - ses sing to God the king, and
sin, where meek souls will re - ceive him still the
tell – O come to us, a - bide with us, our

B♭ F/A Dm/F Dm Am C7 F
met in you to - night.
peace to all the earth.
dear Christ en - ters in.
Lord Em - man - u - el.

216 O little town of Bethlehem

(FOURTH TUNE)
Enmore
Words: P Brooks (1835–1893)
Music: Philip Trumble
Gentle rock
C9 C C9 C C9 C C9 C
1 O lit - tle town of Beth - le - hem,
2 For Christ is born of Ma - ry
3 How si - lent - ly, how si - lent - ly
4 O ho - ly child of Beth - le - hem,
con ped.
Fmaj9/C F/C C9 C C9 C
how still we see you lie! A - bove your deep and
and, gath - ered all a - bove while mor - tals sleep, the
the won - drous gift is given! So God im - parts to
de - scend to us we pray; cast out our sin and
Gm7 Gm7/C C F9 F F9 F G/F
dream - less sleep the si - lent stars go by:
an - gels keep their watch of won - dering love:
hu - man hearts the bless - ings of his heaven:
en - ter in, be born in us to - day!

Am Em9 F9 F
yet in your dark streets shin - ing is ev - er - last-ing light;
O morn-ing stars, to - ge - ther pro - claim the ho - ly birth,
no ear may hear his com - ing, but in this world of sin,
We hear the Christ-mas an - gels the great glad tid-ings tell –
F9 F G7/F A♭ B♭7/A♭ C/G
the hopes and fears of all the years
and prai - ses sing to God the king,
where meek souls will re - ceive him – still
O come to us, a - bide with us,
F/G C9 C 1.2.3. C9 C 4. C9
are met in you to - night.
and peace to all the earth.
the dear Christ en - ters in.
our Lord Em-man - u - el.

217 O Lord, our Lord

(How majestic is your name)

Words and music: Michael Smith

Joyously
mf
D
G
Em7
D/F♯
A
A9/C♯
O Lord, our Lord, how ma - jes - tic is your name in all the earth; O
Lord, our Lord, how maj - es - tic is your name in all the

A A9/C♯ D G Em7 A G/B A7/C♯
earth; O Lord, we praise your
D G Em7 A G/B A7/C♯
name; O Lord, we mag-ni-fy your
D C♯ F♯m E A A/G D/F♯ G
name. Prince of peace, migh-ty God, O Lord God al-
To repeat
Asus A D G Em7 D/F♯
-migh-ty!
last time
Asus A D G Em7 D/F♯ D
migh-ty!

218 O Prince of peace

Capo 3(Em)

Flowing

Words: Timothy Dudley-Smith
Music: Mary Chandler
arranged David Peacock

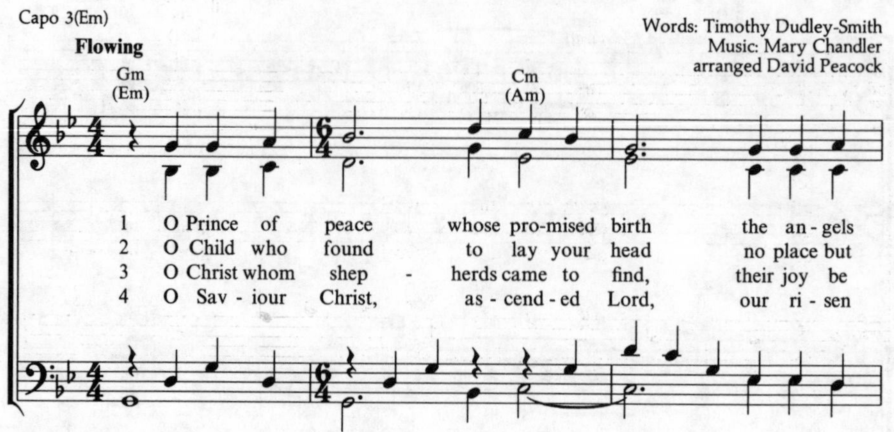
Gm
(Em)
Cm
(Am)
1 O Prince of peace whose pro-mised birth the an-gels
2 O Child who found to lay your head no place but
3 O Christ whom shep - herds came to find, their joy be
4 O Sav - iour Christ, as - cend - ed Lord, our ri - sen

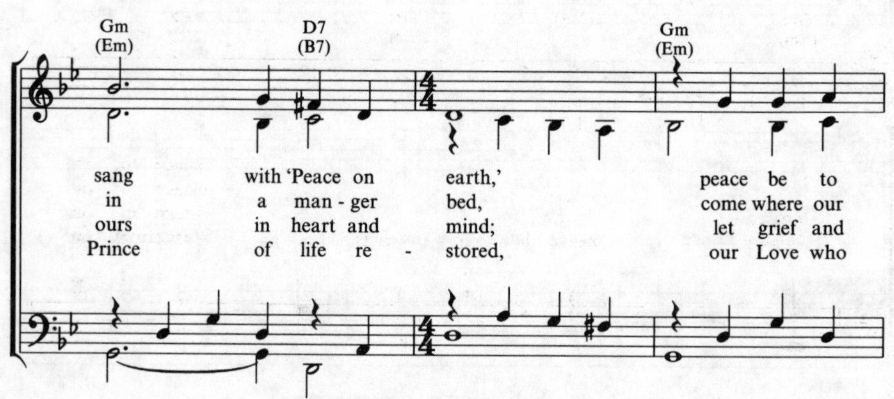
Gm
(Em)
D7
(B7)
Gm
(Em)
sang with 'Peace on earth,' peace be to
in a man - ger bed, come where our
ours in heart and mind; let grief and
Prince of life re - stored, our Love who

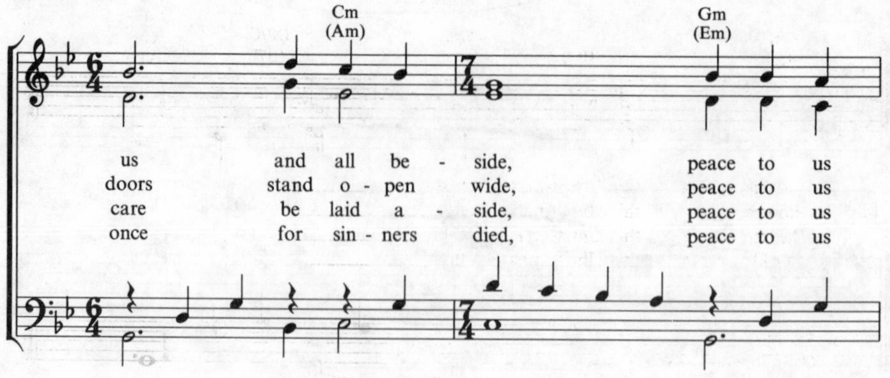
Cm
(Am)
Gm
(Em)
us and all be - side, peace to us
doors stand o - pen wide, peace to us
care be laid a - side, peace to us
once for sin - ners died, peace to us

vv.2.3.4.
Cm
(Am)
vv.3.4.
D7
(B7)
all –
all – peace to the world –
all – peace to the world – peace in our
all – peace to the world – peace in our

vv.4.
Gm
(Em)
Cm
(Am)
Gm
(Em)
E♭
(C)
peace to the
peace in our
homes – peace in our
homes – peace in our hearts – peace with our

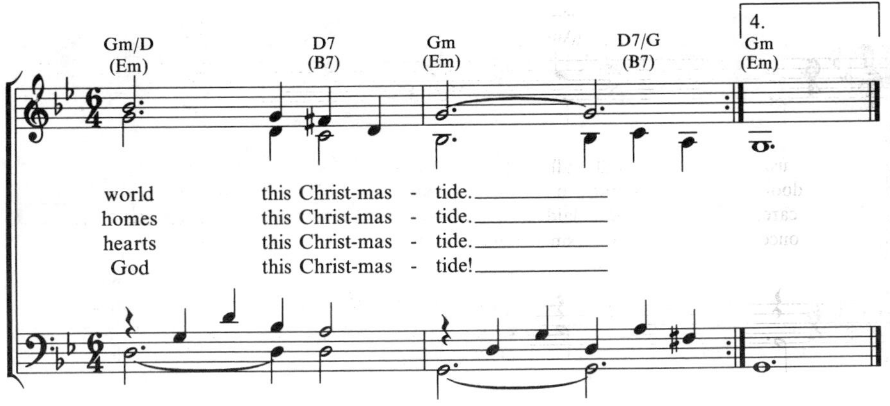
Gm/D
(Em)
D7
(B7)
Gm
(Em)
D7/G
(B7)
4.
Gm
(Em)
world this Christ-mas - tide.
homes this Christ-mas - tide.
hearts this Christ-mas - tide.
God this Christ-mas - tide!

219 O worship the Lord

Was Lebet
Words: J S B Monsell (1811–1875)
Music: Melody from manuscript by J H Rheinhardt, Uttingen (1754)
1 & 5 O worship the Lord in the beauty of holiness, bow down before him, his glory proclaim; with gold of obedience and incense of lowliness, kneel and adore him – the Lord is his name.
2 Low at his feet lay your burden of carefulness, high on his heart he will bear it for you, comfort your sorrows and answer your prayerfulness, guiding your steps in the way that is true.
3 Fear not to enter his courts in the slenderness of the poor wealth you would count as your own; truth in its beauty and love in its tenderness – these are the offerings to bring to his throne.
4 These, though we bring them in trembling and fearfulness, he will accept for the name that is dear; mornings of joy give for evenings of tearfulness, trust for our trembling and hope for our fear.

220 Off to David's town they go

Shepherds' Journey
Capo 5(C)

Words and music: Pete Ratcliffe
arranged David Peacock

Medium pace
F (C) Gm7/F (Dm7) Am/F (Em) Gm7/F (Dm7) F (C) Gm7/F (Dm7) Am/F (Em) Gm7/F (Dm7)
F (C) Gm7/F (Dm7) Am/F (Em) Gm7/F (Dm7) F (C) Gm (Dm)
1 Off to David's town they go, hurrying down the
2 How will they find the baby there – lots of diff-erent places in
Am (Em) Gm/B♭ (Dm) F (C) Am (Em) Dm7 (Am7)
Bethlehem road, shepherds run eagerly to
Bethlehem? No need to fear – the angel
Gm (Dm) C7 (G7) F (C) Dm7 (Am7) Gm (Dm) 3 C7 (G7)
seek out the new-born king.
gave them a holy sign:

F
(C)
Gm7/F
(Dm7)
Am/F
(Em)
Gm7/F
(Dm7)
F
(C)
Gm
(Dm)
Stumb-ling on cheer-ful-ly through the cold night, travel-ling on clo-ser to
'Search for a man-ger,' the an - gel said, 'there in a sta - ble he'll

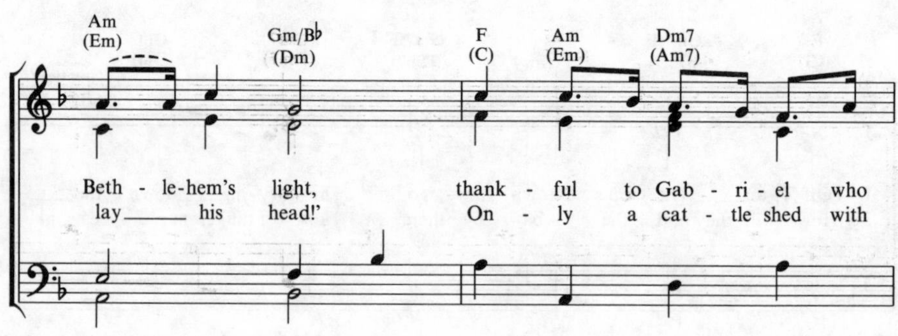
Am
(Em)
Gm/B♭
(Dm)
F
(C)
Am
(Em)
Dm7
(Am7)
Beth - le-hem's light, thank - ful to Gab - ri - el who
lay his head!' On - ly a cat - tle shed with

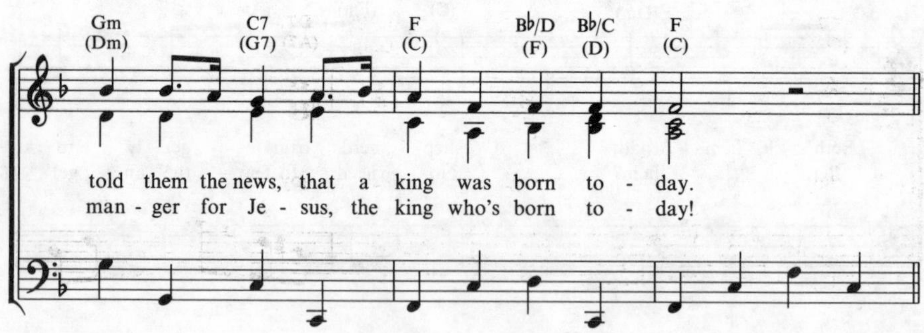
Gm
(Dm)
C7
(G7)
F
(C)
B♭/D
(F)
B♭/C
(D)
F
(C)
told them the news, that a king was born to - day.
man - ger for Je - sus, the king who's born to - day!

Chorus

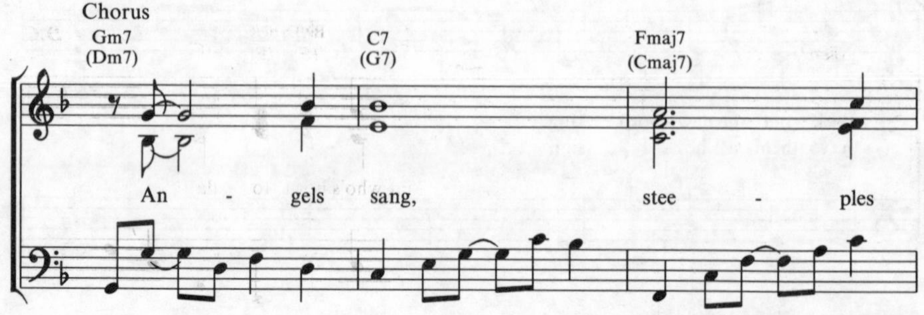
Gm7
(Dm7)
C7
(G7)
Fmaj7
(Cmaj7)
An - gels sang, stee - ples

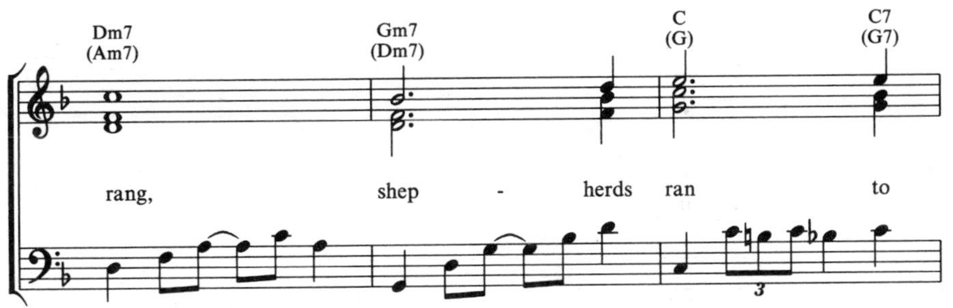
Dm7
(Am7)
Gm7
(Dm7)
C
(G)
C7
(G7)
rang, shep - herds ran to
3
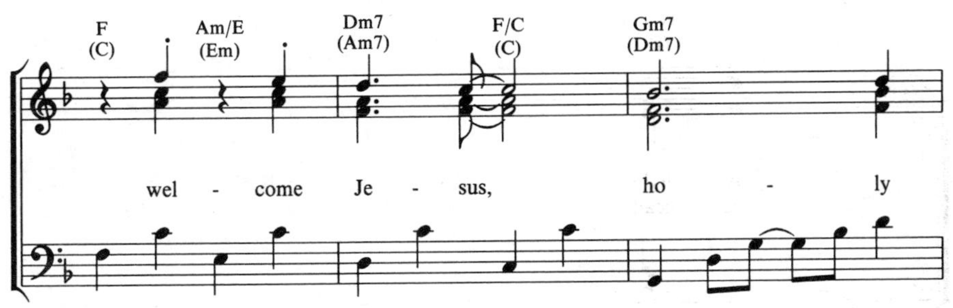
F
(C)
Am/E
(Em)
Dm7
(Am7)
F/C
(C)
Gm7
(Dm7)
wel - come Je - sus, ho - ly
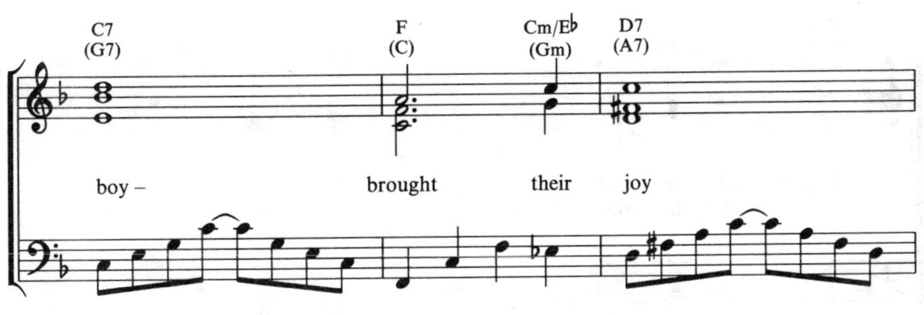
C7
(G7)
F
(C)
Cm/E♭
(Gm)
D7
(A7)
boy – brought their joy

Gm7
(Dm7)
C7
(G7)
F
(C)
B♭/D
(F)
B♭/C
(F)
F
(C)
D.C.
all for Je - sus the king who's born to - day!

221 Oh, the valleys shall ring

Capo 3(D)
Words and music: Dave Bilbrough
Music arranged Norman Warren
Steadily
F (D) C (A) B♭ (G) Gm7 (Em7)
Oh, the val - leys shall ring with the sound of
Am (F♯m) Gm (Em) F (D) C (A)
praise, and the li - on shall lie with the
B♭ (G) Cm/B♭ (Am) B♭ (G) F (D)
lamb; of his gov - ern -
C (A) B♭ (G) Gm7 (Em7) Am (F♯m) Gm (Em) F (D)
- ment there shall be no end and his glo - ry shall

E♭
(C)
F
(D)
fill the earth. May your
Cm
(Am)
D
(B)
E♭
(C)
will be done, may your king - dom
F
(D)
E♭
(C)
come let it rule, let it reign in our
B♭
(G)
F
(D)
lives. There's a shout in the

C (A)
B♭ (G)
Gm7 (Em7)
Am (F♯m)
Gm (Em)
camp as we ans - wer the call: hail the
F (D)
E♭ (C)
F (D)
B♭/F (G)
F (D)
king, hail the Lord of lords!

B♭ melody version

222 Oh where do you think baby Jesus was born

Words and music: Mary Chandler

Gently, not too fast
Em C G Em Am
1 Oh where do you think ba - by Je - sus was born, on that
2 Now Ma - ry and Jo - seph had trav - elled so far on that
3 So where do you think ba - by Je - sus was born, on that
4 Now why do you think ba - by Je - sus was born, on that
Em/B B7 Em C
first Christ-mas night long a - go? Was he born in a house all
first Christ-mas night long a - go; they went to an inn and they
first Christ-mas night long a - go? He was born in a sta - ble so
first Christ-mas night long a - go? He was God's on - ly Son, and he
G Em Am Em/B B7 Em G
co - sy and warm on that first Christ-mas night long a - go? No,
knocked on the door on that first Christ-mas night long a - go. 'No
cold and so bare on that first Christ-mas night long a - go. Yes,
came down to earth on that first Christ-mas night long a - go: for
Dsus D Bm C9 C Em/G B7 Em
no! No, no! Oh where do you think he was born?
room! No room!' the inn - keep-er said, 'There's no room!'
yes! Yes, yes! in a sta - ble – a man - ger his bed.
me, for you – he was born to give life to us all!

223 Over desert, hill and valley

Markam

Words: from Matthew 2
Margaret Clarkson
Music: Norman Warren

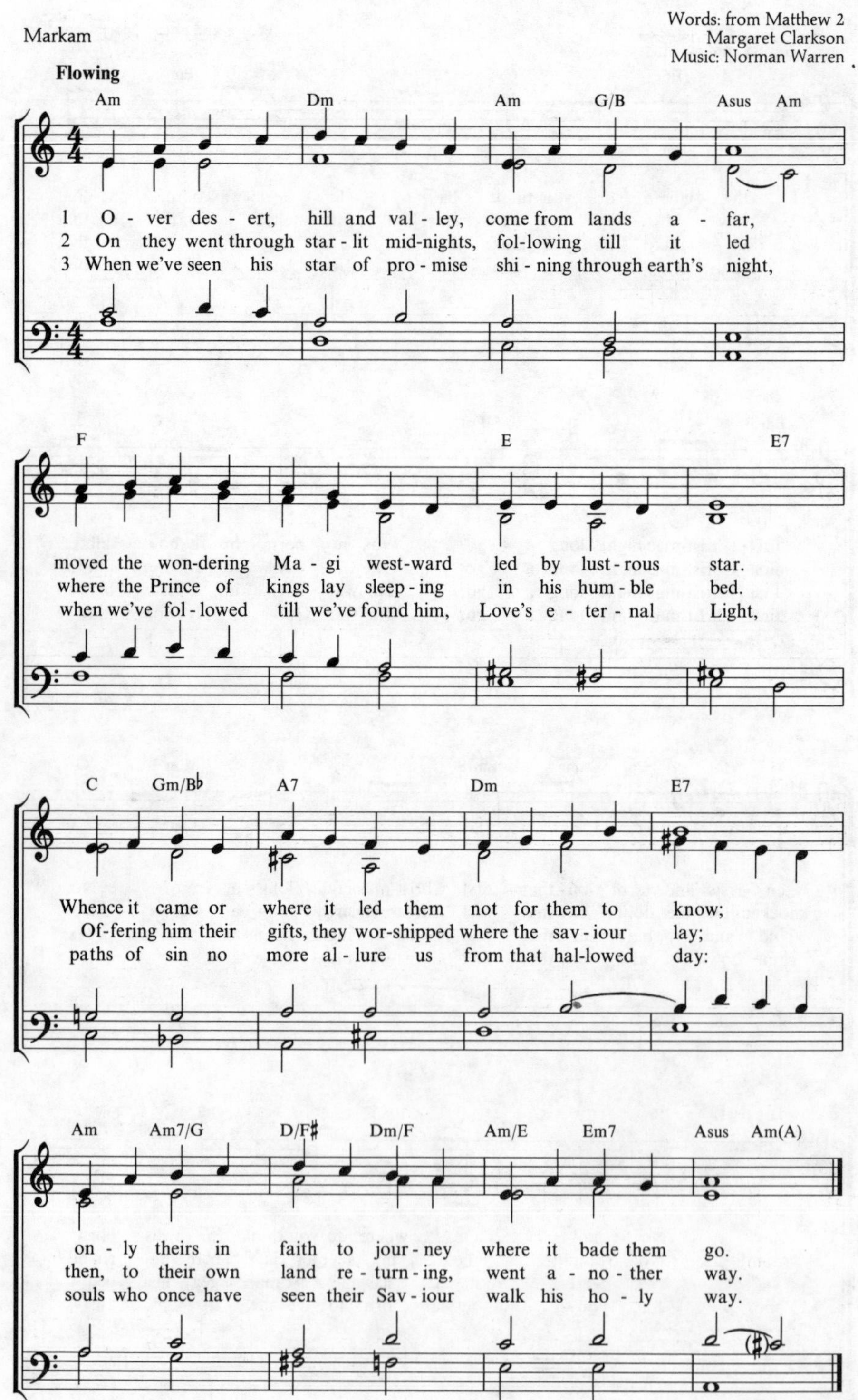

Flowing
Am Dm Am G/B Asus Am
1 O - ver des - ert, hill and val - ley, come from lands a - far,
2 On they went through star - lit mid-nights, fol-lowing till it led
3 When we've seen his star of pro - mise shi - ning through earth's night,
F E E7
moved the won-dering Ma - gi west-ward led by lust - rous star.
where the Prince of kings lay sleep - ing in his hum - ble bed.
when we've fol - lowed till we've found him, Love's e - ter - nal Light,
C Gm/B♭ A7 Dm E7
Whence it came or where it led them not for them to know;
Of-fering him their gifts, they wor-shipped where the sav - iour lay;
paths of sin no more al - lure us from that hal-lowed day:
Am Am7/G D/F♯ Dm/F Am/E Em7 Asus Am(A)
on - ly theirs in faith to jour - ney where it bade them go.
then, to their own land re - turn - ing, went a - no - ther way.
souls who once have seen their Sav - iour walk his ho - ly way.

224 On a night when the world

Twelve days of Christmas

Words: Michael Perry
Music: traditional English melody
arranged David Peacock

G Am7 G Am D7 G
1 On a night when the world in its sin and sor - row lay, the

C G/D D7 G C G/B D7/A
Verses 2–4
G Am7 G
sav - iour Je - sus was born. On a night when the world in its

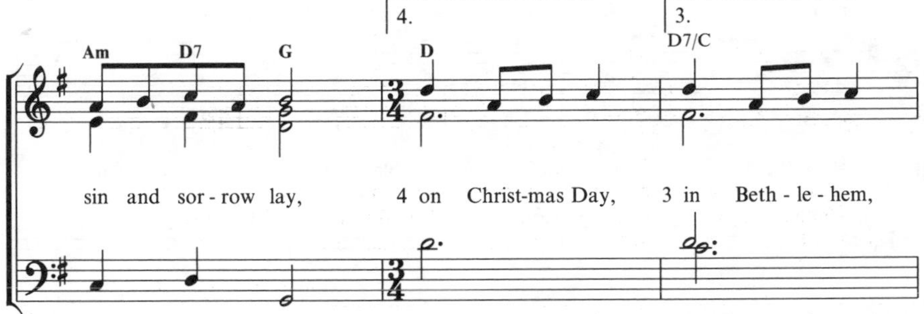
Am D7 G
4.
D
3.
D7/C
sin and sor - row lay, 4 on Christ-mas Day, 3 in Beth - le - hem,

2.
Bm Am7 D7 G C G/D D7 G C G/B D7/A
2 close in a stall, there the sav - iour Je - sus was born. On a

Verses 5–12
G
Am7
G
Am
D7
G
12.
D
Am7
D7
night when the world in its sin and sor-row lay,
12 wise men were rid-ing,

11.
D
Am7
D7
10.
D
Am7
D7
9.
D
11 bright skies were shin-ing,
10 peo - ple were sleep-ing,
9 sheep were re - clin - ing,

8.
D7/C
7.
Bm7
6.
D/A
8 shep - herds were watch-ing,
7 hea - ven was blaz-ing,
6 an - gels were sing-ing,

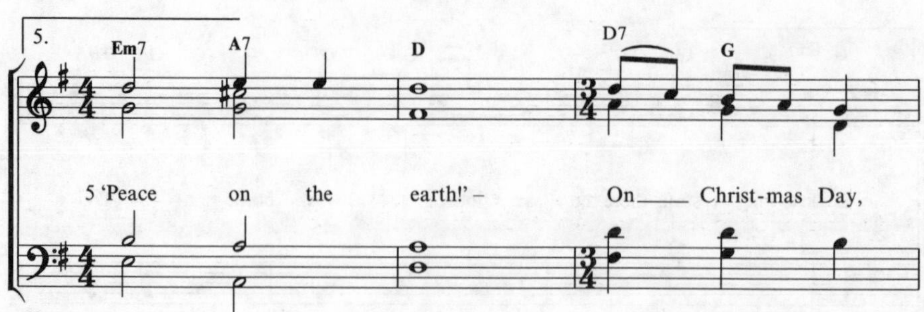
5.
Em7
A7
D
D7
G
5 'Peace on the earth!' –
On Christ-mas Day,

C G/B A D D7
in Beth - le - hem, close in a stall, there the
G C G/D D7
5–11.
G C G/B D7/A
12.
G
sav - iour Je - sus was born. On a born.

In singing this carol, cut during the repeats to the numbered bar for each verse.

Instrument
Verses 2–4.
4.
3.
2.
Verses 5–12.
12.
11.
10.
9.
8.
7.
6.
5.
5–11.
12.

225 Oh what a day for singing

Philippine Carol

Words: Paul Wigmore
Music: Levi Celerio

With vigour
Chorus
Am
E7
Oh what a day for sing - ing – bells in Beth-le-hem are ring - ing;
Am
Oh what a day for sing - ing Christ-mas joy to all the world: so,
A7
Dm
sing songs of ce-le - bra - tion, ring out bells of ju-bi - la - tion,
Am/E
E7
Am
Fine
for Je-sus Christ the Lord has come to be our king on this Christ-mas day!

Verse

G7 C

1 Our God was a - ble to come down on earth,
2 Wise men were rid - ing – through des - erts they came,

E7 Am Dm

born in a sta - ble to bring us new birth; an - gels were prais-ing as
star for their guid-ing and king for their aim; com - ing be - fore him they

Am/E E7

shep - herds were gaz - ing on Je - sus, the Son of God.
knelt to a - dore him with in - cense and gold and myrrh.

B♭ melody version of chorus

226 On Jordan's bank the Baptist's cry

Words: after C Coffin (1676–1749)
J Chandler (1806–1876)
in this version Word & Music
Music: Musikalisches Handbook (1690)
verse 5 arranged with descant John Barnard

Winchester New

Capo 3(G)

B♭ (G) E♭ (C) Cm (Am) F7 (D7) B♭ (G)
1 On Jor - dan's bank the Bap - tist's cry an -
2 Let ev - ery heart be cleansed from sin, make
3 For you are our sal - va - tion, Lord, our
4 To heal the sick, stretch out your hand, and
E♭ (C) B♭ (G) F (D) Dm (Bm) B♭ (G) C (A) F (D) F7 (D7) B♭ (G) Cm (Am) B♭ (G) E♭ (C)
- noun - ces that the Lord is nigh: a - wake and lis - ten
straight the way for God with - in, and so pre - pare to
re - fuge and our great re - ward; with - out your grace we
make the fal - len sin - ner stand; shine out, and let your
Cm (Am) B♭ (G) F (D) B♭ (G) E♭ (C) B♭ (G) Gm (Em) Cm7 (Am7) F (D) B♭ (G)
for he brings glad ti - dings of the King of kings.
be the home where such a migh - ty guest may come.
waste a - way like flowers that wi - ther and de - cay.
light re - store earth's own true love - li - ness once more.

Descant
Bb (G) Eb (C) Cm (Am) F (D) Cm (Am) D (B) G (E)
5 To you, O Christ, all prais - es be, whose
Unison voices
5 To you, O Christ, all prais - es be, whose
Cm (Am) G (E) Cm (Am) Bb (G) Csus (Asus) C (A) F (D) F7 (D7) Bb (G) F7 (D7) Bb (G) Bb7 (G7)
ad - vent sets your peo - ple free; whom with the Fa - ther
ad - vent sets your peo - ple free; whom with the Fa - ther
G7 (E7) Cm (Am) D (B) Gm (Em) Eb (C) Bb (G) Gm (Em) Cm7 (Am7) F7 (D7) Bb (G)
we a - dore and Ho - ly Spi - rit ev - er - more!
we a - dore and Ho - ly Spi - rit ev - er - more!

227 On this very special night

Special night

Words: Elizabeth Cosnett
Music: Ian Sharp

Lightly
Am
Dm
G
E
Am
Dm
Esus
E
Am
E
Am
Am7
Dm7
Esus
E
1 On this ve-ry spe-cial night noise is hushed and stars are bright;
2 Pres - ents glit-ter on the tree, gifts for him or her or me;
3 Shep - herds are the first to see Je - sus and his fa - mi - ly;
Am
Dm
Esus
E
Am
F
Dm6
E7
Am
from the huge and shin-ing sky an - gel songs come drift - ing by.
but we find the best of all hid - den in a cat - tle stall.
news from God has come to them 'Go at once to Beth - le - hem!'
Descant
Am
Dm7
G
C
On the earth and in the
God has giv - en to us
God is ve - ry close to
On the earth and in the sky
God has giv - en to us all
God is ve - ry close to them

Music: © Ian Sharp

Words: © Elizabeth Cosnett

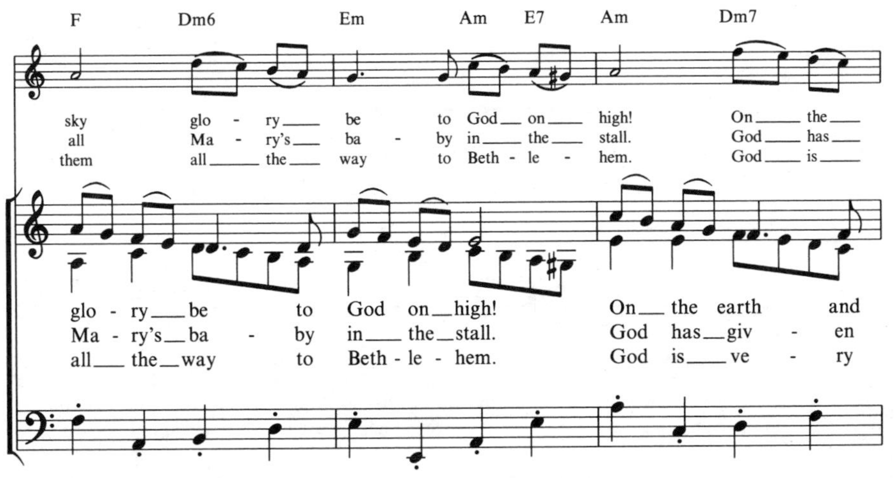
F Dm6 Em Am E7 Am Dm7
sky glo - ry be to God on high! On the
all Ma - ry's ba - by in the stall. God has
them all the way to Beth - le - hem. God is
glo - ry be to God on high! On the earth and
Ma - ry's ba - by in the stall. God has giv - en
all the way to Beth - le - hem. God is ve - ry

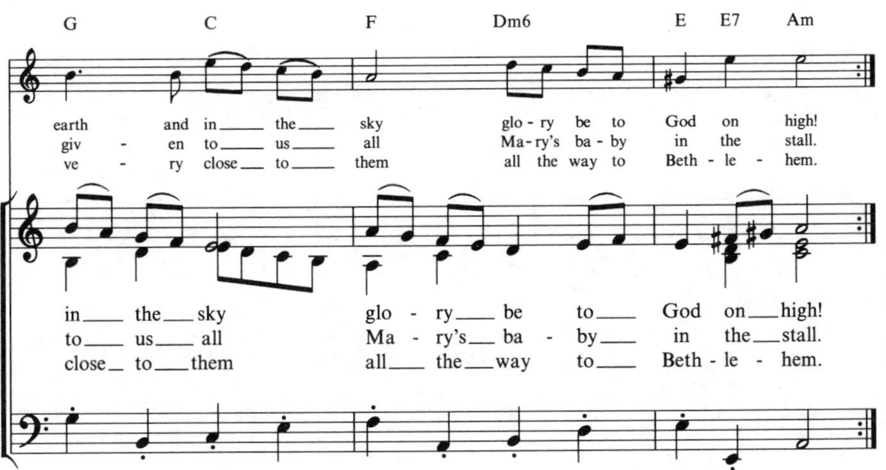
G C F Dm6 E E7 Am
earth and in the sky glo - ry be to God on high!
giv - en to us all Ma - ry's ba - by in the stall.
ve - ry close to them all the way to Beth - le - hem.
in the sky glo - ry be to God on high!
to us all Ma - ry's ba - by in the stall.
close to them all the way to Beth - le - hem.

4 Jesus in the cattle shed
doesn't have a proper bed;
donkey gives a loud hee-haw,
'You may share my yellow straw.
Welcome little friend, hee-haw!
Welcome to my yellow straw!
Welcome, little friend . . .

5 Stars and angels fade away,
sunrise comes on Christmas Day;
child and mother still are there,
safe in Joseph's loving care.
Tell the story everywhere!
Here is joy for all to share!
Tell the story . . .

6 Jesus Christ is here to stay!
Kings arrive from far away.
Incense, gold and myrrh they bring,
presents fit for any king.
All their very best they bring
for the love of Christ, their king
All their very best . . .

228 Once in royal David's city

Irby

Capo 5(C)

Words: C F Alexander (1818–1895)
Music: H J Gauntlett (1805–1876)
arranged with descant Noël Tredinnick

F (C) C7 (G7) F (C) B♭ (F) G7 (D7) C7 (G7) F (C) Dm (Am) Am (Em) B♭ (F) Am (Em)
Descant
6 Not in that poor low - ly sta - ble with the ox - en
1 Once in roy - al Da - vid's ci - ty stood a low - ly
2 He came down to earth from hea - ven who is God and
3 And through all his won - drous child - hood he would hon - our
B♭ (F) C7 (G7) F (C) C7 (G7) Dm (Am) G7 (D7) C7 (G7) F (C)
stand - ing by, we shall see him, but in hea - ven,
cat - tle shed, where a mo - ther laid her ba - by
Lord of all; and his shel - ter was a sta - ble
and o - bey, love and watch the gen - tle mo - ther
Dm (Am) Am (Em) B♭ (F) Am (Em) Gm (Dm) C7 (G7) F (C) B♭ (F) C7 (G7) Am (Em) F/A (C)
set at God's right hand on high: there his child - ren
in a man - ger for his bed: Ma - ry was that
and his cra - dle was a stall: with the poor and
in whose ten - der arms he lay: Christ - ian child - ren

Gm (Dm) C7 (G7) F (C) B♭ (F) C7 (G7) Am (Em) Dm (Am) Gm7 (Dm) C7 (G7) F (C)
ga - ther round bright like stars, with glo - ry crowned.
mo - ther mild, Je - sus Christ, her lit - tle child.
meek and lowly lived on earth our sav - iour holy.
all should be kind, o - bed - ient, good as he.

4 For he is our childhood's pattern:
day by day like us he grew;
he was little, weak and helpless –
tears and smiles like us he knew:
and he feels for all our sadness,
and he shares in all our gladness.

5 And our eyes at last shall see him,
through his own redeeming love;
for that child, so dear and gentle,
is our Lord in heaven above:
and he leads his children on
to the place where he has gone.

6 Not in that poor lowly stable
with the oxen standing by,
we shall see him, but in heaven,
set at God's right hand on high:
there his children gather round
bright like stars, with glory crowned.

B♭ melody and descant versions

Descant
F* (C) C7 (G7) F (C) C7 (G7) F (C)
Melody
C7 (G7) F (C) C7 (G7) F (C)
B♭ (F) F (C) C7 (G7) F (C) B♭ (F) F (C) C7 (G7) F (C)

* Simplified guitar chords not compatible with keyboard part

229 Our God has turned to his people

St. Mary Lewisham

Words: from Luke 1 (*The Song of Zechariah / Benedictus*)
Timothy Dudley-Smith
Music: David Wilson

D F/G Em7 A7 D Am7 D G D F♯7

1 Our God has turned to his peo - ple, he has saved them and set them free and
2 Our God has stooped to re - deem us in a co - ve - nant a - ges long, from
3 And you, O Child, are the pro - phet, the fore - run - ner of God most high, to

Bm C♯ F♯m Bm7 Bm7/E A

raised up a migh - ty Sav - iour who has giv - en them vic - to - ry – a
all who would seek to hurt us, from the hands of ___ ma - lice and wrong: the
show how in ten - der mer - cy he will put our of - fen - ces by. The

Am7 Am7/D D G Am C D7 G B7

King in the house of ___ Da - vid as his ho - ly ___ pro - phets fore - told! Our
oath he ___ swore to our fa - thers, that, de - liv - ered and free ___ from fears, we
day shall dawn on our dark - ness and the light of ___ heaven in - crease, to

Em A7 D Am7/G Em7 A7 D

God has re - deemed his ___ peo - ple as he prom - ised in days of ___ old.
serve with a ho - ly ___ wor - ship in his pre - sence for all our ___ years.
guide our ___ feet from the sha - dows that we walk in the path of ___ peace.

230 One shall tell another

New wine

Words and music: Graham Kendrick
Music arranged Chris Rolinson

Hebrew style
Verse
Em
Am
1 One shall tell a - no - ther, and he shall tell his friends;
(2) -pass-ion of the Fa - ther is rea - dy now to flow; through
(3) longs to do much more than our faith has yet al - lowed, to
B7
Em
B7
hus-bands, wives and child-ren shall come fol - low - ing on. From
acts of love and mer - cy we must let it show. He
thrill us and sur - prise us with his sove - reign power. Where
Em
Am
house to house in fam - i - lies shall more be gath-ered in; and
turns now from his an - ger to show a smil - ing face, and
dark-ness has been dark - est, the bright-est light will shine; his

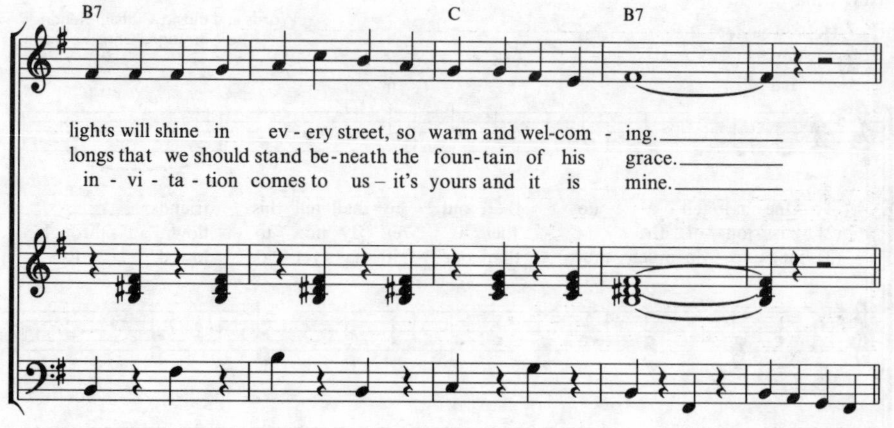
B7
C
B7
lights will shine in ev - ery street, so warm and wel-com - ing.
longs that we should stand be-neath the foun-tain of his grace.
in - vi - ta - tion comes to us – it's yours and it is mine.

Chorus

Em
Am
Em
C
D
Come on in and taste the new wine, the wine of the

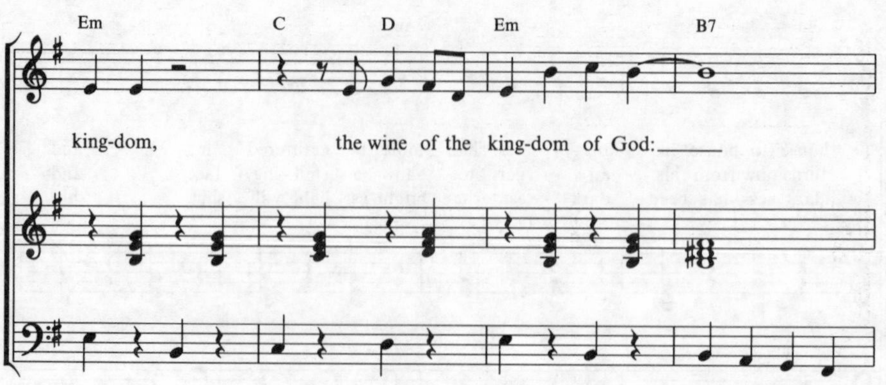
Em
C
D
Em
B7
king-dom, the wine of the king-dom of God:

Em
Am
Em
C
D
here is heal - ing and for - give-ness, the wine of the

Em
C
D
Em
B7
king-dom, the wine of the king-dom of God.

repeat to verse
or chorus
to end
Em
2 Com-
3 He

231 Pass through the gates

Capo 5(C)

From Isaiah 62
Words and music: Pete Lawry

With excitement
Chorus
Bb/C (F) F (C) Bb (F) F/A (C) Bb (F) F (C)
Pass through, pass through the gates; pre - pare the way for the
F/C (C) C (G) Bb/C (F) F (C) Bb (F) F/A (C)
peo - ple. Build up, build up the road; rem-ove the
Gm (Dm) F/A (C) Gm7/Bb (Dm7) C (G) F (C) Bb/C (F) F (C)
Fine
stones, raise a ban-ner for the na - tions!
Verse
C/E (G) Dm (Am) Gm (Dm) Dm (Am)
1 I have post - ed watch-men on your walls, O Je - ru - sa - lem,
2 I de - clare you will be called the Ho - ly Peo - ple, the Re -

Music: © Pete Lawry / Music for the King †

Words: © NIV adapted †

Bb (F) C (G) Dm (Am) Gm/D (Dm) Dm (Am)
they will ne - ver be si - lent: you who call on the
- deemed of the Lord; you will be called the
Gm (Dm) Dm (Am) Bb (F) C (G) Dm (Am)
Lord, give your - selves and give him al - so no rest till he est -
Loved One, Sought Af - ter, the Ci - ty No Lon-ger Laid Waste, when he est -
C (G) Dm (Am)
- ab - lish-es Je - ru - sa - lem, and
- ab - lish-es Je - ru - sa - lem, and
D.C. al Fine
Bb (F) Gm (Dm) A7 (E7) Bb/C (F)
makes her the praise of the earth!
makes her the praise of the earth!

232 People walking in the dark

(Unto us a child is born)

From Isaiah 9
Words and music: Mark Cheesman and Chris Jeffrey
Capo 3(D)
Andante
Dm(Bm)
C♯dim/D (B♭dim)
Dm9 (Bm9)
Dm (Bm)
D♭/E♭ (B♭)
A7 (F♯7)
Dm7 (Bm7)
A/D (F♯)
A
D.𝄋 instrumental
1 Peo-ple walk - ing in the dark, peo-ple
(2&4) us a child is born, un - to
Am7/D (F♯m)
D (B)
Gm (Em)
B♭/F (G)
liv - ing in a land of sha - dows now their dark - ness is dis -
us a son is giv - en, and the gov - ern-ment is
1.3.
Cm7/E♭ (Am7)
D♯5 (G♯5)
D7 (B7)
Gm/E (Em)
A7 (F♯7)
- pelled, for a light has dawned. 2&4 Un-to

2.4.
Eb/F
(C)
G/A
(E)
A/B
(F#)
Bb/C
(G)
his, and he is called:
F
(D)
C/F
(A)
Won - der-ful
Coun-sel-lor,
R.H.
R.H.
Bb
(G)
F/A
(D)
Gm7
(Em7)
F
(D)
Migh - ty God,
Ev - er - last - ing
Fa - ther,
1.
Eb/Bb
(C)
Bb
(G)
Gm7
(Em7)
C7
(A7)
Prince of peace.

2.
Cm7
(Am7)
B♭/C
(G)
to Coda
F
(D)
Prince of peace.
E♭/F
(C)
Dm/F
(Bm)
B♭maj7/E
(Gmaj7)
A
(F♯)
A7
(F♯7)
3 He will reign for ev - er, his
Dm
(Bm)
Fmaj7/C
(Dmaj7)
B♭7sus
(G7sus)
B♭7
(G7)
E♭
(C)
peace will ne - ver end; he will bring us
B♭/E♭
(G)
A♭/E♭
(F)
joy, will bring us life, our free - dom de -

Bb/Eb
(G)
Eb
(C)
Bb/Eb
(G)
- fend.
(Instrumental)

D.𝄋 al Coda
Ab/Eb
(F)
Bb/Eb
(G)
Eb9
(C9)
A7
(F#7)
(Instrumental . . .)

CODA
Gm7
(Em7)
Am
(F#m)
Bb
(G)
Bb/C
F
(D)
Bb/F
(G)
Eb/F
(C)
F
(D)
Prince of peace!

233 Play your pipe, bang your drum

Shepherds' Dance
Words and music: Judy Davies
Music arranged David Peacock
Lively
Chorus
D
Em
F♯m7
B7
Play your pipe, bang your drum, sing to Christ the
E7
A
D
Em
Sav - iour; come and wor - ship, come and wor - ship,
A
D
Fine
G
D
wor - ship Christ our king!
1 Shep-herds come a - danc - ing,
2 Peace - ful in the man - ger
3 Lis - ten to the an - gels,
A7
D
G
D/F♯
E7
A7
D.C.
bring your pipe and drum; come and see the ba - by – run, run, run!
see him ly - ing there; gent - ly ga - ther round him – Oh take care!
can you hear them sing – wel - com - ing the sav - iour? He's our king!

× indicates Clap, Bang, Toot – or whatever is appropriate

234 Praise God today

Crucifer
Words: from Isaiah 12
Christopher Idle
Music: S H Nicholson (1875–1947)
Chorus
Praise God to - day: his
1 glor - ies
2 mer - cies
3 bless - ings ne - ver end;
4 tri - umphs
5 won - ders
our judge be-comes in Christ our great-est friend.
Fine
Verses – Harmony
1 God brings us com - fort where his an - ger burned,
2 Wells of sal - va - tion streams of life will bring;
3 Songs shall be his for this vic - tor - ious day:
4 Love lives a - mong us, Is - rael's ho - ly One
so judge - ment and fear to peace and trust are turned:
with joy we shall draw from this re - fresh-ing spring.
give thanks to his name, and teach the earth to say,
who comes to the res - cue – see what God has done!

235 Praise for coming of the King

Jonathan Charles

Words: Brian Black and Word & Music
Music: David Peacock

Brightly
G
Instrument
Am7/G
G
Am7/G D7
tr
G
(flutes octave higher)
1 Praise for com - ing of the
2 Praise for shin - ing star on
3 Praise for gift of God's own
4 Praise for Christ-mas – all our
C
D7
G
King,
high,
Son,
days,
praise for song the an - gels sing,
praise for hum-ble shep-herds nigh,
praise for vic-tory he has won,
heart and soul and voice shall raise
G7
C
Dsus
praise for gifts the wise men bring,
praise for ba - by Je - sus' cry,
praise while time-less a - ges run,
love for God in all his ways,
praise for Christ - mas –
'Praise for Christ - mas!' –
praise for Christ - mas –
praise for Christ - mas –

1.2.3.
D
D7
G
Am7/G
G
Am7/G
D7
tr
ring __ bells, ring!
hearts re - ply.
praise be done!
sound his

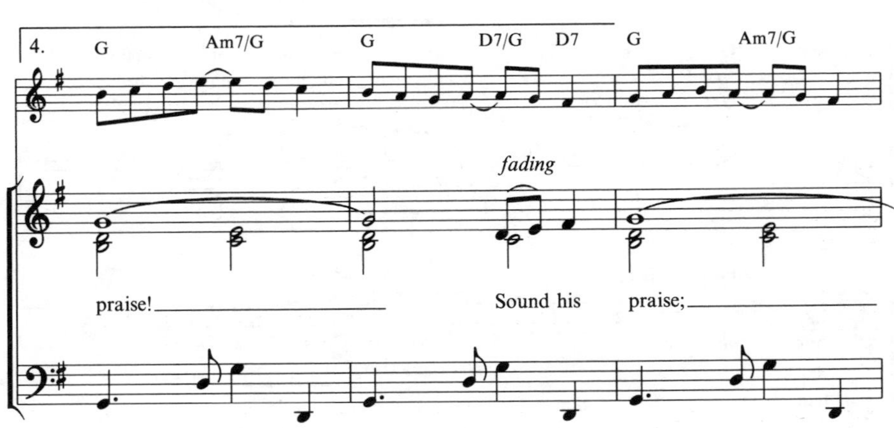
4.
G
Am7/G
G
D7/G
D7
G
Am7/G
fading
praise!
Sound his praise;

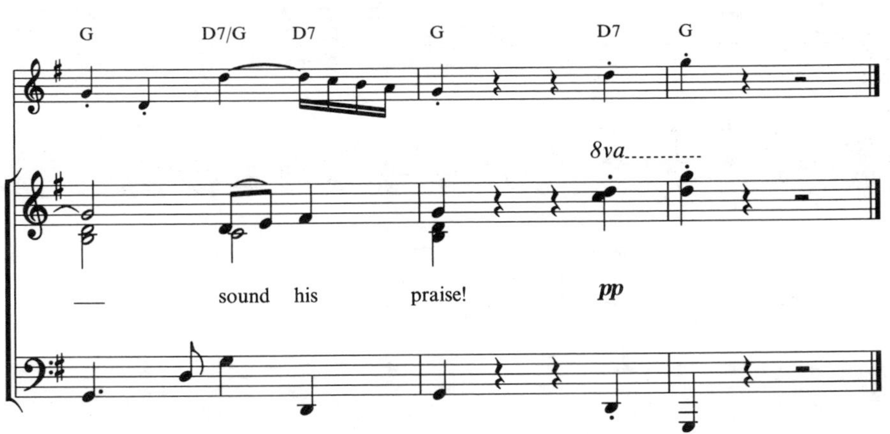
G
D7/G
D7
G
D7
G
8va
sound his praise!
pp

236 Praise him, praise him

Ludgrove
Words: F van Alstyne (1820–1915)
and in this version Word & Music
Music: C G Allen (1838–1878)
Joyfully
G D/F♯ Em Bm/D Am A7/D D G/B
1 Praise him, praise him – Je - sus, our migh - ty re - deem - er;
2 Praise him, praise him – Je - sus, our migh - ty re - deem - er;
3 Praise him, praise him – Je - sus, our migh - ty re - deem - er;
G D/F♯ Em Bm/D C A7/E A7 D
sing, O earth, his won - der - ful love pro - claim:
for our sins he suff - ered, and bled, and died:
heaven - ly arch - es, loud with ho - sann - as ring!
G D/F♯ Em Bm/D Am A7/D D G/B
hail him, hail him, high - est arch - an - gels in glo - ry;
he – our rock, our hope of e - ter - nal sal - va - tion –
Je - sus, Sav - iour, reign - ing for ev - er and ev - er:
G G7 C Am/C G/D D7 G
strength and hon - our give to his ho - ly name!
hail him, hail him, Je - sus, the cru - ci - fied!
crown him, crown him, pro - phet and priest and king!

D G/D D Am D7 G D
Like a shep - herd, Je - sus will guard his child - ren,
Sound his prai - ses – Je - sus who bore our sor - rows:
Christ is com - ing, o - ver the world vic - tor - ious;
G D7 Em G/B C A7/E A7 D
in his arms he'll car - ry them all day long.
love un - bound - ed, won - der - ful, deep, and strong.
power and glo - ry now to the Lord be - long:
Chorus
G D/F♯ Em Bm/D Am A7/D D G/B
Praise him, praise him, tell of his ex - cel - lent great - ness;
G G7 C Am/C G/D D7 G
praise him, praise him ev - er in joy - ful song!

237 Praise to God and peace on earth

Anellen
Capo 3(D)

Words: from Luke 2
Christopher Idle
Music: Roger Mayor

Joyfully
N.C.
F (D) C/E (A) Dm (Bm)
1 Praise to God and
2 Shep-herds have no
3 Ma - ry won - ders
4 An - gels' mu - sic,
Gm (Em) Gm7 (Em7) F/A (D) B♭ (G) Gm7 (Em7) F/A (D) Gm/B♭ (Em) F/C (D)
peace on earth! hear what hea - ven's an - gels say;
time to lose, come to wor - ship, go their way
at her child, keeps in mind as well she may
shep - herds' word, we shall sing as well as they;
C (A) C/E D/F♯ (B) Gm (Em) D7/A (B7) Gm7/B♭ (Em7) G7 (E7) C (A) C/E F9 (D9)
fear shall die at glo - ry's birth
burst - ing with the lat - est news
pro - mi - ses in him ful - filled
Ma - ry's Son is Christ the Lord
B♭ (G) B♭/D F/C (D) Dm7 (Bm7) Gm7 (Em7) C7 (A7) F (D) D.C.
* Je - sus is a - live to - day!

* On Christmas Day may be sung: 'Jesus Christ is born today!'

238 Praise to God the Father

Words: from Colossians 1
Christopher Idle
Music: Gordon Hartless
arranged David Peacock
Tersanctus
1 Praise to God the Fa - ther! he who saves his peo - ple,
2 For-ces seen and un - seen made in the be - gin - ning,
3 Or - i - gin and First - born of the church, his bo - dy,
res - cues us from dark - est powers and ty - ran - nies_ of night,
depths of spi - rit, heights of_ mind, and worlds in time and space:
raised from death to be its_ Head in sov-ereign-ty__ a - lone:
brings us lib - er - a - tion by his Son, Christ Je - sus,
all in Christ cre - a - ted, by and through and for_ him,
God's full na - ture shar - ing, u - ni - verse - re - claim-ing,
who bears the like - ness____ of im - mor - tal light.
in Christ ex - ist - ing____ find in him their place.
peace - mak - ing Sav - iour____ praise to Christ the Son!
1.2.
3.

239 Praise to our God

Capo 5(Am)

Words and music: Graham Kendrick

Flowing
Dm
(Am)
C
(G)
1 Praise to our God who a-lone is the migh-ty One
2 Bring to him now, as an of-fering of fra-grance sweet,
Bb
(F)
robed in ma-jes-ty! Come and bow down, wor-ship and a-
all the pray-ers of your heart to his throne; with thanks-giv-ing,
Asus
(Esus)
A7
(E7)
Dm
(Am)
-dore.
come!
The Lord Al-migh-ty
Gm
(Dm)
C
(G)
Dm
(Am)
D
(A)
his love en-dures for ev-er, his

Gm
(Dm)
C7
(G7)
F
(C)
grace
and mer - cy ev - er sure;
A
(E)
Dm
(Am)
Gm
(Dm)
C
(G)
his power will ne - ver,
ne - ver fail or
Dm
(Am)
D
(A)
Gm
(Dm)
C7
(G7)
fal - ter,
or his love
grow
to repeat
F
(C)
Asus
(Esus)
A7
(E7)
Last time
F
(C)
B♭
(G)
F
(C)
cold.
cold.

240 Praise to the mighty Lord

Song of Zechariah

From Luke 1 (*The Song of Zechariah / Benedictus*)
Words and music: Elaine Davies

Capo 3(Em)

Smoothly

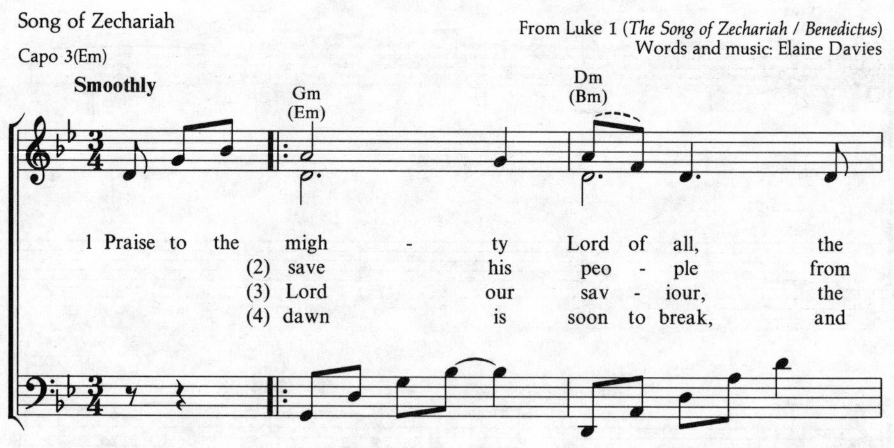

Gm
(Em)
Dm
(Bm)
1 Praise to the migh - ty Lord of all, the
(2) save his peo - ple from
(3) Lord our sav - iour, the
(4) dawn is soon to break, and

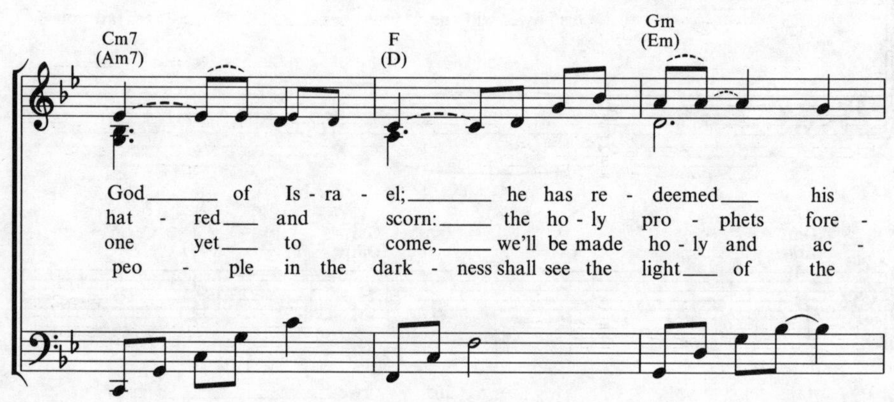

Cm7
(Am7)
F
(D)
Gm
(Em)
God of Is - ra - el; he has re - deemed his
hat - red and scorn: the ho - ly pro - phets fore -
one yet to come, we'll be made ho - ly and ac -
peo - ple in the dark - ness shall see the light of the

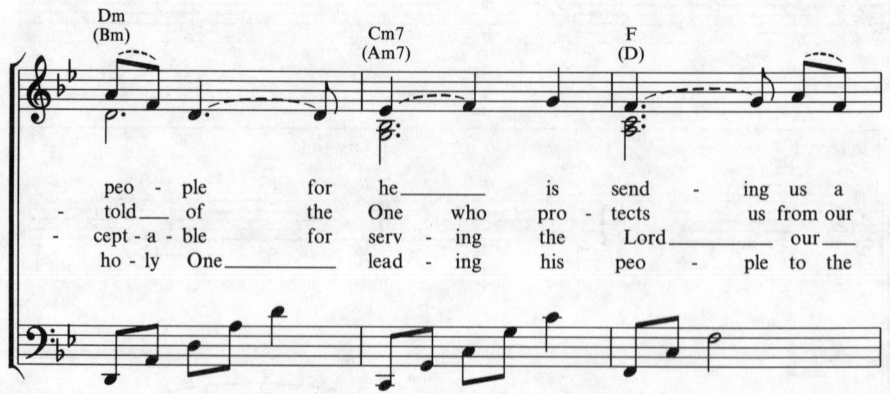

Dm
(Bm)
Cm7
(Am7)
F
(D)
peo - ple for he is send - ing us a
- told of the One who pro - tects us from our
- cept - a - ble for serv - ing the Lord our
ho - ly One lead - ing his peo - ple to the

Chorus
Gm (Em)
Cm (Am)
F (D)
sav - iour.
en - e - mies.
God.
path of peace.
And through him his word will be ful -
- filled;
yes, through him his word
will be ful - filled.
1.2.3.
4.
2 Some-one to
3 And with the
4 Hea-ven's

241 Prepare the way for Jesus

From Isaiah 40
Words and music: Pip and Alison Roseblade

Moderato
Em
G/A
Dmaj7
1 Pre - pare the way for Je - sus to re - turn,
2 Ev - ery val - ley shall be raised up,
3 And the glo - ry of the Lord shall be re - vealed,
Em
G/A
D
in the de - sert make a high - way;
ev - ery moun-tain, hill, brought low;
as he pu - ri - fies our lives;
Em
G/A
Dmaj7
through the wil - der - ness make straight the way for him,
and all the rough ground shall be made smooth,
and the whole wide world shall see the bride pre - pared,
Em
G/A
D
G/D
where streams of liv - ing wa - ter may flow.
and the rug - ged pla - ces a plain.
as the dark - ness comes to the light.

Chorus
D
B7
Em
A7
We'll make a high - way for the Lord, we'll make a
F♯m
Bm
Em
high - way for King Je - sus; we'll make a high - way for the
A7
D
B7
Em
Bride-groom to come. We'll make a high-way for the Lord,
A7
F♯m
Bm
we'll make a high - way for King Je - sus; we'll make a
Em
A
A7
D
G/D
D
high-way for the Bride - groom to re - turn.

242 Prepare the way of the Lord

Words and music: Mary Smail
Music arranged David Peacock

Brightly
C
Em
F
C/E
1&3 Pre - pare the way of the Lord,
(2) come to us as he came be - fore,
Dm
G
Dm
G
G7
make his paths straight; o - pen the gates that he may
clothed in his glo - ry to stand in our place; and we be -
C
Em
F
C/E
en - ter free - ly in - to our lives. Ho -
- hold him, now our priest, Lord and king. Ho -
Dm
G
G7
C
Chorus
- san - na! we cry to the Lord. And we will
- san - na! we sing to the Lord.

Em
F
C/E
fill the earth with the sound of his praise:
Dm
G
Dm
G
G7
Je - sus is Lord let him be a - dored! Yes, we will
C
Em
F
C/E
have this man to reign o - ver us, ho -
Dm
G
G7
1.2.
C
3.
C
- san - na – we fol - low the Lord! 2 And he will Lord.

243 Prepare the way, the way for the Lord

Words and music: Susie Killen and Anne Johnson
arranged Christopher Norton

Brightly
Chorus
E
A/E
E
A
Pre - pare the way, the way for the Lord, make straight the high-way for our
Bsus
B
F♯m7
B
E/G♯
God. Do you not know? Have you not heard? He
last time
to Coda
A
E
A
E
F♯m7 G♯m/B
E
A/E
left the throne to come to his own to re - deem them.
E
Verses
A
1 The Word, through whom all things were cre -
2 The Light has ne - ver been ex -

E
A
E
A/E
E
F♯m7
- a - ted, brought light, light that gives life to us all,
- ting-uished, though dark-ness bruised it with its e - vil sin;
B7
E
A
be - came flesh and lived for a while a -
grace and truth and right - eous-ness have
E
A
E
- mong us, re - vealed his glo - ry, the glo - ry of the
tri-umphed: freed from our sin we wor - ship him who
CODA
F♯m7/A
C♯m/G♯
F♯m7
B
one, true God. Pre -
reigns for - ev - er.
E

244 Rejoice and be merry

Gallery Carol
Capo 3(D)

Words: traditional, and in this version Word & Music
Music: English traditional melody
arranged David Iliff

Joyfully
C (A) F (D) C (A) F (D) C (A) F (D) B♭ (G) C (A) B♭ (G) F (D)
1 Re - joice and be mer - ry in songs and in
2 A hea - ven - ly vi - sion ap - peared in the
3 And soon in the sky a bright star did ap -
4 They came and they of - fered myrrh, in - cense and
C (A) F (D) B♭ (G) F (D) B♭ (G) C (A) C7 (A7) F (D) B♭ (G) C (A)
mirth; O praise our re - deem - er, all mor - tals on
sky; vast num - bers of an - gels the shep - herds did
- pear, which led the wise men from the east to draw
gold – for God's gra - cious pur - pose these trea - sures fore -
F (D) C7 (A7) F (D) C7 (A7) F (D) B♭ (G) F (D) B♭ (G) F (D) C7 (A7) F (D)
earth! for this is the birth - day of Je - sus our
spy, pro - claim - ing the birth - day of Je - sus our
near; they found the mes - si - ah, Christ Je - sus our
- told: then wor - shipped for ev - er be Je - sus our
C (A) F (D) Dm (Bm) B♭ (G) F (D) C (A) B♭ (G) F (D) Dm (Bm) C (A) F (D)
king, who brought us sal - va - tion – his prais - es we'll sing!

245 Rejoice with heart and voice

Gaudete

Capo 3(C)

Words: from the Latin
Michael Perry
Music: medieval carol
arranged John Barnard

Lively

Cm (Am) Gm (Em) Cm (Am) B♭ (G) E♭ (C) B♭ (G) Cm (Am) Gm (Em)

Re - joice with heart and voice! now is our Sav - iour

Cm (Am) B♭ (G) Cm (Am) Gm (Em) F (D) B♭ (G) F (D) Gm (Em) Cm (Am) *Fine*

of the vir - gin Ma - ry born – so re - joice!

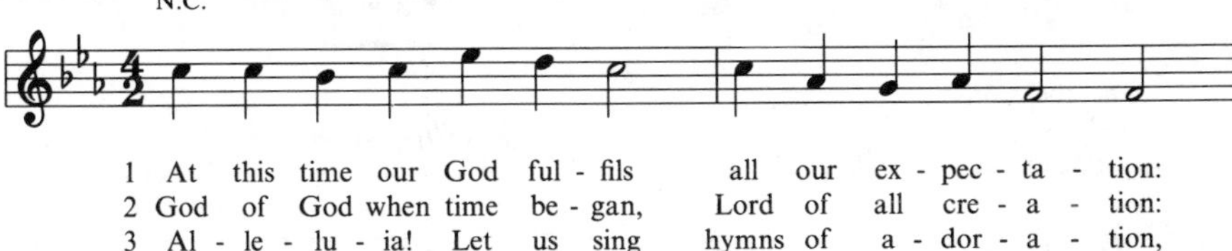

N.C.
1 At this time our God ful - fils all our ex - pec - ta - tion:
2 God of God when time be - gan, Lord of all cre - a - tion:
3 Al - le - lu - ia! Let us sing hymns of a - dor - a - tion,

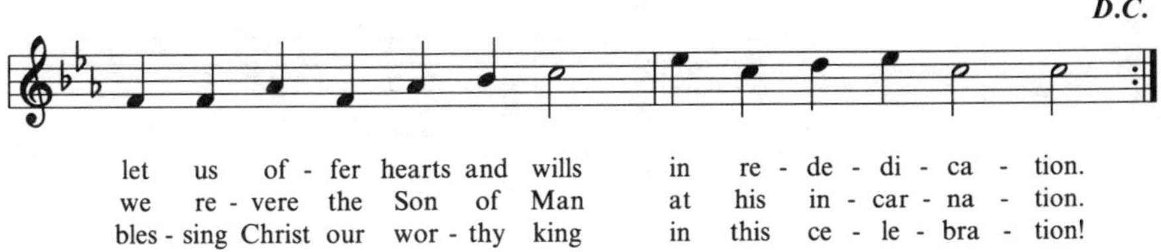

D.C.
let us of - fer hearts and wills in re - de - di - ca - tion.
we re - vere the Son of Man at his in - car - na - tion.
bles - sing Christ our wor - thy king in this ce - le - bra - tion!

246 Rejoice, rejoice, a saviour has come

Words and music: Frank Hernandez
Music arranged David Peacock
Bright and lively
1 Re - joice, re-joice, a sav-iour has come: to God be glo - ry! We hail his birth with 'Peace on earth!' for Christ the Lord is he.
(2) joice, re-joice, a vir-gin has born a child most mar-vel - lous! The scrip-tures tell Em - man - u - el means 'God is with us'.
(3) joice, re-joice, for he will save his peo - ple from their sins; and he shall bless with right-eous-ness the one who trusts in him.
Chorus
Won-der-ful Coun-sel-lor, Migh-ty God – this shall be his name; E - ter-nal Fa - ther,

Bm F♯m G D/F♯ G A D
1.2.
G A D
Prince of peace – with jus - tice he shall reign! 2 Re -
3 Re -
3.
G A D G D Bm
4 And he shall be great, he shall be
F♯m G D G D G D G D G D
great, and there shall be no end to his king-dom; and he shall reign for
G D G F♯m7 Em7 A D G A D
ev - er-more: Je - sus Christ the Lord!

247 Rejoice, rejoice! Christ is in you

Rejoice

Words and music: Graham Kendrick

Triumphantly
Chorus
D G D A7 D Bm7
Re - joice, re-joice! Christ is in you – the hope of glo - ry in
Em7 A D G D A7 D
our hearts. He lives, he lives! his breath is in you. A -
Bm7 Em7 A D Dmaj7
- rise! A might - y ar - my we a - rise!
Em7 Dmaj7 D Dmaj7 Em7 Dmaj7 D
Fine

Verse
A
Bm
1 Now is the time for us__ to march up - on the land ___ in - to our
2 God is at work in us__ his pur-pose to per-form __ build - ing a
3 Though we are weak, his grace is ev - ery-thing we need ___ we're made of
G
A
D
hands he will give the ground we claim;
king - dom of pow - er not__ of words;
clay, but this trea - sure is__ with - in;
A
Bm
he rides in ma - jes - ty__ to lead us in - to vic - to - ry,__
where things im - poss - i - ble__ by faith shall be made poss - i - ble:__
he turns our weak-ness-es__ in - to his op - por - tun - i - ties,__
G
Bm
Em7
Asus
A
the world shall see that Christ is Lord. Re -
let's give the glo - ry to him now. Re -
so that the glo - ry goes to him. Re -

248 Rejoice, rejoice, for the king Messiah's born

Messiahmas Carol

From Matthew 1 and Luke 2
Words and music: Stuart Dauermann
Music arranged David Peacock

Lively Hebrew style
Chorus
Em
Am
Em/B
B7
Re - joice, re - joice, for king Mes - si - ah's
Em
D
G
B7
Em
Em/D
Em/C
Em/B
born in Beth - le - hem; re - joice, the
Am
Em/B
B7
1.3.5.
Em
2.4.6.
Em
Fine
Son of Da - vid's come! Re - come!
Verses
Em
F♯7
1 'Where is the One who's born the king Em -
2 My eyes have seen the day of your sal -

B
Em
- man - u - el,
for we have come with
- va - tion,
ful - fil - ment of your
F♯7
B
frank - in - cense to Is - ra - el?'
The
word of rev - e - la - tion,
a
Am
Em/B
B7
Em
Em7/D
east - ern star of Beth - le - hem has led us here to
light to light - en Gen - tiles well, and glo - ry for God's
F♯7/C♯
F♯7
B
Em/C♯
B
D.𝄋
wor - ship him. O sons of men:
Re -
Is - ra - el – of him they tell.
Re -

249 Restore, O Lord

Words and music: Graham Kendrick and Chris Rolinson
Music arranged David Peacock
Steadily, with feeling
Descant last verse
D
Em/D
D
1&4 Re - store, O Lord, the hon - our of your
(2) store, O Lord, in all the earth your
(3) us, O Lord, where we are hard and
Em/D
Bm
A
Gmaj7
Asus
A
hon - our of your name
works of sov - ereign
name in works of sov - ereign pow - er; come
fame, and in our time re - vive the
cold, in your re - fin - er's fire; come
Bm
Gmaj7
F♯sus
F♯
Em
Asus
A
power;
shake the earth a - gain
shake the earth a - gain that all may
Church that bears your name; and in your
pu - ri - fy the gold: though suff - ering

D
F♯7
Bm
Bm/A
that all may come with rev - erent fear to the
see, and come with rev - erent fear to the
ang - er, Lord, re - mem - ber mer - cy – O
comes, and ev - il crouch - es near, still our
G
F♯m7
Em7
G/A
Gmaj9
liv - ing God whose King - dom
liv - ing God whose King - dom
liv - ing God whose mer - cy
liv - ing God is reign - ing –
1.2.3.
4.
Em7
G/A
D
Em7
D/F♯
Asus A
D
shall out - last the years.
shall out - last the years. 2 Re - 4 years.
shall out - last the years. 3 Bend
he is reign - ing here! 4 Re -

250 Riding out across the desert

The Camel Shuffle
Words and music: Pete Ratcliffe
Lightly in "20's style"
Gmaj7/F♯
E♭7/D♯
G/D
N.C.
G/D F♯/D D
Verses
G
1 Rid-ing out a-cross the de - sert,
leav-ing all their friends be - hind them,
2 Wise men on their de-sert jour - ney,
how they long to wor-ship Je - sus and
A7
trav-elling o - ver san - dy plains,
gui - ded by the star so bright,
travel - led ma - ny miles so far –
hon - our him with ro - yal gifts –
D7
comes a com - pa - ny of wise men, mov - ing
now they've got to keep on go - ing – must not
though they're get - ting tired and wea - ry, town of
hearts are full of joy and won - der as they're

1.3.
G
C
E♭7
G
N.C.
stea - di - ly a - long their way;
let the star get out of
Beth - le - hem is not too far:
search - ing for the new born

2.4.
Chorus
G
E
E7
sight.
king.
Ri - ding through the de - sert,
3

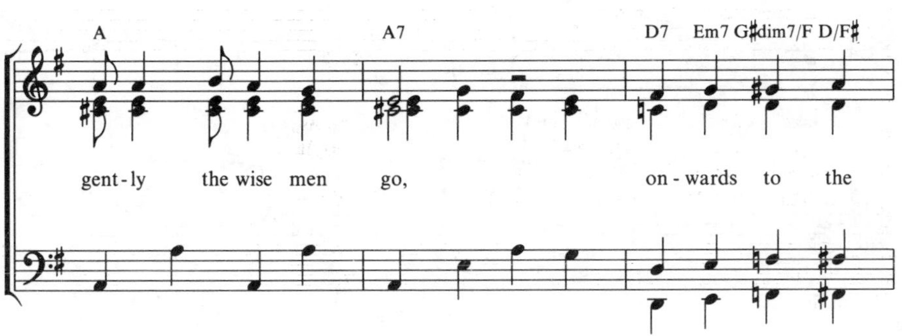
A
A7
D7 Em7 G♯dim7/F D/F♯
gent - ly the wise men go,
on - wards to the

D7
G
Am/C F♯/C♯
G
king who was pro-mised long a - go;

E7
but they don't know where they're going to find him –
3
A A7 D Em G♯dim7/F D/F♯
there's ma - ny towns to search – so they'll keep on
D N.C. G C E♭7
fol - low-ing the star, for it will lead them to his place of
G D.𝄋 To end Gmaj7/F♯ E♭7
birth.
G/D D7 G

251 Ring out the bells

Past three a clock

Words: Michael Perry
Music: English traditional melody
arranged David Iliff

N.C.
f
G C Am D G Em D
Ring out the bells – the joy - ful news is break - ing;
G C Am Dsus D D7 G D7 G Fine
ring out the bells for Je - sus Christ is born!
G D G D G Am Em D G
1 An - gels in won - der sing of his glo - ry;
2 Let all cre - a - tion wor - ship be - fore him;
3 Pro - phets have spo - ken – hark to their warn - ing:
Em C G D7 Em D Em D G C
shep - herds re - turn - ing tell us the sto - ry.
earth bring him hom - age, hea - ven a - dore him!
sha - dows are pas - sing, soon comes the morn - ing!

252 Ring, bells of Bethlehem

Words: Michael Perry
Music: traditional
arranged Norman Warren

Capo 3(C)

Bells
F (D)
Fmaj7 (Dmaj7)
Gm7/F (Em7)
F (D)
1 Ring, bells of Beth - le-hem,
2 Come, as the wise of old, ding-dong-ding, ding-a-dong-a-ding;
3 Ring, bells of Beth - le-hem,
F (D)
Fmaj7 (Dmaj7)
Gm7/F (Em7)
Fsus (Dsus) F (D)
rise up, Je - ru - sa-lem, joy - ful - ly sing.
frank - in - cense, myrrh and gold joy - ful - ly bring:
rise up, Je - ru - sa-lem, joy - ful - ly sing.
Gm (Em)
Dm (Bm)
Gm (Em)
C (A)
Dm (Bm)
C (A)
Come from your lands a - far,
in - cense shows wil - ling prayers, ding - dong - ding, ding - a - dong - a - ding;
Come and be - fore him bow,

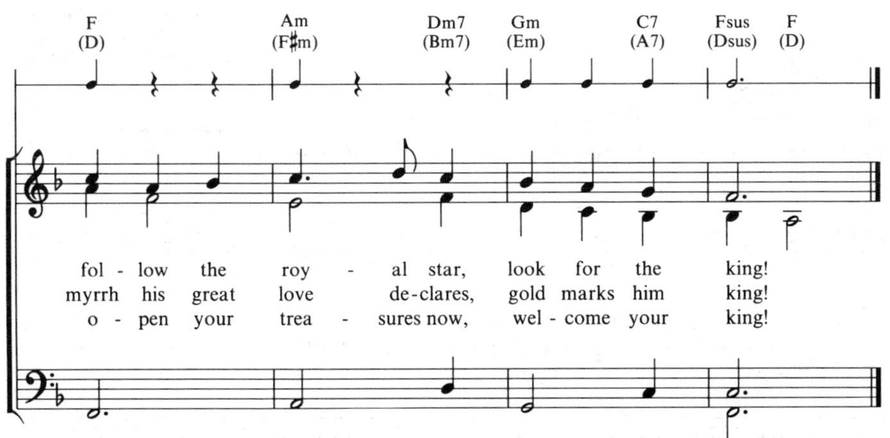
F (D)
Am (F♯m)
Dm7 (Bm7)
Gm (Em)
C7 (A7)
Fsus (Dsus)
F (D)
fol - low the roy - al star, look for the king!
myrrh his great love de-clares, gold marks him king!
o - pen your trea - sures now, wel - come your king!

B♭ melody version

Chime bar accompaniment (F, G, A, B♭, C)

253 Ring the bells

Words and music: Harry Bollbach
Music arranged David Peacock

Joyfully
C Em F C
1 Ring the bells, ring the bells, let the whole world know
Dm G/B G7 C Am Dm G G7 C
Christ was born in Beth-le-hem ma-ny years a - go:
Am Em7 F Gm Asus A
2 Born to die that we might live, came to earth new life to give;
Dm7 G E Am Dm G G7 C
born of Ma - ry, born so low, ma-ny years a - go.

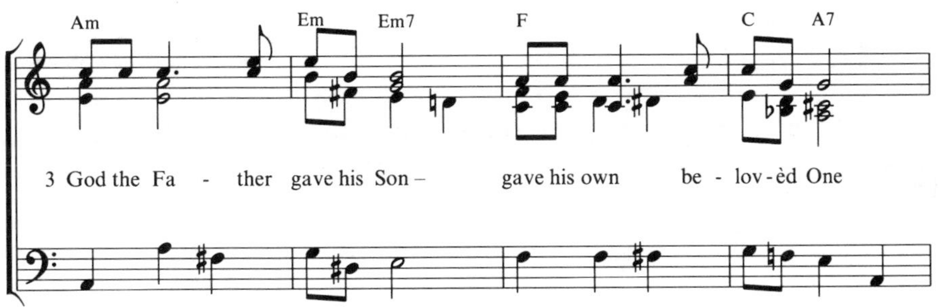
Am
Em
Em7
F
C
A7
3 God the Fa - ther gave his Son –
gave his own
be - lov - èd One

Dm7
G
C
Am
Am7
D
D7
Gsus
G
B♭
to this wick - ed, sin-ful earth,
to
bring man-kind his love – new birth!

E♭
Gm
A♭
E♭
4 Ring the bells,
ring the bells,
let the whole world
know

Fm
B♭/D
B♭7
E♭
Cm
Cm7
Fm7
B♭7
E♭
rall.
Christ the sav - iour
lives to-day,
as he
did
so long a - go.

254 Royal sons of a royal king

Capo 3(D)
Words and music: Barbara McArthur
Music arranged David Peacock
Slowly with majesty
F (D) Gm7 (Em7) Csus (Asus) C (A) F (D)
1 Roy - al sons of a roy - al king,
2 Lord, we of - fer roy - al praise –
Dm (Bm) Gm (Em) C (A) C7 (A7) F (D)
made to wor - ship, made to praise –
gold and frank - in - cense and myrrh;
F♯dim7 (D♯dim7) Gm7 (Em7) Csus (Asus) C (A) A7 (F♯7)
kings and priests to the King of kings,
Lord, we come in ho - li - ness,
Dm (Bm) Gm (Em) C (A) C7 (A7) 1. F (D) Gm7 (Em7) Gm7 /C C7 (A7) 2. F (D)
made to wor - ship him.
Lord, we wor - ship you.

255 Sent away to a cattle shed

Candles and crowns
Capo 3(D)
Words: Frances Norton
Music: Christopher Norton
arranged David Peacock
Moderately
F (D) B♭ (G) C (A) C7 (A7) F (D)
1 Sent_ a - way to a cat - tle shed! Can you i - ma-gine our
2 Born in a man - ger while ox - en fed – can you i - ma-gine our
3 But what sweet sense in our sav-iour's birth – the les-sons all there for
B♭ (G) C (A) C7 (A7) Am7 (F♯m7) Dm7 (Bm7) G (E)
Lord's sweet head_ laid_ to rest_ on a pil-low of straw?
sweet sav-iour's head was laid on a blan - ket_ of straw and hay?
us_ to learn,_ no need for trum - pets,_ jew-els or crowns!
Chorus
Dm7 (Bm7) G (E) Gm7 (Em7) C7 (A7) Am (F♯m) Dm (Bm) Gm (Em) C7 (A7)
Can-dles and crowns and cribs were there none, on - ly Ma-ry and
1.2. 3.
Cm6/A (Am6) D (B) Gm7 (Em7) Gm7/C F (D) B♭ (G) C (A) C7 (A7) F (D)
Jo - seph and the stars a - bove. - bove.
rit.
a tempo

256 See, amid the winter snow

Humility

Words: E Caswall (1814–1878)
and in this version Jubilate Hymns
Music: J Goss (1850–1880)

G Am7 Bm C D7/C G
1 See, a - mid the win - ter snow,
2 Low with - in a man - ger lies
TREBLE VOICES 3 Say, you hum - ble shep - herds, say
D/F♯ C/E G G/D D D7 G/B G Am Bm
born for us on earth be - low; see, the gen - tle
he who built the star - ry skies; he who, throned in
what your joy - ful news to - day? Tell us why you
C D7/C G D/F♯ Em G/D C Dsus D7 G
Lamb ap - pears, pro - mised from e - ter - nal years:
height sub - lime, reigns a - bove the cher - u - bim:
left your sheep on the lone - ly moun - tain steep:
Chorus
G C/G G D7/F♯ G D G/B C G
Hail, O ev - er - bless - èd morn; hail, re - demp - tion's

Am G/B D Em A7 Bm Em7/G A7 D D7/C
hap - py dawn! Sing through all Je - ru - sa - lem:
G/B C Am7 D7 G
'Christ is born in Beth - le - hem!'

4 MEN
'As we watched at dead of night,
all around us shone a light;
angels singing Peace on earth
told us of a Saviour's birth.'
Hail, O ever-blessèd morn . . .

5 Sacred infant, king most dear,
what a tender love was here,
thus to come from highest bliss
down to such a world as this!
Hail, O ever-blessèd morn . . .

6 Holy Saviour, born on earth,
teach us by your lowly birth;
grant that we may ever be
taught by such humility.
Hail, O ever-blessèd morn . . .

B♭ melody version

G* C G D G
C G D7 G
Chorus
G D
G D Em A7 D G C D7 G

* Simplified guitar chords not compatible with keyboard part

257 See him lying on a bed of straw

Calypso Carol
Words and music: Michael Perry
Music arranged mainly by Stephen Coates
D
Em/G
Em7
1 See him ly - ing on a bed of straw: a
2 Star of sil - ver, sweep a - cross the skies,
3 An - gels, sing a - gain the song you sang,
4 Mine are rich - es, from your pov - er - ty,
A7
D
Aaug
draugh - ty sta - ble with an o - pen door;
show where Je - sus in the man - ger lies;
bring God's glo - ry to the heart of man;
from your in - no - cence, e - ter - ni - ty;
D
Em/G
Em7
Ma - ry cra - dl - ing the babe she bore the
shep - herds, swift - ly from your stu - por rise to
sing that Beth - l'em's lit - tle ba - by can
mine for - give - ness by your death for me,
A7
D
D7
prince of glo - ry is his name.
see the sav - iour of the world!
be sal - va - tion to the soul.
child of sor - row for my joy.

Chorus
G
D/F♯
Bm
O now car - ry me to Beth - le - hem to
Em
A7
D
Aaug
see the Lord ap - pear to men
D
B
Em
just as poor as was the sta - ble then, the
A7
D
prince of glo - ry when he came.

258 See the dawn appearing

Words: Stanley Johnson
Music: David Cooper
Slowly
D Bm/A Em/A Dmaj7/F♯ Em7/G F♯m/A
1 See the dawn ap - pear - ing, light - ing the sky –
2 Ox and ass are stir - ring – though they draw near
3 Cru - el day a - waits you, dawn's ic - y breath,
Em7/B D A A7 D
though sha - dows fly, don't you a - wake! The
no need to fear, don't you a - wake. Though
sor - row and death, when you a - wake. Rough
Bm/A Em/A Dmaj7/F♯ Em7/G F♯m/A
day - light break - ing shines bright and clear –
shep - herds greet you kneel - ing to pray,
hands will seize you – scorned and de - nied,
Em7/B D A A7 D G/D D
though day is near, don't you a - wake.
king born to - day, don't you a - wake.
nailed, cru - ci - fied when you a - wake.
Music: © David Cooper
Words: © Stanley Johnson

D Em A D C Am7
An - gels have sung you their lul - la - bies –
Wise men will bring you their gifts of gold,
Though peo - ple hail you to - day as king,
D Em D Em/G A
cap - ture this mom - ent be - fore it dies.
born to be king as the pro - phets told.
they will not hear the Good News you bring.
D Bm/A Em/A D7 G/D G/D F♯m/C♯
See the dawn ap - pear - ing light - ing the sky –
Em7/B Daug/A♯ A A7 D Em/D D
though shad - ows fly, don't you a - wake!

259 See, to us a child is born

Rebecca

Words: Timothy Dudley-Smith
Music: David Peacock

Joyfully
Dm
Gm
1 See, to us a child is born –
3 Migh - ty God, who mer - cy brings –
A7
Dm
A7
glo - ry breaks on Christ - mas morn!
Lord of lords and King of kings!
Dm
Gm
Now to us a Son is given –
Fa - ther of e - ter - nal days –
A7
Dm
Am7
Dm
praise to God in high - est heaven!
ev - ery crea - ture sing his praise!

Lines 1 and 3: choir or solo
Lines 2 and 4: all

Dm
Gm
2 On his shoul - der rule shall rest –
4 Ev - er - last - ing Prince of peace –
C
F
in him all the earth be blessed!
truth and right - eous - ness in - crease!
B♭
Gm6/E
Wise and won - der - ful his Name –
He shall reign from shore to shore –
A
1.
Dm
2.
Dm
hea - ven's Lord in hu - man frame!
Christ is King for ev - er - more!

260 Shepherds came, their praises bringing

Words: From *Quem pastores laudavere* (fifteenth century)
G B Caird (1917–1984)
Music: German carol melody
arranged R Vaughan Williams (1872–1958)
Quem pastores laudavere
Capo 3(D)
F (D) C/E (A) F (D) B♭/D (G) B♭ (G) Csus (Asus) C7 (A7)
1 Shep - herds came their prais - es bring - ing,
2 Wise men whom a star had guid - ed
3 Je - sus born the king of hea - ven,
F (D) Gm (Em) C7 (A7) Dm (Bm) G (E) C (A)
who had heard the an - gels sing - ing:
in - cense, gold, and myrrh pro - vi - ded,
Christ to us through Ma - ry gi - ven,
F (D) B♭/D (G) F/A (D) B♭ (G) Csus (Asus) C7 (A7) A/C♯ (F♯) Dm (Bm)
'Far from you be fear un - ru - ly,
made their sac - ri - fi - ces tru - ly
to your praise and ho - nour du - ly
Gm (Em) Am (F♯m) Dm (Bm) Gm7 (Em7) C7 (A7) F (D)
Christ is king of glo - ry born.'
to the king of glo - ry born.
be re - sound - ing glo - ry done.

261 Small wonder the star

No small wonder

Words: Paul Wigmore
Music: Paul Edwards

Thoughtfully
B Em D/E Em Bm/E Am9 D7
1 Small won - der the star, small won - der the
2 Small won - der the kings, small won - der they
3 Small won - der the love, small won - der the
G D/F♯ Em Am D G Bm7/F♯
light, the an - gels in cho - rus, the
bore the gold and the in - cense, the
grace, the pow - er, the glo - ry, the
Em Em/C♯ F♯7 B Em9 Em7/D C
shep - herds in fright; but sta - ble and
myrrh, to a - dore; but God gives his
light of his face; but all to re -
Am G G7 C Am Am7 Bm7/E Em
man - ger for God – no small won - der!
life on a cross – no small won - der!
- deem my poor heart – no small won - der!

262 Shepherds, leave your drowsy sheep

He's the Lord of creation

Words: Peter Brown
and in this version Word & Music
Music: Peter Brown

G
*
Singers, large glockenspiel
C
Am
1 Shep - herds, leave your drow - sy sheep,
2 An - gels, sing your song of praise,
3 Na - tions, leave your cares be - hind,
Pitched percussion
and Recorders
(tr)
(desc.)
Triangle
Tambourine
p
tr
mp
D7
G
shep - herds, see the babe a - sleep:
an - gels, on this day of days,
na - tions, come, your Lord to find –
tr

Verse 3 may be repeated as a round (from *), then the chorus sung together.

Chorus
G7
C
see him in a sta - ble.
praise him as you're a - ble. He's the
Je - sus is no fa - ble!
take wood block (pref. two-tone)
G
Em
A7
D7
C7
G
Lord of cre-a - tion come down from hea - ven – such is his love.
1 2 3 1 2 3 1 2 1 2 3 1 2 3 1 2

263 Shepherds, leave your flocks

Words: Douglas Coombes
Music: traditional Porto Rican melody
arranged David Peacock

Lively
Dm A/D Dm7 D6 Gm7 Am7
Dm Am Dm
1 Shep-herds, leave your flocks, and
2 Shep-herds, do not fear, though
3 Shep-herds, now re - turn, with
Gm A A7
jour - ney to the man - ger: there in Beth - le - hem you'll
winds are get - ting strong - er: Beth - le - hem is near, the
joy your hearts are la - den; spread the joy - ful news of
Dm A Dm
find the child, the sav - iour. He is born this night to
way is not much long - er. There's the sta - ble door – go
Je - sus and the maid - en: God has kept his word, his

Gm
Dm/A
A
gen - tle mai - den Ma - ry –
shep-herds, come with me,
this
in and kneel be - fore him:
Je - sus, gen - tle king,
ac -
Son is born to save us –
tra - vel on your way,
sing

1.2.
A7
D
Am
3.
A7
Dm
mir - a - cle to see.
- cept the praise we bring!
praise this Christ-mas Day!

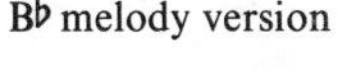
B♭ melody version

4

264 Shepherds, wake to news of joy

The Fields of Bethlehem
Medieval style
gently with mystery
Words: Michael Perry
Music: Norman Warren
Recorder/flute
(Drum rhythm:)
Brightly
Dm Gm Am Dm
1 Shep-herds, wake to news of joy – God's en - voy
2 Run to greet him – Christ the Lord, God's own Word,
B♭ Dm Gm Dm G Dm
comes to say that for you is born a boy
now ar - rayed not with clothes the rich af - ford,
Gm Dm Am Dm Dm
Part 1
close in Da - vid's town to - day!
but in hum - ble man - ger laid! 3 Hear the mid - night

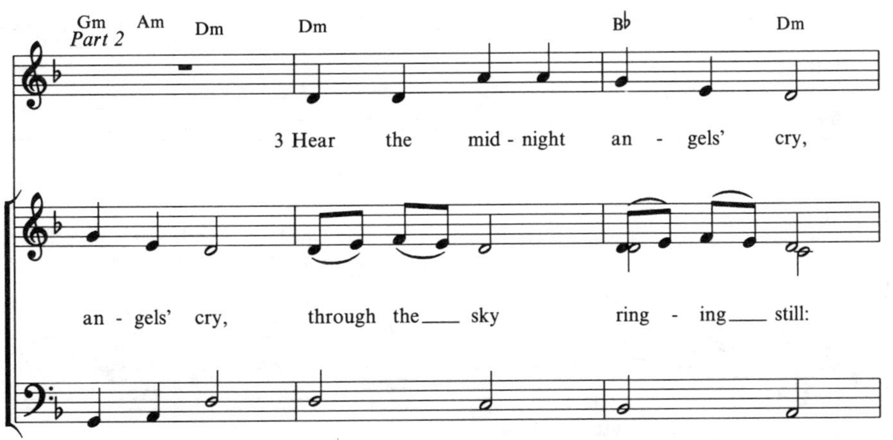
Gm Am Dm Dm B♭ Dm
Part 2
3 Hear the mid - night an - gels' cry,
an - gels' cry, through the sky ring - ing still:

Gm Dm G Dm Gm Dm
through the sky ring - ing still: 'Glo - ry be to
'Glo - ry be to God on high; peace on earth – to

Am Dm Gm Dm Am Dm
God on high; peace on earth – to all, good - will!
all, good - will; peace on earth – to all, good - will!

265 Shout aloud, girls and boys

Personent hodie

Words: from the Latin
Michael Perry
Music: Piae Cantiones (1582)
arranged G Holst (1874–1934)

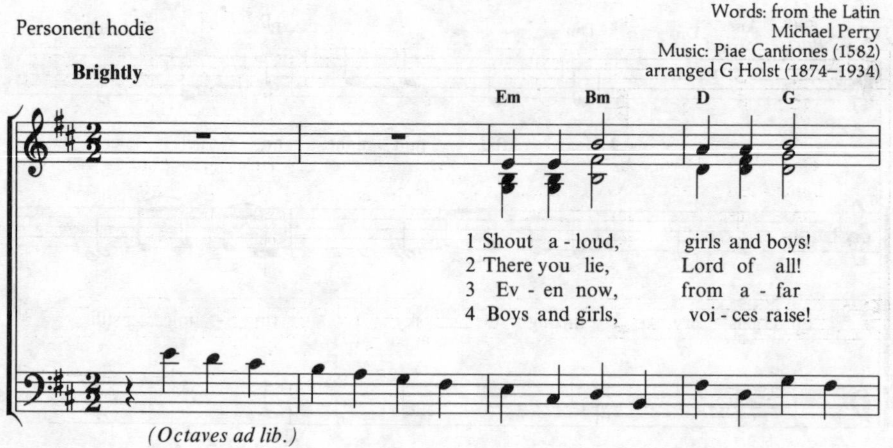

Brightly
Em Bm D G
1 Shout a - loud, girls and boys!
2 There you lie, Lord of all!
3 Ev - en now, from a - far
4 Boys and girls, voi - ces raise!
(Octaves ad lib.)

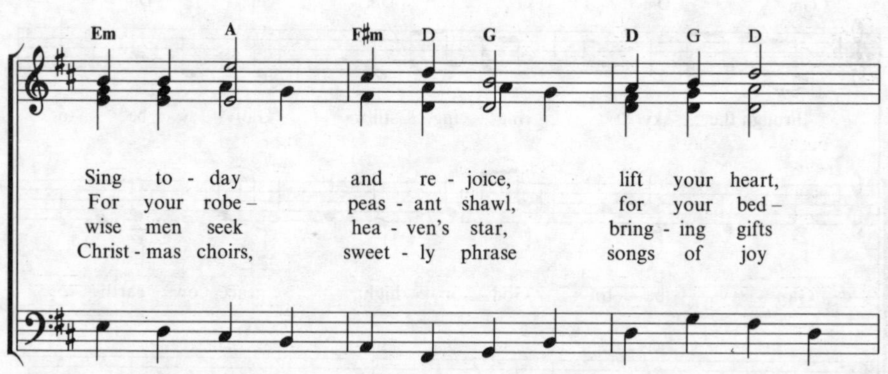

Em A F#m D G D G D
Sing to - day and re - joice, lift your heart,
For your robe – peas - ant shawl, for your bed –
wise men seek hea - ven's star, bring - ing gifts
Christ - mas choirs, sweet - ly phrase songs of joy

A Bm Em F#m7 Bm Em
raise your voice; come and do not wa - ver,
ox - 's stall, for your throne a man - ger,
where you are: gold to bow be - fore you,
and of praise; leave all care and wor - ry,

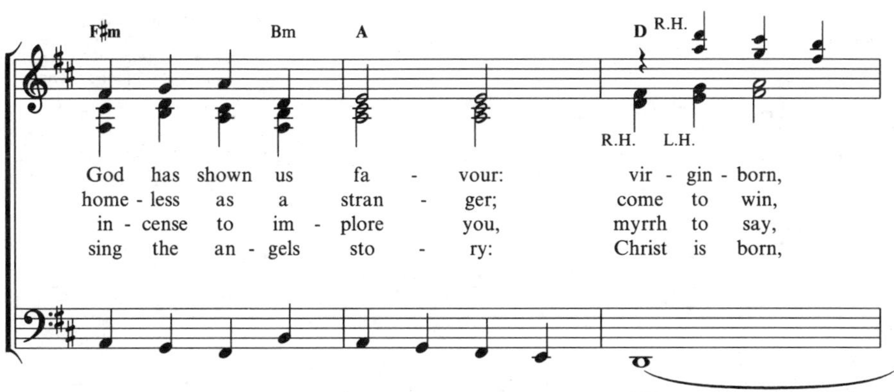
F♯m
Bm
A
D
R.H.
R.H.
L.H.
God has shown us fa - vour: vir - gin - born,
home - less as a stran - ger; come to win,
in - cense to im - plore you, myrrh to say,
sing the an - gels sto - ry: Christ is born,

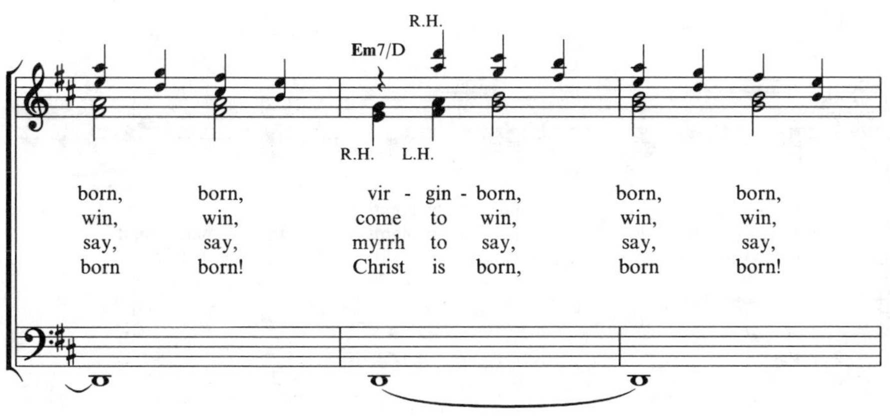
R.H.
Em7/D
R.H.
L.H.
born, born, vir - gin - born, born, born,
win, win, come to win, win, win,
say, say, myrrh to say, say, say,
born born! Christ is born, born born!

D
A7/D
D
Bm
E
vir - gin - born, Ma - ry's child, Christ is here – our sav - iour!
come to win hell's do - main – spurn-ing death and dan - ger!
myrrh to say 'sac - ri - fice' – there-fore we a - dore you!
Christ is born: Peace on earth, and to God be glo - ry!

266 Silent night

Stille nacht

Capo 3(G)

Words: after J Möhr (1792–1848)
J F Young (1820–1885)
Music: F X Gruber (1787–1863)
arranged Noël Tredinnick

Cm7 (Am7) F7 (D7) Gm (Em) C9 (A9) B♭/F (G) F7 (D7) B♭ (G)
Introduction
B♭ (G) B♭maj7 (Gmaj7) B♭7 (G7) B♭6 (G6) Cm7 (Am7) F7 (D7)
Optional descant v.3
3 Si - lent night! ho - ly night! Son of God,
1 Si - lent night! ho - ly night! all is calm,
2 Si - lent night! ho - ly night! shep - herds quail
3 Si - lent night! ho - ly night! Son of God,
B♭ (G) Cm (Am) Dm (Bm) E♭ (C) B♭ (G) B♭7 (G7)
love's pure light: ra - diant beams your ho - ly face
all is bright round the vir - gin and her child:
at the sight, glo - ry streams from hea - ven a - far:
love's pure light: ra - diant beams your ho - ly face

E♭ (C)
Cm7 (Am7)
Fm (Dm)
G7 (E7)
Cm7 (Am7)
F7 (D7)
with the dawn of sav - ing grace, Je - sus, Lord, at your
ho - ly in - fant, so gen - tle and mild, sleep in hea - ven - ly
hea - venly hosts sing, 'Al - le - lu - ia, Christ the sav - iour is
with the dawn of sav - ing grace, Je - sus, Lord, at your
Gm7 (Em7)
C9 (A9)
B♭/F (G)
Fsus (Dsus)
F7 (D7)
B♭ (G)
birth, Je - sus Lord, at your birth.
peace; sleep in hea - ven - ly peace!
born, Christ the sav - iour is born.'
birth, Je - sus, Lord, at your birth.
B♭ melody version
B♭* (G)
F (D)
B♭ (G)
E♭ (C)
B♭ (G)
E♭ (C)
B♭ (G)
F (D)
B♭ (G)
F7 (D7)
B♭ (G)

* Simplified guitar chords not compatible with keyboard arrangement

267 Silver star

Polovtsian Dance
Capo 3(D)

Words: Michael Perry
Music: A Borodin (1834–1887)
arranged Norman Warren

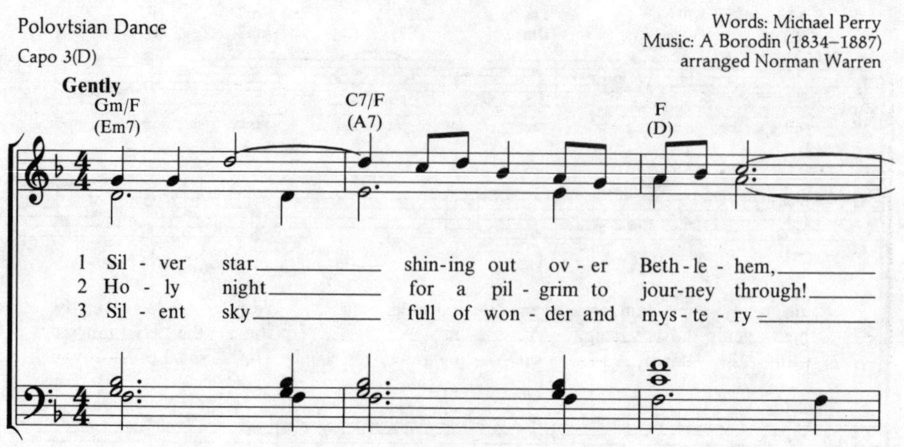
Gently
Gm/F
(Em7)
C7/F
(A7)
F
(D)
1 Sil - ver star shin-ing out ov - er Beth - le - hem,
2 Ho - ly night for a pil - grim to jour-ney through!
3 Sil - ent sky full of won - der and mys - te - ry –

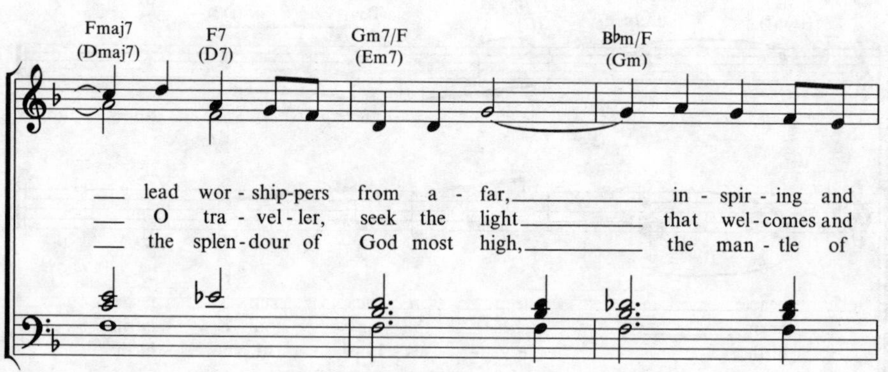
Fmaj7
(Dmaj7)
F7
(D7)
Gm7/F
(Em7)
Bbm/F
(Gm)
lead wor - ship-pers from a - far, in - spir - ing and
O tra - vel - ler, seek the light that wel - comes and
the splen - dour of God most high, the man - tle of

F
(D)
Dm
(Bm)
Gm
(Em)
guid - ing them! They look for the in - fant King –
beck - ons you! You come to the brink of heaven,
ma - jes - ty! Yet God lays a - side his crown –

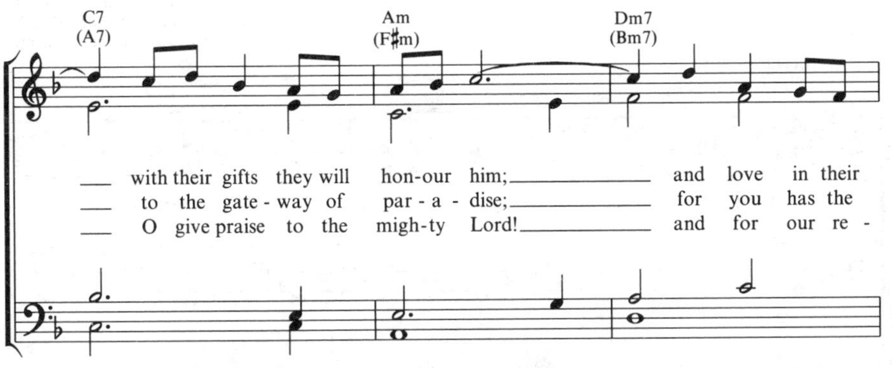
C7
(A7)
Am
(F♯m)
Dm7
(Bm7)
with their gifts they will hon-our him; and love in their
to the gate-way of par-a-dise; for you has the
O give praise to the migh-ty Lord! and for our re-

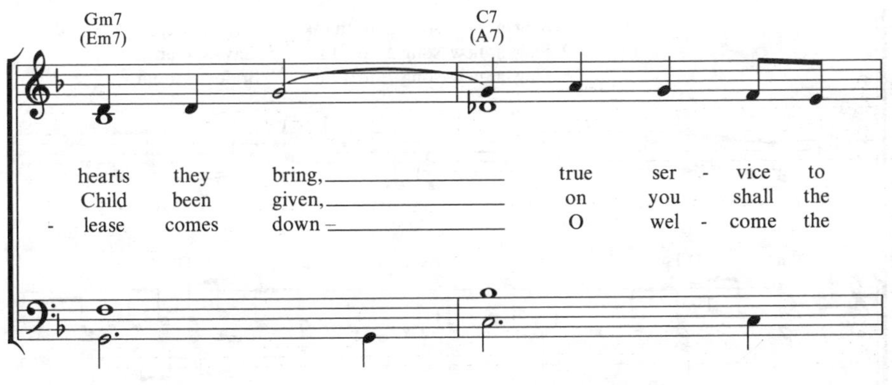
Gm7
(Em7)
C7
(A7)
hearts they bring, true ser-vice to
Child been given, on you shall the
-lease comes down – O wel-come the

1.2.
Dm7/F
(Bm7)
N.C.
3.
F
(D)
of-fer him.
Sun a-rise.
liv-ing Word!

268 Sing a new song of thanksgiving

He's coming back

Words and music: Martin Cox

Rhythmically
D
Em7 Asus A
D G/D
Bm
1 Sing a new song of thanks - giv - ing, the
2 Sing a new song to the Sav - iour,
3 Sing a new song to the Bride - groom,
Em7 D/F♯ G Asus A D G/D
Lord is re-turn - ing to claim his own; he's com-ing back to heal your
stand and name him your Lord and king; praise and a - dore him for he
raise your voi - ces to praise his name; be rea - dy to greet him: you'll not
F♯sus F♯ Bm Em7 D/F♯ G Asus G/A D
hurt and pain, to har-vest all the seed he's sown.
gave his life, to con-quer fear and death's sharp sting.
know the hour when joy - ful - ly he'll call your name.

Chorus
D7
G
A
He's coming back,
he's coming back,
F♯m
Bm
1.
Em
A7
G/A
A7
he's coming back
to claim his
D
Em/D
D7
2.
Em
own;
he's coming back,
and his
A7
D
D.𝄋
to end
glo - ry will be shown.

269 Sing a song, a joyful song

A joyful song

Words and music: Colleen O'Meara
Music arranged Betty Pulkingham

With a lilt
E
B7/E
B7
A/E*
A/E
B7
1 Sing a song, a joy - ful song, sing un - to the Lord; Sing a song, a joy - ful song, sing un - to the Lord.
2 See the ba - by in a man - ger, see the ba - by soft - ly sleep - ing; see the ba - by in a man - ger – come with me and see.
3 See the mo - ther rock the ba - by, rock the ba - by, rock the ba - by; see the mo - ther rock the ba - by – come with me and see.
Clap your hands, all you peo - ple, clap your hands un - to the Lord;

* use single strums when played with piano accompaniment

A/E
E
E
B7
dance your feet, all you peo - ple, dance un - to the
E
E
E
E
E
Lord!

4 Hear the donkey hee and hawing,
hee and hawing, hee and hawing;
hear the donkey hee and hawing,
come with me and see.
Clap your hands . . .

5 Shepherds on the hills a-watching,
hills a-watching, hills a-watching;
shepherds on the hills a-watching:
come with me and see.
Clap your hands . . .

6 See the stars so brightly shining,
brightly shining, brightly shining;
see the stars so brightly shining,
come with me and see.
Clap your hands . . .

7 Kings upon their camels riding,
camels riding, camels riding;
kings upon their camels riding,
bringing gifts to him.
Clap your hands . . .

The song appeals to young children, and the verses themselves to simple miming by a group of children and leader. Gather the children together on verse 1, dance the chorus in a circle.

Ideas for verses include 'see the baby' (pointing to manger); 'softly sleeping' (tilt head and rest it on folded hands); 'rock the baby' (make a cradle of your arms); 'hear the donkey' (one hand cupped over ear); 'hee and hawing' (place hands straight up on either side of head to form donkey ears).

270 Sing alleluia to the Lord

Words: verse 1 Linda Stassen,
verses 2–4 anonymous
Music: Linda Stassen
arranged David Peacock

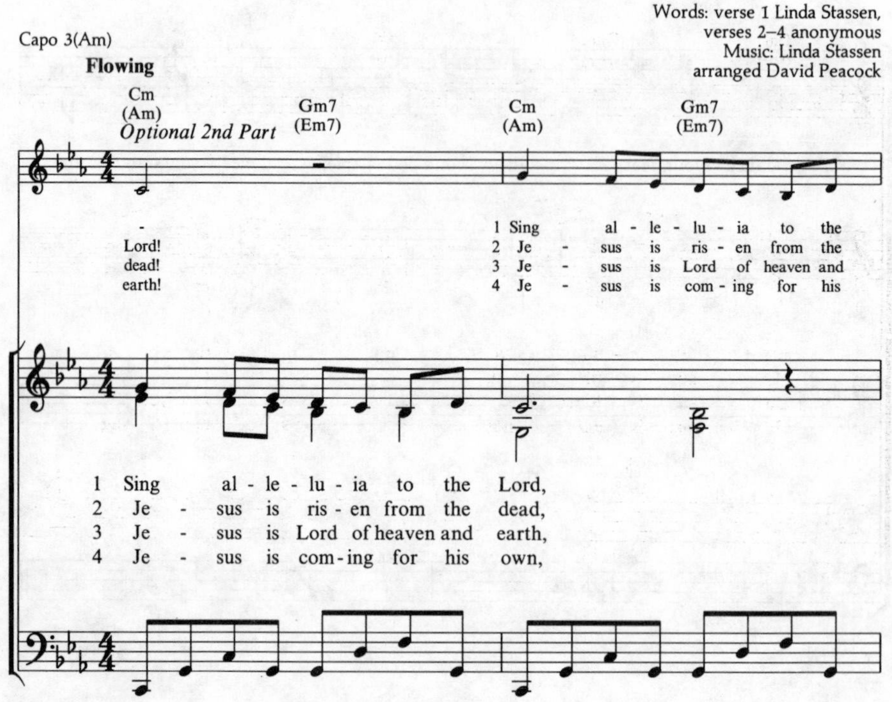

Capo 3(Am)
Flowing
Cm (Am)
Optional 2nd Part
Gm7 (Em7)
Cm (Am)
Gm7 (Em7)
1 Sing al - le - lu - ia to the
Lord! 2 Je - sus is ris - en from the
dead! 3 Je - sus is Lord of heaven and
earth! 4 Je - sus is com - ing for his
1 Sing al - le - lu - ia to the Lord,
2 Je - sus is ris - en from the dead,
3 Je - sus is Lord of heaven and earth,
4 Je - sus is com - ing for his own,

Cm (Am)
Dm (Bm)
E♭ (C)
F (D)
Gsus (Esus)
G (E)
Lord, sing al - le - lu - ia
dead, Je - sus is ris - en
earth, Je - sus is Lord
own, Je - sus is com - ing
sing al - le - lu - ia to the Lord,
Je - sus is ris - en from the dead,
Je - sus is Lord of heaven and earth,
Je - sus is com - ing for his own,

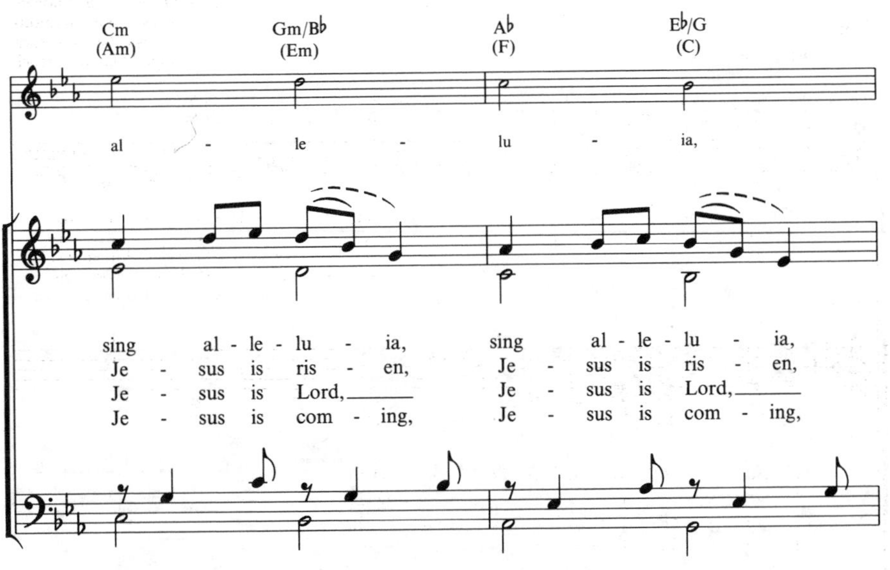

Cm
(Am)
Gm/B♭
(Em)
A♭
(F)
E♭/G
(C)
al - le - lu - ia,
sing al - le - lu - ia, sing al - le - lu - ia,
Je - sus is ris - en, Je - sus is ris - en,
Je - sus is Lord, Je - sus is Lord,
Je - sus is com - ing, Je - sus is com - ing,

Fm9
(Dm9)
Gm7
(Em7)
Cm
(Am)
Gm7
(Em7)
4.
Cm
(Am)
sing al - le - lu - ia to the
Je - sus is ris - en from the
Je - sus is Lord of heaven and
Je - sus is com - ing for his own.
sing al - le - lu - ia to the Lord!
Je - sus is ris - en from the dead!
Je - sus is Lord of heaven and earth!
Je - sus is com-ing for his own.

271 Sing a new song to the Lord

Onslow Square

Words: from Psalm 98 (*Cantate Domino*)
Timothy Dudley-Smith
Music: David Wilson

Vigorously
G F G F G Dm
1 Sing a new song to the Lord, he to whom won-ders be -
2 Now to the ends of the earth see his sal - va - tion is
3 Sing a new song and re - joice, pub - lish his prais - es a -
4 Join with the hills and the sea thun - ders of praise to pro -
G F Em A
- long! Re - joice in his tri - umph and
shown; and still he re - mem - bers his
- broad! Let voi - ces in chor - us, with
- long! In judge - ment and just - ice he
Em F D7 G Dm
tell of his power - O sing to the
mer - cy and truth, un - chang - ing in
trum - pet and horn, re - sound for the
comes to the earth - O sing to the
Am7 D7 G Am7 1.2.3. Gmaj7 Am7 4. G
Lord a new song!
love to his own.
joy of the Lord!
Lord a new song!

272 Sing glory, glory

Words: Unknown
in ths version Word & Music
Music: Unknown
arranged Stephen Coates and David Peacock

Joyfully
A C♯ F♯m A7
1 Sing glo - ry, glo - ry al - le - lu - ia – an - gel
(2) glo - ry, al - le - lu - ia – tell the
(3) glo - ry, al - le - lu - ia – to his
D A/C♯ C7 E7/B E7
hosts the skies a - dorn; sing glo - ry,
news of 'Peace on earth!'; sing glo - ry,
ci - ty make your way; sing glo - ry,
A C♯ Dmaj7 B7/D♯
glo - ry al - le - lu - ia – our re -
glo - ry, al - le - lu - ia – come and
glo - ry, al - le - lu - ia – our re -
OR ON CHRISTMAS DAY: Je - sus
A/E F♯m Bm7/D E7 1.2. A E7 3. A
- deem - er, Christ is born! 2 Sing glo - ry
ce - le - brate his birth! 3 Sing glo - ry
- deem - er lives to - day!
Christ is born to - day!

Music arrangement: © Stephen Coates

273 Sing heaven, shout for joy

Words and music: Bob Fraser

Joyfully
D
G
Sing heav-en, shout for joy, O earth; let the
D
A7
D
moun-tains burst in-to song, for the sav - iour comes and he will
G
D/A
A7
D
rule in glo-ry – your re-deem-er will not be long. Al - le-lu-ia,
G
D
A7
al - le-lu - ia, al - le-lu - ia, come, Lord Je - sus;
D
G
D
A7
D
al - le-lu-ia, al - le-lu-ia, al - le-lu - ia,___ come!

On repeat, men sing 'Sing heaven' while ladies sing 'Alleluia', then ladies sing 'Sing heaven' while men sing 'Alleluia'.

274 Sing lullaby

The infant king

Words: S Baring-Gould (1834–1924)
Music: Basque noël
arranged Norman Warren

E F♯m7/E B7/E E B7 E A A B E E/D♯
1 Sing lul - la - by! lul - la - by ba - by, now re - clin - ing:
2 Sing lul - la - by! lul - la - by ba - by, sweet - ly sleep - ing:
3 Sing lul - la - by! lul - la - by ba - by, gent - ly doz - ing:
4 Sing lul - la - by! lul - la - by! Is the ba - by wa - king?
C♯m F♯m B7 Esus E A B F♯7/C♯ F♯7 Bsus B
(1–3) sing lul - la - by! Hush, do not wake the in - fant king;
(4) sing lul - la - by! Hush, do not stir the in - fant king;
B7 E G♯m7 A F♯m E G♯m7 E F♯m7/E B7
an - gels are watch - ing, stars are shin - ing o - ver the place where
soon will come sor - row with the morn - ing, soon will come bit - ter
soon comes the cross, the nails, the pierc - ing, then in the grave at
dream - ing of East - er, joy - ful morn - ing, con - quer - ing death, its
C♯m E F♯m E/G♯ E F♯m B7 E
he is ly - ing:
grief and weep - ing: sing lul - la - by!
last re - pos - ing: sing lul - la - by!
bond - age break - ing:

275 Soft the evening shadows fall

The March of the Christmas Pilgrims

Words: Timothy Dudley-Smith
Music: Michael Paget

With life

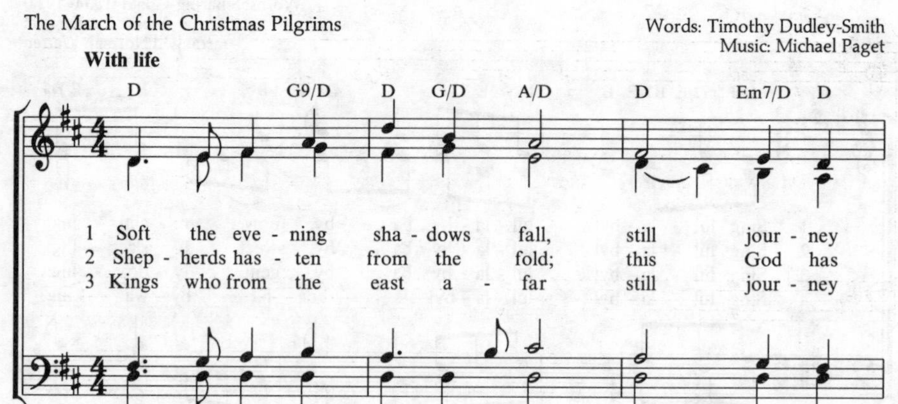
D
G9/D
D
G/D
A/D
D
Em7/D
D
1 Soft the eve - ning sha - dows fall, still jour - ney
2 Shep - herds has - ten from the fold; this God has
3 Kings who from the east a - far still jour - ney

Gmaj7/D
D
Bm
Bm7
on; dark - ness soon be o - ver all,
done. Here in hu - man form be - hold
on, seek - ing Christ be - neath a star,

Em7
Bm
F♯m
D
A/C♯
Bm7
Em/G
still jour - ney on. Wea - ry now, and
this God has done. Christ the Lord of
still jour - ney on. For his wor - ship

F♯m/A A7 Bm Em A Bm7 F♯m7 Em7 Bm7
tra - vel - worn, night must come be - fore the morn:
Da - vid's line, born a sa - viour and a sign,
in - cense bring, gold to crown an in - fant King,

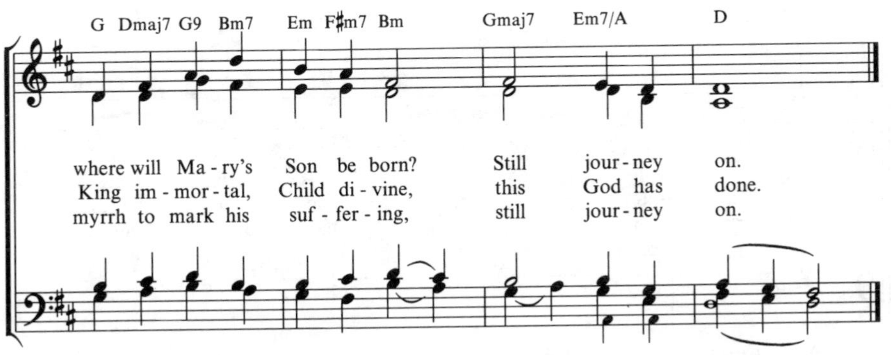
G Dmaj7 G9 Bm7 Em F♯m7 Bm Gmaj7 Em7/A D
where will Ma - ry's Son be born? Still jour - ney on.
King im - mor - tal, Child di - vine, this God has done.
myrrh to mark his suf - fer - ing, still jour - ney on.

4 Lord of all, enthroned above,
  God sent his Son.
God of everlasting love,
  God sent his Son.
He himself a ransom gave,
bowed himself to cross and grave,
came himself to seek and save,
  God sent his Son.

5 So the Christmas story tell;
  still journey on.
At the last shall all be well;
  still journey on.
Love be ours, and joy and praise,
one with Christ to walk his ways,
in his service all our days
  still journey on.

276 Softly, a shepherd is singing

Words: Paul Wigmore
Music: Czech traditional melody
arranged David Peacock

The Angels and the Shepherds

Capo 3(D)
1 Soft - ly, a shep - herd is sing - ing his song o - ver the Beth - le - hem hills all night long:
2 Her - ald - ing an - gels are sing - ing their song, won - der - ful words that to hea - ven be - long:
3 Lov - ing - ly, Ma - ry is sing - ing her song, bear - ing the child who will bear all our wrong:
4 Wor - ship - ping Je - sus, we sing a new song – Beth - le - hem's ba - by, our sav - iour so strong:
Chorus
Night-time is pass - ing – wait for the dawn-ing! Praise him who brings us joy in the morn-ing: Al - le - lu - ia!

277 Songs of gladness

Frère Jacques

Words: Michael Perry
Music: French traditional melody
arranged David Peacock

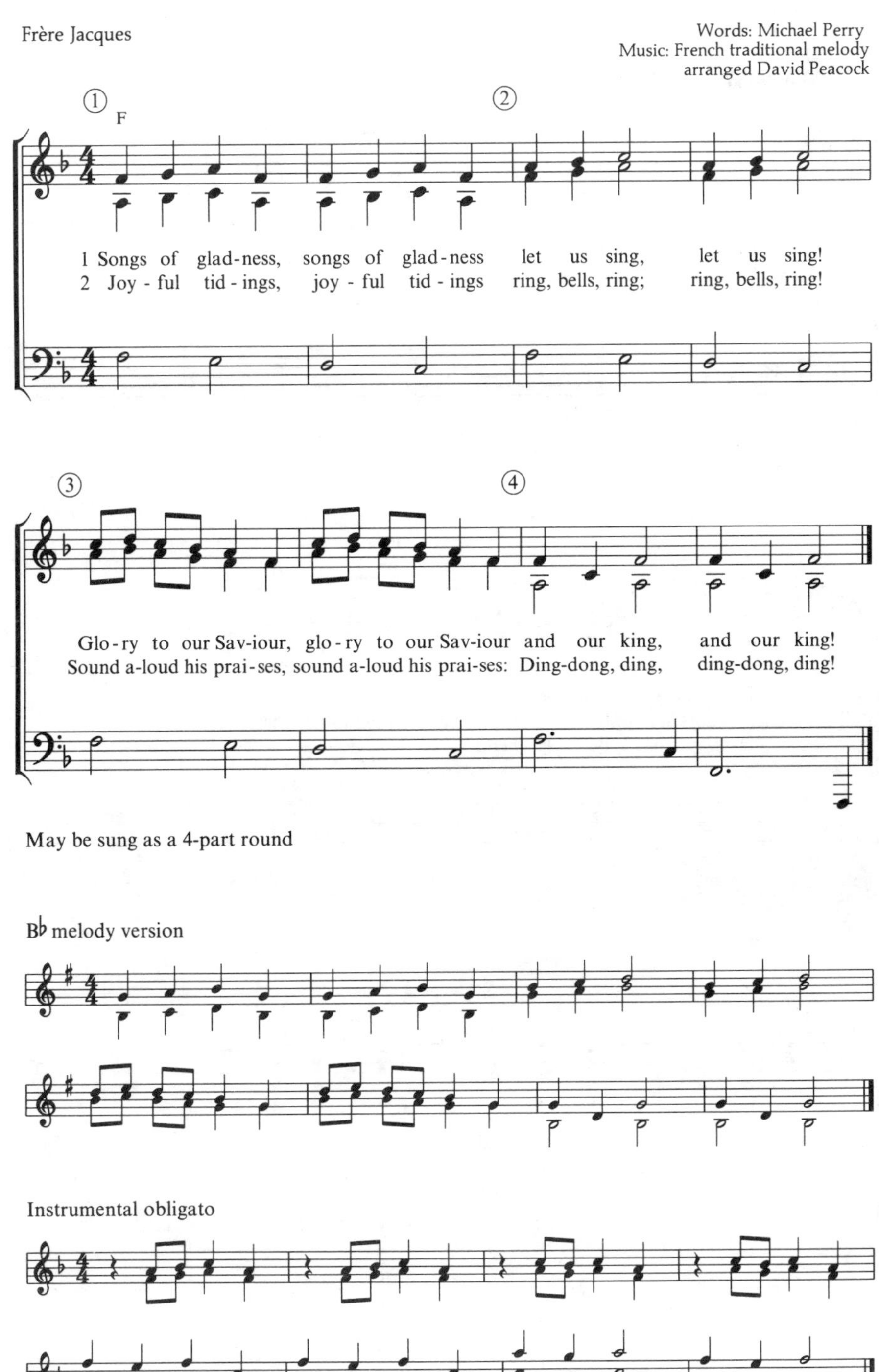

F
1 Songs of glad-ness, songs of glad-ness let us sing, let us sing!
2 Joy - ful tid - ings, joy - ful tid - ings ring, bells, ring; ring, bells, ring!
Glo-ry to our Sav-iour, glo-ry to our Sav-iour and our king, and our king!
Sound a-loud his prai-ses, sound a-loud his prai-ses: Ding-dong, ding, ding-dong, ding!
May be sung as a 4-part round
B♭ melody version
Instrumental obligato

278 Soldiers marching

Carol of the Drum
Capo 3(D)

Words: Michael Perry
Music: Harry Simeone and Henry Onorati
arranged David Peacock

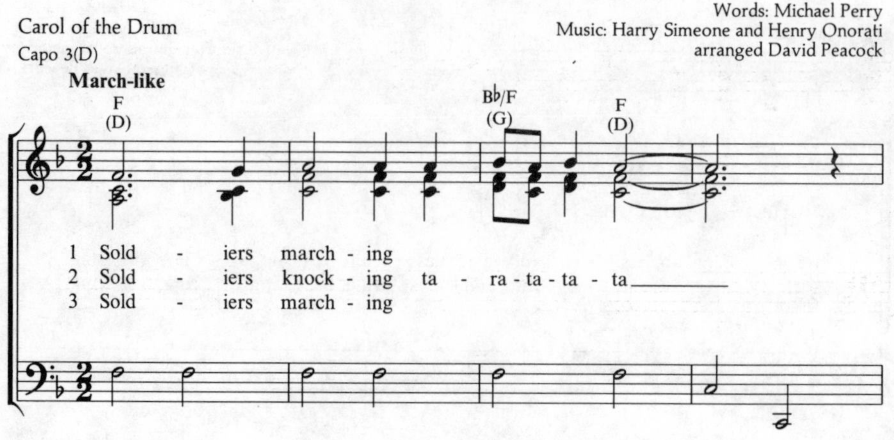

March-like
F
(D)
B♭/F
(G)
F
(D)
1 Sold - iers march - ing
2 Sold - iers knock - ing ta - ra - ta - ta - ta
3 Sold - iers march - ing

B♭/F
(G)
F
(D)
the streets of Beth - le - hem,
on doors of Beth - le - hem, ta - ra - ta - ta - ta
a - way from Beth - le - hem,

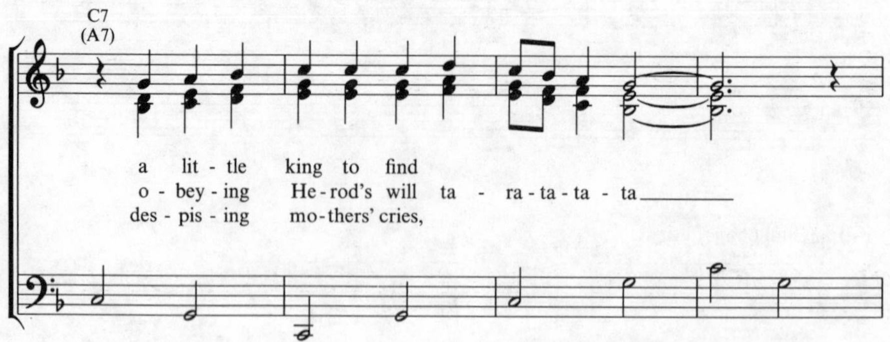

C7
(A7)
a lit - tle king to find
o - bey - ing He - rod's will ta - ra - ta - ta - ta
des - pis - ing mo - thers' cries,

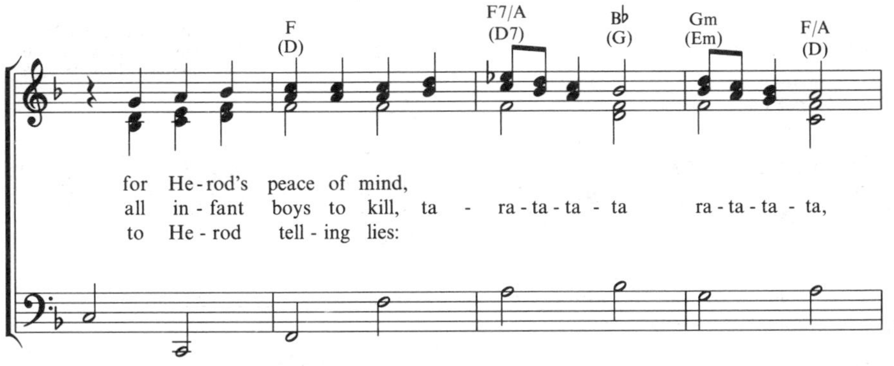
F
(D)
F7/A
(D7)
B♭
(G)
Gm
(Em)
F/A
(D)
for He-rod's peace of mind,
all in-fant boys to kill, ta - ra-ta-ta - ta ra-ta-ta - ta,
to He-rod tell-ing lies:

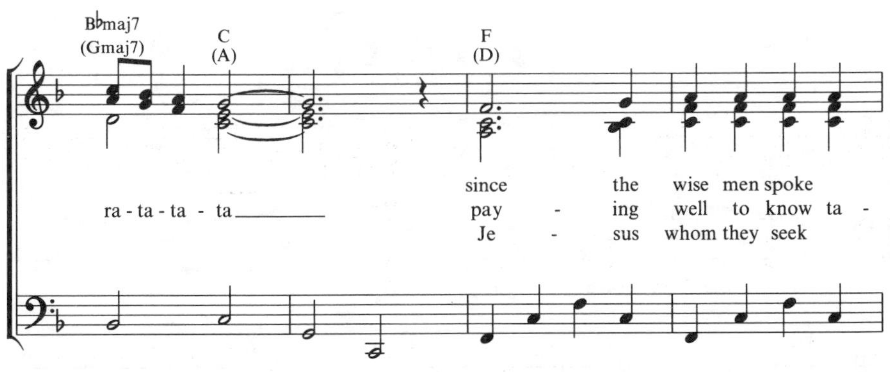
B♭maj7
(Gmaj7)
C
(A)
F
(D)
since the wise men spoke
ra-ta-ta - ta pay - ing well to know ta -
Je - sus whom they seek

Gm/C
(Em)
F
(C)
1.2.
3.
of a star.
- ra-ta-ta-ta where they are.
is a - far.

279 Soon – and very soon

Capo 3(D)
Words and music: Andrae Crouch
Music arranged David Peacock
Joyfully
F (D)
Gm7/C (Em7)
F (D)
1&4 Soon – and ve - ry soon –
2 No more cry - ing there,
3 No more dy - ing there,
we are go-ing to see the King,
Gm7/C (Em7)
Gm7
C (A)
Gm7/C (Em7)
soon – and ve - ry soon –
No more cry - ing there,
No more dy - ing there,
we are
F (D)
C7 (A7)
F (D)
A7/E (F♯7)
go-ing to see the King,
soon – and ve - ry soon –
No more cry - ing there,
No more dy - ing there,
Dm (Bm)
B♭m/D♭ (Gm)
F/C (D)
F
we are go-ing to see the King.
Al - le -

F7 (D7) Gm7/B♭ (Em7) B♭m (Gm) F/C (D)
- lu - ia, al - le - lu - ia, we're go-ing to see the King!
1.2. F C7 (A7)
3.4. F (D) Dm7 (Bm7) G7 (E7) C7 (A7) F (D) Dm7 (Bm7)
Al - le - lu - ia, al - le -
G7 (E7) C7 (A7) F (D) Dm7 (Bm7) G7 (E7) C7 (A7)
p
- lu - ia, al - le - lu -
F (D) Dm7 (Bm7) G7 (E7) C7 (A7)
f
v.3 F (D) D.C.
v.4 F (D)
- ia, al - le - lu - ia! - ia!

280 Sound on the trumpet

The Bridegroom Song

Words and music: John McNeil
Music arranged David Peacock

Strong and joyful
Increase in tempo with each repeat
Dm/B♭
Trumpets
Gm7
Asus
A
D
Dmaj7/C♯
marcato
Chorus
marcato
Sound on the trum-pet,
Break out the ban-ners,
Bm7
Dmaj7/A
Gm
D
call to the peo - ple, sing your new song –
join in the danc - ing, no time for gloom –
last time to Coda
Gm
D
A7
1.
D Asus A
our Bride - groom's com - ing, it won't be long.
pre-pare the ban - quet, he's com - ing soon.

2.
D
Asus
A
Dm
a3
Verses
1 If you're one of God's
2 Go out in tears and
C
F
peo - ple, re - joice in praise and
weep - ing to bring the har - vest
A
Gm
song; come lift up your hearts be -
home: it's time for the joy of

Dm
A7
- fore him and give your voi - ces
reap - ing; in joy the sheaves now
D.𝄋
Dm
Dm/B♭ Asus A
in praise and song.
are com - ing home.
CODA
D
A7
D
(shout)
ban - quet, he's com - ing soon. Yes!

281 Still, still, still

Words: from the German
Paul Wigmore
Music: Austrian traditional melody
arranged John Barnard

Tenderly
D Bm Em D/F♯ Em/G Em A A7 D
D Bm A7 D/F♯ Em/G Em A A7 D
1 Still, still, still, the ba - by lies a - sleep: yet
2 Love, love, love, no great - er love than his; while
A A7 D A A7 D
far a - way are her - ald voi - ces – hea - ven sings and earth re - joi - ces!
'Christ the Lord' the an - gels name him, we with fer - vent hearts ac - claim him.
Bm A7 D/F♯ Em/G Em A A7 D
Still, still, still, the ba - by lies a - sleep.
Love, love, love, no great - er love than his!

282 Standing in the rain

Words and music: Sydney Carter
Music arranged David Peacock

Not too slow
Dm
Instrument
Dm7/C
B♭maj7
A7
Chorus
Stand-ing in the rain, knock-ing on the win-dow,
Gm
Gm7
Dm/A
A7
Dm
knock-ing on the win-dow on a Christ-mas day.
Dm
Dm/C♯
Dm7/C
Dm/B
B♭maj7
F/A
Gm
Gm/F
There he is a-gain, knock-ing on the win-dow,

Fine
A7/E Gm D7 Gm Dm/A A7 Dm
knock - ing on the win - dow in the same old way.
Verses
D G
1 No use knock-ing on the win-dow, there is
2 No, we have - n't got a man - ger, no, we
G/A A7 G/D D F♯m7
noth - ing we can do, sir; all the beds are booked al -
have - n't got a sta - ble: till you woke us with your
D.C.
Em A Dm Am7 Dm Am7
- rea - dy, there is noth-ing left for you, sir!
knock-ing, we were sleep-ing like the dead, sir!

283 Sweet was the song

Howgate

Words: W Ballet (c.1600)
and in this version Word & Music
Music: Norman Warren

Gently
Am
Dm7/A
Em/A
Am7/G
F
F/E
Dm
Em7/D
1 Sweet was the song that Ma-ry sang when she to Beth-le-hem
2 'Sweet babe,' she sang, 'my dar-ling son, for our sal-va-tion
Em7/C
Am/C
Esus/B
E7/B
Ju-dah came, and was de-liv-ered of a son – the sav-iour, Je-sus
time-ly born, whom God has pro-mised from on high to vis-it those by
Dm/F
F/A
Gsus
G
C
Fmaj7/C
Dm7/C
G7/C
Am7
Christ by name: 'Lul-la-by, lul-la-by; lul-la-by,
sor-row worn!' 'Lul-la-by, sweet
Em7
Asus
lul-la-by.'
Em7/B
babe,' she sang, and rocked him gen-tly on her knee.

284 Take heart and praise our God

Christchurch

Words: from Psalm 47
David Mowbray
Music: C Steggall (1826–1905)

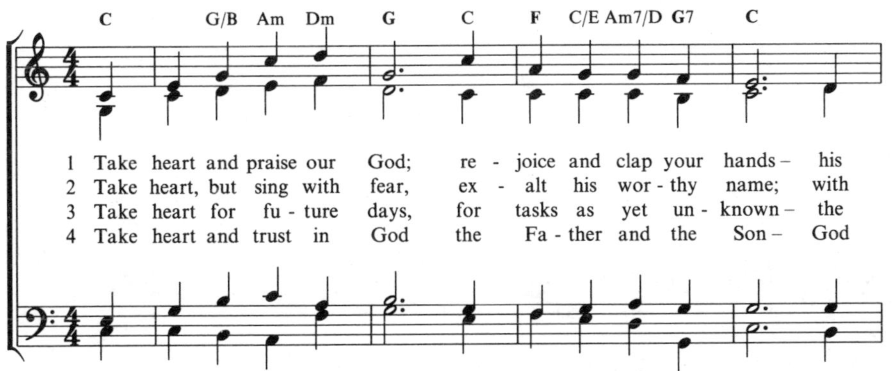
C G/B Am Dm G C F C/E Am7/D G7 C
1 Take heart and praise our God; re - joice and clap your hands – his
2 Take heart, but sing with fear, ex - alt his wor - thy name; with
3 Take heart for fu - ture days, for tasks as yet un - known – the
4 Take heart and trust in God the Fa - ther and the Son – God

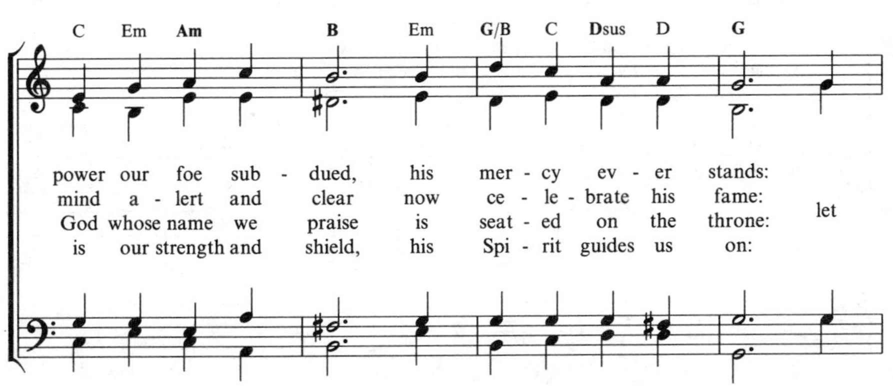
C Em Am B Em G/B C Dsus D G
power our foe sub - dued, his mer - cy ev - er stands:
mind a - lert and clear now ce - le - brate his fame:
God whose name we praise is seat - ed on the throne:
is our strength and shield, his Spi - rit guides us on:
let

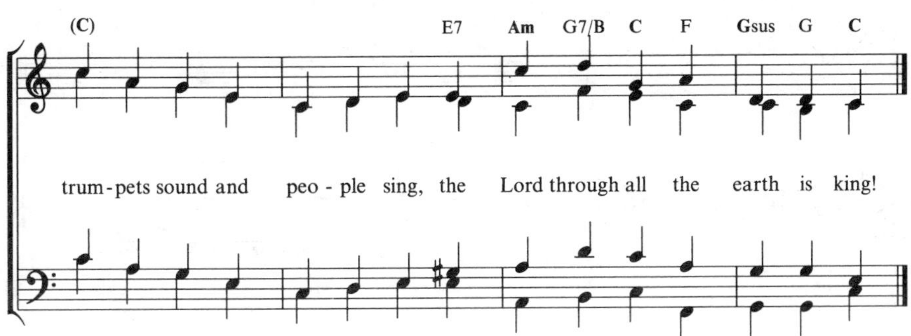
(C) E7 Am G7/B C F Gsus G C
trum - pets sound and peo - ple sing, the Lord through all the earth is king!

285 Tell out, my soul, the greatness of the Lord

Woodlands

Words: from Luke 1 (*The Song of Mary / Magnificat*)
Timothy Dudley-Smith
Music: W Greatorex (1877–1949)

A D G A D

1 Tell out, my soul, the great - ness__ of the Lord!
2 Tell out, my soul, the great - ness__ of his name!
3 Tell out, my soul, the great - ness__ of his might!
4 Tell out, my soul, the glo - ries__ of his word!

A Bm D A7 D Em Em/G F♯

un - num - bered bless - ings give my spi - rit voice;
make known his might, the deeds his arm has done;
powers and do - min - ions lay their glo - ry by.
firm is his pro - mise, and his mer - cy sure.

B7 Em Em7/D A7

ten - der to me the pro - mise of his word;
his mer - cy sure, from age to age the same;
Proud hearts and stub - born wills are put to flight,
Tell out, my soul, the great - ness of the Lord

D G D G A D Em7/G A Asus D

in God my sav - iour shall my heart re - joice.
his ho - ly name – the Lord, the migh - ty one.
the hun - gry fed, the hum - ble lift - ed high.
to child - ren's child - ren and for ev - er - more!

286 The angel Gabriel from heaven came

Gabriel's Message

Words: S Baring Gould (1834–1924)
and in this version Word & Music
Music: Basque noël
arranged C E Pettman (1866–1943)

Am Dm6/A Am Dm6/A Esus E7
1 The an - gel Ga - bri - el from hea - ven came, his
2 'Fear not, for you shall bear a ho - ly child, by
3 Then gen - tle Ma - ry hum - bly bowed her head: 'To
Am Dm6/A Am Dm6 Am/C Esus Em Am
wings as drift - ed snow, his eyes as flame:
him shall we to God be re - con - ciled;
me be as it plea - ses God,' she said,
C Dm/F D7/F♯ G9 G C
'From God, all hail,' the an - gel said to Ma - ry, 'most
his name shall be Em-man - u - el, the long - fore - told: most
'My soul shall praise and mag - ni - fy his ho - ly name.' Most
Dm Esus E7 F Dm7 Am/C Esus Em Am
high - ly fa - voured la - dy!' Glo - ri - a!
high - ly fa - voured la - dy!' Glo - ri - a!
high - ly fa - voured la - dy!' Glo - ri - a!

4 'And so,' she said, 'how happy I shall be!
All generations will remember me;
for God has kept his promises to Israel.'
Most highly favoured lady!
Gloria!

5 Of her, Emmanuel – the Christ – was born
in Bethlehem, upon that Christmas morn.
And Christian folk throughout the world
will ever say,
'Most highly favoured lady!
Gloria!'

287 Tell me, why do you weep

From Matthew 25
Words and music: Graham Kendrick
Music arranged David Peacock

With pace
Chorus
Am
Am/G♯
Am
Am7
Tell me, why do you weep; tell me, why do you mourn; tell me,
Am
Am6
E
Am
Am/G♯
why do you look so sad? Tell me, why don't you dance; tell me,
Am/G
Am/F♯
Am/F
Am/E
Am
E
why don't you sing; tell me, why don't you look to the sky?
Verses
Am
E
1&5 Don't you know that your king is com - ing; don't you
2 Don't you know that the feast is rea - dy – rea - dy
3 Don't you know you are the Lord's in - vi - ted; don't you
4 Come a - rise, my love, my fair - est daugh - ter: the

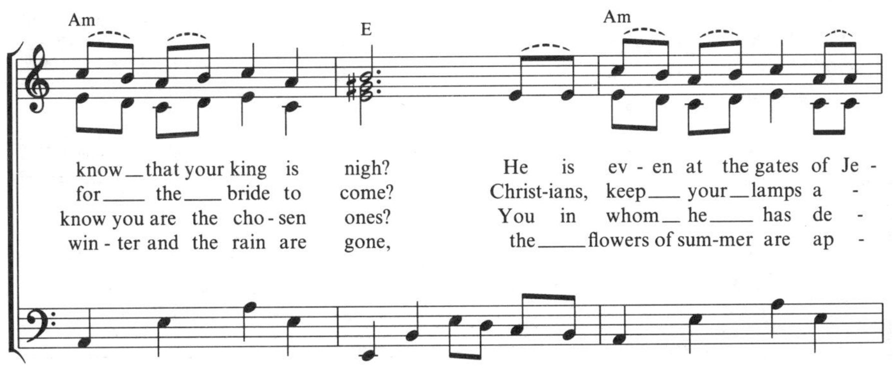
Am
E
Am
know — that your king is nigh? He is ev - en at the gates of Je -
for — the — bride to come? Christ-ians, keep — your — lamps a -
know you are the cho - sen ones? You in whom — he — has de -
win - ter and the rain are gone, the — flowers of sum-mer are ap -

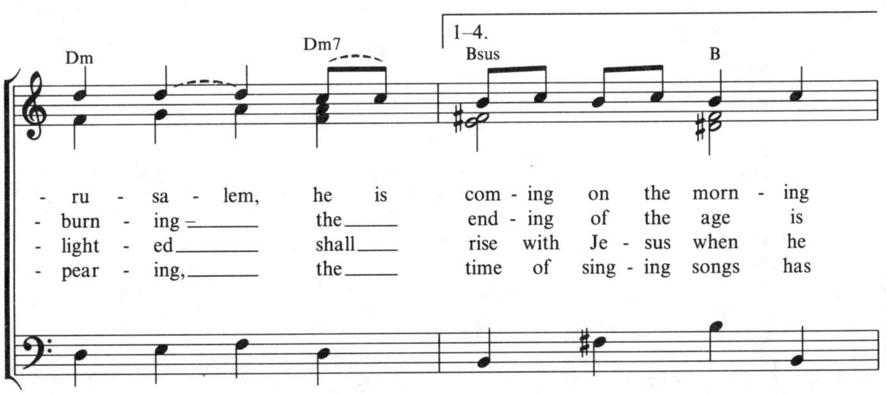
Dm
Dm7
1–4.
Bsus
B
- ru - sa - lem, he is com - ing on the morn - ing
- burn - ing — the — end - ing of the age is
- light - ed — shall — rise with Je - sus when he
- pear - ing, — the — time of sing - ing songs has

E
5.
Bsus/F♯
B
E7
Am
sky.
come.
comes.
come.
Tell me com-ing on the morn - ing sky.

288 The bells ring out at Christmas-time

Sweet Chiming Christmas Bells
Capo 3(C)

Words: Miriam Richards
and in this version Word & Music
Music: Unknown
arranged David Peacock

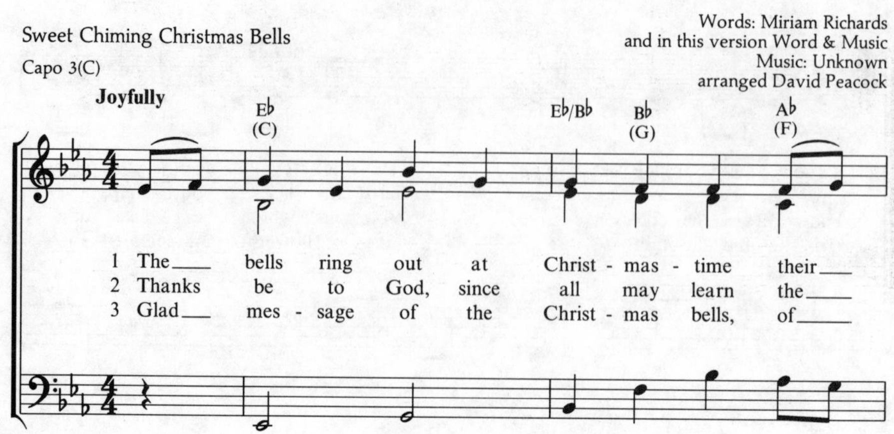

Joyfully
E♭ (C)
E♭/B♭
B♭ (G)
A♭ (F)
1 The___ bells ring out at Christ - mas - time their___
2 Thanks be to God, since all may learn the___
3 Glad___ mes - sage of the Christ - mas bells, of___

Fm7 (Dm7)
B♭7 (G7)
E♭ (C)
E♭7 (C7)
mes - sage loud and clear; our___ hearts are stirred as
bells' ex - ult - ant theme – the___ babe of Beth - le -
God whose name is love – O___ may this mu - sic

Fm (Dm)
B♭7 (G7)
E♭ (C)
on the air the___ joy - ful sound we hear:
- hem was born this___ lost world to re - deem: Ring
all our days our___ hope and com - fort prove!

Ab/Bb (F) Eb/Bb (C) Bb (G) Ab/Bb (F) Eb/Bb (C)
out the Christ - mas bells, ring out the Christ - mas
Bb (G) Eb (C) Fm7 (Dm) Eb/G (C) Ab (F)
bells! The__ sav - iour comes – make straight his way, ring
Eb/Bb (C) Bb (G) Eb (C) Fm7 (Dm7)
out those bells! The__ sav - iour comes – make
Eb (C) Ab (F) Eb/Bb (C) Bb7 (G7) Eb (C)
straight his way, ring out those bells!

289 The darkness turns to dawn

(FIRST TUNE)

Saigon

Words: Timothy Dudley-Smith
Music: Norman Warren

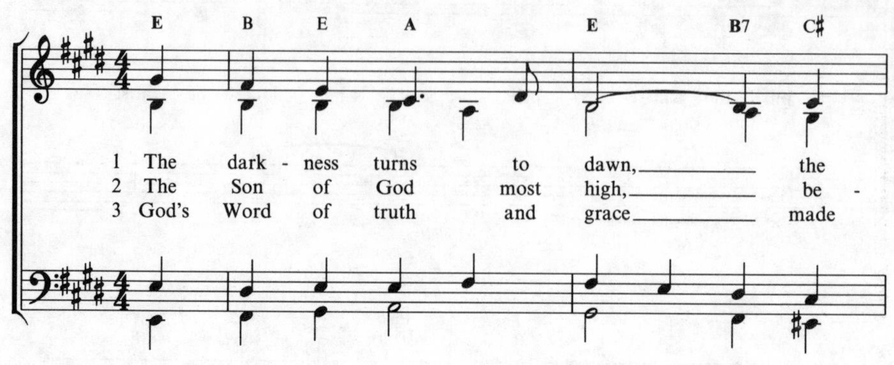
E B E A E B7 C♯
1 The dark - ness turns to dawn, the
2 The Son of God most high, be -
3 God's Word of truth and grace made

F♯m E Bsus B E A/G♯ B7/F♯ G♯m/F♯ C♯m
day - spring shines from heaven; for un - to us a
- fore all else be - gan, a vir - gin's son be -
flesh with us to dwell; the bright - ness of the

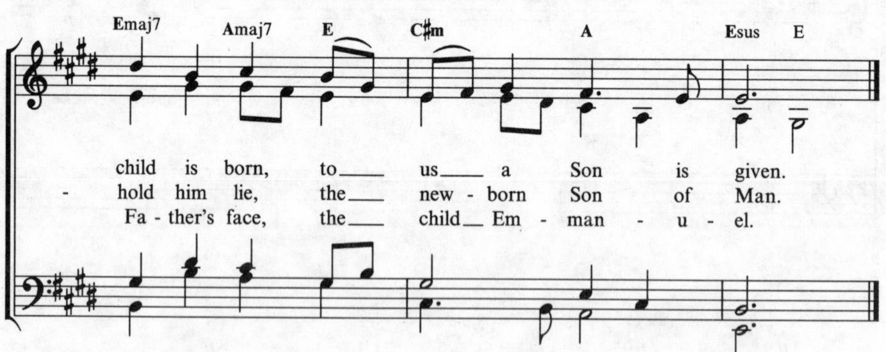
Emaj7 Amaj7 E C♯m A Esus E
child is born, to us a Son is given.
- hold him lie, the new - born Son of Man.
Fa - ther's face, the child Em - man - u - el.

4 How rich his heavenly home!
How poor his human birth!
As mortal man he stoops to come,
the light and life of earth.

5 A servant's form, a slave,
the Lord consents to share;
our sin and shame, our cross and grave,
he bows himself to bear.

6 Obedient and alone
upon that cross to die,
and then to share the Father's throne
in majesty on high.

7 And still God sheds abroad
that love so strong to send
a saviour, who is Christ the Lord,
whose reign shall never end.

290 The darkness turns to dawn

(SECOND TUNE)

Sandys

Words: Timothy Dudley-Smith
Music: English traditional melody
from W Sandys *Christmas Carols* (1833)

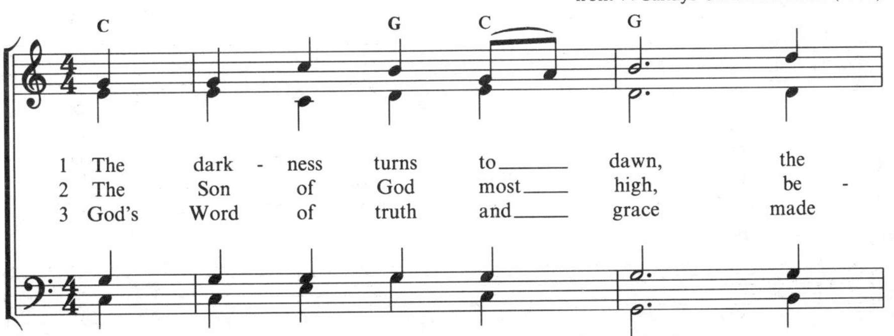

C G C G
1 The dark - ness turns to dawn, the
2 The Son of God most high, be -
3 God's Word of truth and grace made

D7/A G Am D G G7/F C/E F C
day - spring shines from heaven; for un - to us a
- fore all else be - gan, a vir - gin's son be -
flesh with us to dwell; the bright - ness of the

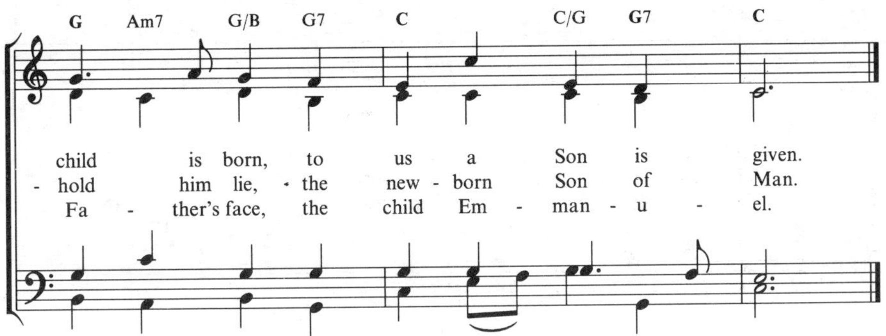

G Am7 G/B G7 C C/G G7 C
child is born, to us a Son is given.
- hold him lie, the new - born Son of Man.
Fa - ther's face, the child Em - man - u - el.

4 How rich his heavenly home!
How poor his human birth!
As mortal man he stoops to come,
the light and life of earth.

5 A servant's form, a slave,
the Lord consents to share;
our sin and shame, our cross and grave,
he bows himself to bear.

6 Obedient and alone
upon that cross to die,
and then to share the Father's throne
in majesty on high.

7 And still God sheds abroad
that love so strong to send
a saviour, who is Christ the Lord,
whose reign shall never end.

291 The earth was dark

Lights to the world

Words and music: John Daniels and Phil Thomson
Music arranged G Baker

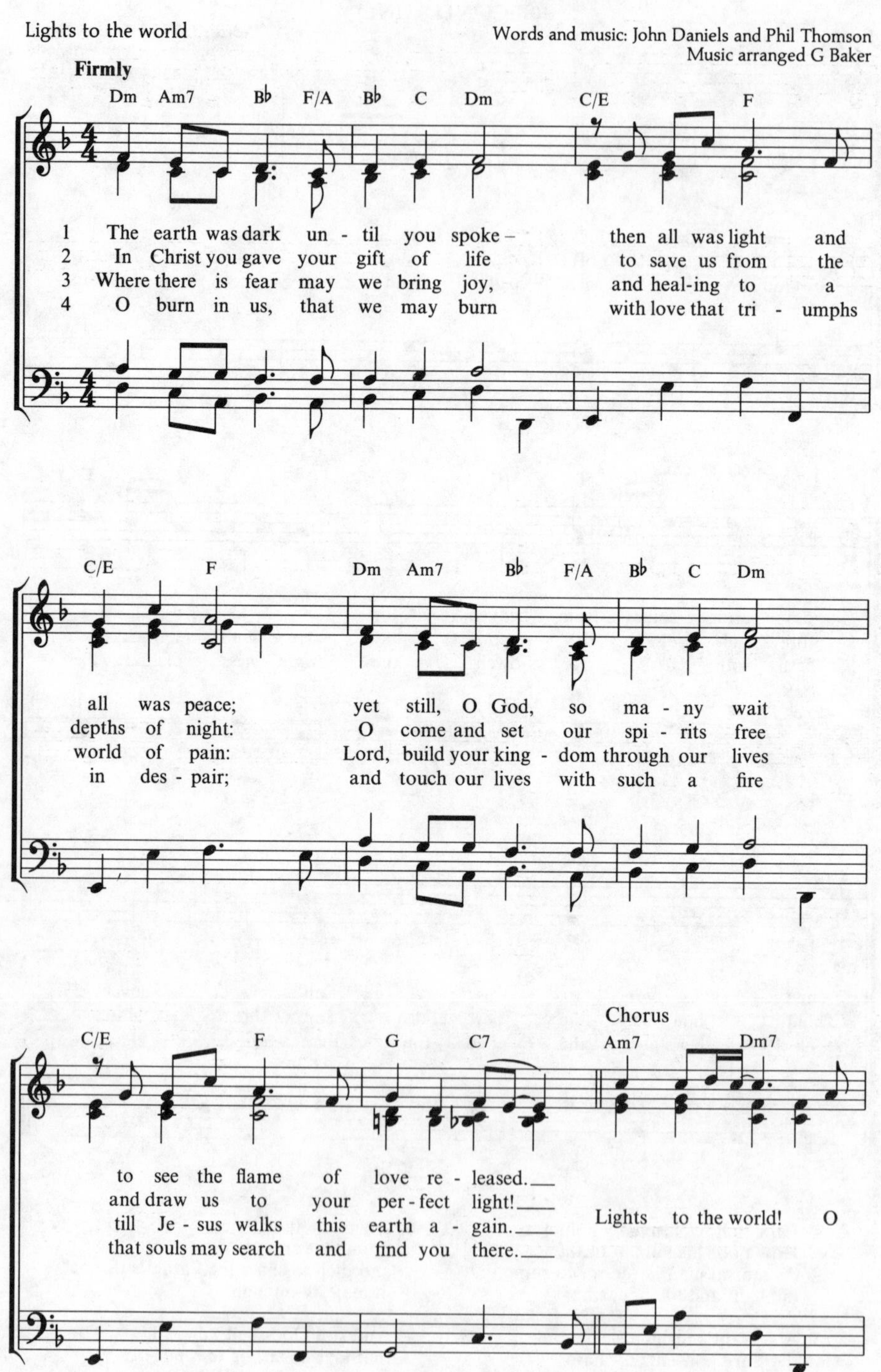

Firmly
Dm Am7 B♭ F/A B♭ C Dm C/E F
1 The earth was dark un - til you spoke – then all was light and
2 In Christ you gave your gift of life to save us from the
3 Where there is fear may we bring joy, and heal-ing to a
4 O burn in us, that we may burn with love that tri - umphs
C/E F Dm Am7 B♭ F/A B♭ C Dm
all was peace; yet still, O God, so ma - ny wait
depths of night: O come and set our spi - rits free
world of pain: Lord, build your king - dom through our lives
in des - pair; and touch our lives with such a fire
C/E F G C7
to see the flame of love re - leased.
and draw us to your per - fect light!
till Je - sus walks this earth a - gain.
that souls may search and find you there.
Chorus
Am7 Dm7
Lights to the world! O

Gm7
C9
C7
Am7
Dm7
Gm7
C9
C
Light di - vine, kin - dle in us a migh - ty flame,

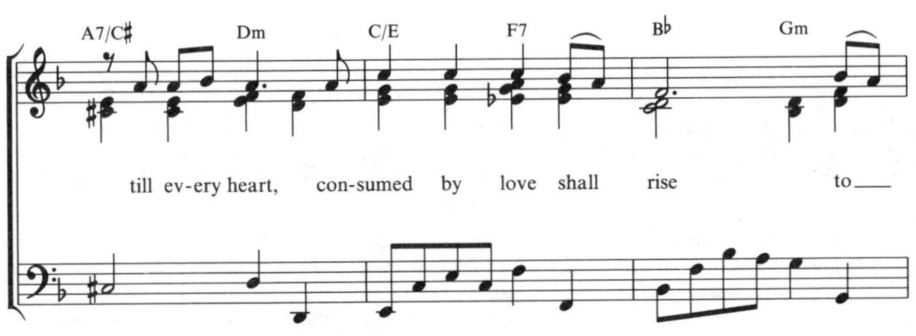
A7/C♯
Dm
C/E
F7
B♭
Gm
till ev-ery heart, con-sumed by love shall rise to

Gm/C
C7
1.2.3.
F
F/A
Gm
B♭/C
C
4.
F
praise your ho - ly name!
name!

292 The first nowell

Words: Unknown (c. seventeenth century)
and in this version Word & Music
Music: English traditional melody
arranged J Stainer (1840–1901)
Descant: Noël Tredinnick

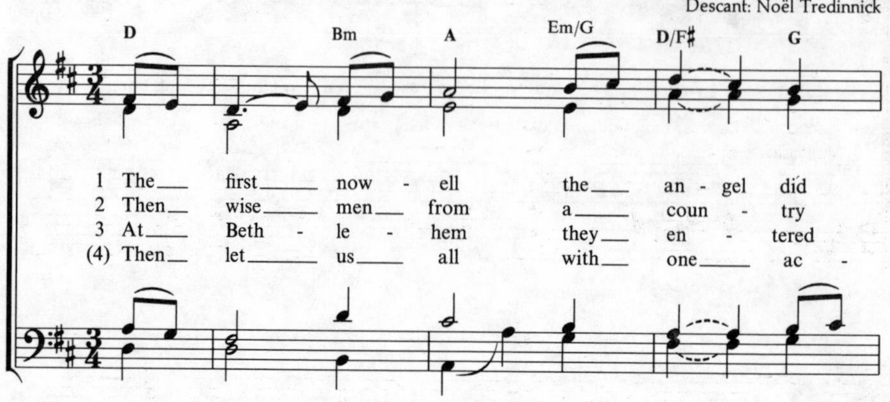
D
Bm
A
Em/G
D/F♯
G
1 The first now - ell the angel did
2 Then wise men from a coun - try
3 At Beth - le - hem they en - tered
(4) Then let us all with one ac -

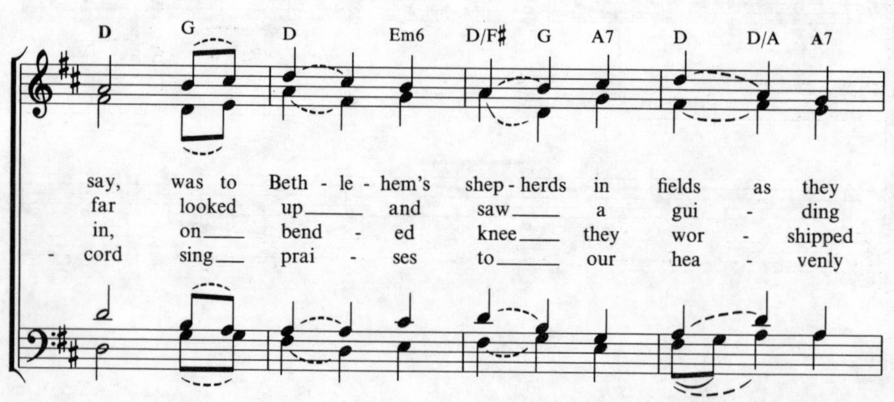
D
G
D
Em6
D/F♯
G
A7
D
D/A
A7
say, was to Beth - le - hem's shep - herds in fields as they
far looked up and saw a gui - ding
in, on bend - ed knee they wor - shipped
- cord sing prai - ses to our hea - venly

D
A7
D
Bm
A
Em/G
D/F♯
G
lay; in fields where they lay keep - ing their
star; they tra - velled on by night and
him; they of - fered there in his pre -
Lord; for Christ has our sal - va - tion

D G D Em6 D/F♯ G A7 D D/A A7 D
sheep on a cold win - ter's night that was so deep:
day to reach the place where Je - sus lay:
- sence their gold and myrrh and frank - in - cense:
wrought and with his blood our life has bought:
A7 D Bm F♯m D G D A
Now - ell, now - ell, now - ell, now - ell,
Bm Dmaj7/A G D A7/E D/F♯ D/A A7 D
born is the king of Is - ra - el!
Descant
A7 Bm G D/F♯ Bm/G♯ Bm7 E7
4 Then let us all with one ac -

A G D/F♯ A/E E/D A/C♯ Em/B F♯7 Bm Em7 A7
- cord sing prai - ses to our hea - venly

D F♯ Bm9 E7 Gm D/F♯ Bm7 Bm/G♯ C♯7
Lord; for Christ has our sal - va - tion

F♯m C♯7 Bm C♯ F♯m G♯dim7 B♭dim7 Bm7 Em7 A7
wrought and with his blood our life has

A little slower
B9
F♯
G9
C9
F9
D/F♯
bought: Now - ell, now - ell, now -
ff
G♯m
C♯7
F♯m
Em
A7
Bm/G♯
C♯7
- ell, now - ell, born is the
F♯m
Em
A7
F7
Em7
E♭7
D9
D
king of Is - ra - el!
rit.

293 The God we seek

Christopher

Words: B Rees (1911–1983)
Music: David Peacock

Flowing

Em
Am
1 The God we seek, be - yond all thought, has
2 Love is the man - ger where he lies,
(3) - to the love of Christ the king our

D7
Gmaj7
Em/C♯
now his Christ - mas won - der wrought: be - hold, the seek -
love is the cross on which he dies: strong - er than death
lives, our world, in faith we bring: the sin, the pain,

F♯
Bsus
B
- er is the sought!
shall love a - rise!
the suf - fer - ing.

Am7
D
Gmaj7
Wait - ing end - ed, earth be -
Glor - ious meek - ness, power in
God es - teems us, Christ re -
Cmaj7
F♯m7
G/A
- friend - ed – Je - sus is born!
weak - ness – Je - sus is born!
- deems us – Je - sus is born!
A/B
1.2.
E
Am7
A/B
Bsus
3.
E
2 -
3 In -

294 The heaviness of travel

The birthplace of the King
Words and music: Don Wyrtzen
Gently, not too fast
Dm Dm7 G7 Gm7
1 The hea - vi - ness of tra - vel to an
2 No roy - al home was o - pen to the
Dm/A Am7 Dm
o - ver - crowd - ed town had
wea - ry man and his wife, but
Dm7 G7 Gm7
pressed down on the sim - ple girl, who
on - ly a sta - ble cave was left to
Dm/A Am7 Dm
rode with - out a sound; al -
greet the cry of life; the

slightly faster
F G F G
- rea - dy now the qui - et pain of
sheep and ox - en shared the joy that
F G Asus A7
a tempo
child - birth had be - gun, and
made all hea - ven sing: that
Dm Dm7 G7 Gm7
all the inns turned them a - way was there no
straw - strewn cave was changed in - to the
Dm/A Am7 Dm
room for God's on - ly Son?
birth - place of the King.

295 The holly and the ivy

Words: traditional
and in this version Word & Music
Music: English traditonal melody
arranged Noël Tredinnick
Capo 3(D)
Merrily
f
resoluto
F (D)
Gm (Em)
F (D)
B♭ (G)
F9 (D9)
Dm (Bm)
Gm (Em)
1 The holly and the ivy when they are both full
2 The holly bears a blossom as white as any
3 The holly bears a berry as red as any
C (A)
F (D)
B♭ (G)
Am (F♯m)
Dm (Bm)
Gm9 (Em9)
C7 (A7)
B♭ (G)
Am (F♯m)
grown – of all the trees that are in the wood, the holly bears the crown.
flower; and Mary bore sweet Jesus Christ to be our sweet saviour.
blood; and Mary bore sweet Jesus Christ to die for all our good.
Chorus
Gm (Em)
F (D)
Gm7 (Em7)
Am7 (F♯7)
B♭ (G)
Am (F♯m)
Dm (Bm)
4 part choir (optional keyboard)
Oh, the rising of the sun and the
Keyboard

Gsus (Esus)
G7 (E7)
C (A)
F (D)
A7 (F♯7)
run-ning of the deer, the___ play-ing of the
B♭ (G)
Am (F♯m)
Dm (Bm)
Gm7 (Em7)
C7 (A7)
F (D)
mer - ry or - gan, sweet sing - ing in the choir!
8va

4 The holly bears a prickle,
as sharp as any thorn;
and Mary bore sweet Jesus Christ
to wear a cruel crown.
Oh, the rising . . .

5 The holly bears a bark
as bitter as any gall;
and Mary bore sweet Jesus Christ
to suffer for us all.
Oh, the rising . . .

6 The holly and the ivy
when they are both full grown –
of all the trees that are in the wood,
the holly bears the crown.
Oh, the rising . . .

296 The light of Christ

From John 3 etc
Words and music: Don Fishel
Music arranged Noël Tredinnick
Flowing
Chorus
A D Bm Em
2nd part The light of Christ has
The light of Christ has come in -
last time to Coda
Asus A7 D
come in - to the world, the
- to the world, the light of
Bm G D Em A7 D D7
light of Christ has come.
Christ has come in - to the world. (v.3 The)

Verses
G
Em
F♯m
Bm
1 We all must be born a - gain to
2 God gave up his on - ly Son out of
(3) light of God has come to us so that
G
A7
D
G
A7
see the king - dom of God; the wa - ter and the
love for the world, so that all those who be -
we might have sal - va - tion; from the dark - ness of our
D
Bm
Em
A7
Spi - rit bring new life in God's love.
- lieve in him will live for ev - er. The
sins we walk in - to glo - ry with Christ Je - sus.
CODA
Bm
G
D
Em
A7
D
light of Christ has come.
Christ has come in - to the world.

297 The little baby Jesus is asleep

Baby Jesus

Words and music: Alice Pullen (1889–1983)
Words in this version Word & Music
Music arranged David Peacock

Quietly and lightly

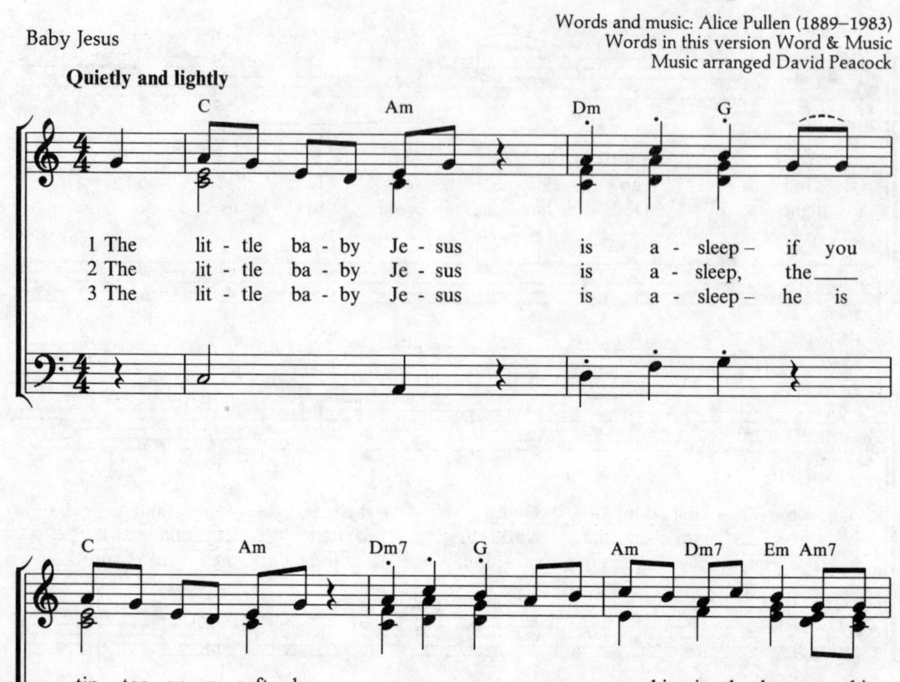

C Am Dm G
1 The lit - tle ba - by Je - sus is a - sleep – if you
2 The lit - tle ba - by Je - sus is a - sleep, the
3 The lit - tle ba - by Je - sus is a - sleep – he is
C Am Dm7 G Am Dm7 Em Am7
tip - toe ve - ry soft - ly you may peep: can you see him in the hay on this
shep-herds in the fields have left their sheep; they have heard the an-gels sing, and have
far too small to walk, or e - ven creep; but the sto - ry's just be - gun for he

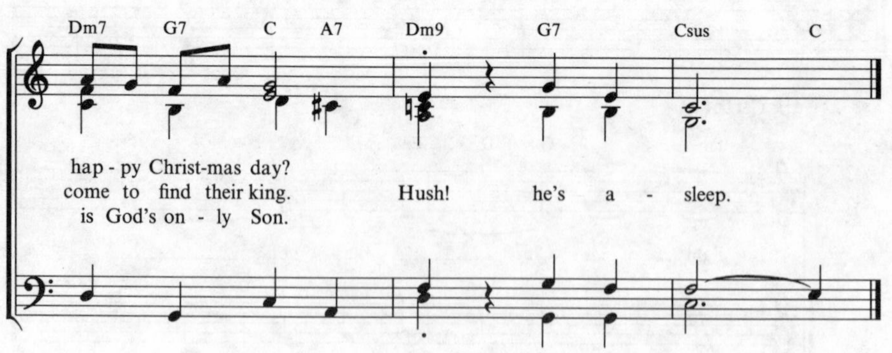

Dm7 G7 C A7 Dm9 G7 Csus C
hap - py Christ-mas day?
come to find their king. Hush! he's a - sleep.
is God's on - ly Son.

298 The people who in darkness walked

Words: from Isaiah 9
J Morison (1750–1798) and in this version Jubilate Hymns
Music: *Scottish Psalter*, Edinburgh (1615)

Dundee

Capo 3(C)

E♭ (C) A♭ (F) B♭ (G) E♭ (C) D♭ (B♭) B♭ (Gm) A♭ (F) E♭ (C)
1 The peo - ple who in dark - ness walked have
2 To greet you, Sun of right - eous - ness, the
3 For now to us a child is born, to
B♭ (G) Cm (Am) A♭ (F) B♭ (G) E♭ (C) B♭ (G) Cm (Am) B♭ (G)
seen a glor - ious light: that light shines out on
gath - ering na - tions come; re - joic - ing as when
us a son is given; and on his shoul - der
Cm7 (Am7) F (D) B♭ (G) E♭ (C) Fm (Dm) Cm (Am) B♭ (G) E♭ (C)
those who lived in sha - dows of the night.
reap - ers bring their har - vest trea - sures home.
ev - er rests all power in earth and heaven.

4 His name shall be the prince of peace,
eternally adored;
most wonderful of counsellors,
the great and mighty Lord.

5 His peace and righteous government
shall over all extend;
on judgement and on justice based,
his reign shall never end.

299 The Lord is king

Capo 4(C)

Words and music: Graham Kendrick

Triumphantly
E (C) Asus2 (G) A (F) E (C)
The Lord is king, he is migh - ty in bat - tle,
A (F) E (C) C♯m (Am) F♯m (Dm)
work-ing won - ders, glor-ious in ma - jes -
F♯m/B (G) E/B (G) A/B (G) B7 (G7) E (C) Asus2 (G) A (F) E (C)
- ty. The Lord is king – so ma - jes - tic in pow - er!
A (F) E (C) C♯m (Am) F♯m (Dm) B7 (G7)
His right hand has shat-tered the en - e - my.

E (C)
G♯m7 (Em7)
F♯m7 (Dm7)
B (G)
E (C)
G♯m7 (Em7)
1st part
This is my God and I will praise him;
2nd part
This is my God
F♯m7 (Dm7)
B (G)
E (C)
G♯m7 (Em7)
F♯m7 (Dm7)
B (G)
My strength and song and my sal - va -
and I will praise him;
E (C)
G♯m7 (Em7)
F♯m7 (Dm7)
A (F)
B7 (G7)
E (C)
- tion, and my sal - va - tion.
my strength and song and my sal - va - tion.

300 The shepherd guards his sheep

Battle Hymn
Words: Michael Perry
Music: American traditional melody
arranged Noël Tredinnick
Capo 3(G)
Bb (G) C (A) Bb/F (G) F (D) Bb (G) F7 (D7) Bb (G) F7 (D7) Bb (G) Gm (Em)
1 The shep-herd guards his sheep up - on the
2 The wise man in the east is glad to
3 So let us make our plea-sure hum-ble
Cm7 (Am7) F7 (D7) Bb (G) Eb (C) Gm7 (Em7) Cm7 (Am7)
hill - side late at night – he is wo - ken from his sleep to see a
see the shin - ing star – he is sad - dling up his beast to go to
ser - vice to the king as we of - fer him our trea - sure and the
F7 (D7) Bb (G) F7 (D7) Bb (G)
flash of blind - ing light, a voice that makes him leap pro-claims the
Beth - le-hem a - far: we find our king and priest, sal - va - tion
prai - ses that we bring: with love in full - est mea - sure God has

Gm (Em) D7 (B7) Gm (Em) Cm7 (Am7) E♭/F (C) F7 (D7) B♭ (G)
news with great de-light that Je - sus Christ is born!
comes where sin - ners are as Je - sus Christ is born!
blessed us – so we sing that Je - sus Christ is born!
F7 (D7) B♭ (G) Gm7 (Em7) Cm (Am) F7 (D7) B♭ (G)
Glo - ry, glo - ry, al - le - lu - ia;
E♭ (C) F7 (D7) B♭ (G) F7 (D7) B♭ (G)
glo - ry, glo - ry, al - le - lu - ia; glo - ry, glo - ry, al - le -
1.2. 3.
Gm (Em) D7 (B7) Gm (Em) Cm7 (Am7) E♭/F (C) F7 (D7) B♭ (G) B♭(G)
- lu - ia – for Je - sus Christ is born! born!

301 The sky shall unfold

We shall behold him

Words and music: Dottie Rambo

Hushed, with expression
F
C/E
Dm7/G
mp
1 The sky shall un -
(2) an - gel shall
mp
mp
C
G/B
F/A G G/F
C/E
G/D
- fold pre - par - ing his en - trance, the
sound the shout of his com - ing, the
C
G/B
Am
Am7/G
Am/F♯
D9
stars will ap - plaud him with thun - ders of
sleep - ing will rise from their slum - ber - ing

Dm7/G F/G C G/B
praise; the sweet light in his eyes shall en -
place; and those who re - main shall be
F/A G G/F C/E G/D C F♯dim
- hance those a - wait - ing, we shall be -
changed in a mo - ment, and we shall be -
C/G Am F/G G7 F/C C
- hold him then, face to face.
- hold him then, face to face.
Chorus
Dm7/G C Em7 F G G/F
mf
We shall be - hold him, we shall be -
mf

C/E G/D C F
- hold him – face to
Em7 Fmaj7 F6 Am/F♯ Dm7/G F/G Dm7/G
face in all of his glo - ry; we shall be -
C Em7 F G G/F C/E
- hold him, we shall be - hold
2nd time to Coda
G/D C F♯dim C/G
him, face to face,

Am7
Dm7
G7
F/C
C
Dm7/G
our sav-iour and Lord!
mp
2 The
CODA
F♯dim
C/G
Am7
Dm7
Dm7/G
E7/G♯
face to face,
our sav-iour and
Am
Am7/G
Am/F♯
D9
C/G
Lord;
face to face,
Am7
Dm7
Dm7/G
G7
C
E♭/B♭
A♭maj7
D♭maj9
C
cresc.
f
our sav-iour and Lord!
8va

302 The star in the east

From Matthew 2
Words and music: David Jenkins
Music arranged David Peacock

Moderate, bright tempo
E C♯m Amaj7 A6 G♯m7 C♯m
1 The star in the east shone__ bright o - ver Beth - le - hem,
2 The star in the east, so____ bright o - ver Beth - le - hem,
3 The time will___ come when the star of____ Beth - le - hem
F♯m7 F♯m7/B B7 E A E
clear in the eve - ning sky;
shines in the world to - day;
gleams once a - gain in the sky;
C♯m Amaj7 A6 G♯m7 C♯m
that was the night when they heard____ in Beth - le - hem the
Je - sus____ Christ, who was born____ in Beth - le - hem___
and on that night____ the star____ of Beth - le - hem will
F♯m7 F♯m7/B B7 A/E E
sound of a ba - by's cry:
shows us the right - eous way:
shine like a flame on high: and

C♯m
A
G♯7/B♯
C♯m
for there was born in a hum - ble man - ger an
lead - ers may rise with their new phi - lo - so - phies, but
who will re - turn to a new cre - a - tion, and
Bm7
Bm6
Amaj7
B7
un - known child, just a lit - tle stran - ger. But
deep in our hearts are the an - cient pro - phe - sies that
bring to a suf - fer - ing world sal - va - tion? The
E/G♯
B
E
B/D♯
C
E/B
three wise men who came and a - dored,
God's own Son the wise men a - dored is
king the three wise men a - dored
Amaj7
B7
A/E
E
knew he was Christ, our Lord.
des - tined to be our Lord.
Je - sus Christ our Lord.

303 The stars danced

Words and music: Barbara Gillard
Music arranged V Fleetwood

With an easy swing
Verses
G Em Am D G Em Am D
1 The stars danced, the an-gels sang the night God came to earth; the whole vault of hea-ven rang to ce-le-brate his birth.
2 Ma-ry, his mo-ther, smiled to see her babe new-born. Shep-herds came hur-ry-ing, left their flocks for-lorn.
3 Wise men who saw his star, knew their Lord was here, came with their of-fer-ings, in-cense, gold and myrrh.
4 We too will give to him, gifts of love and praise, dance for him, sing for him, re-joice in him al-ways.
Chorus
G Em Am D
We will dance, we will sing, we will praise our heaven-ly king at his birth.
1.2.3. G
4. G
birth.

Words and music: © St Paul's Outreach Trust †

304 The story has broken

The ash grove
Capo 5(C)
Words: Michael Perry
Music: Welsh traditional melody
arranged Norman Warren
Obligato: David Peacock
Flute obligato
C7 (G7) F (C) C7 (G7) F (C) Gm7 (Dm7)
1 The story has broken, an angel has
3 The shepherds returning, and wise men of
C (G) F (C) B♭ (F)
spoken, and this is the token that
learning their saviour discerning, his
F/C (C) C7 (G7) F (C) C7 (G7) F (C) C7 (G7) F (C)
Jesus is here: he comes as a stranger re-
praises will sing: as those who first saw him and

Gm7
(Dm7)
C
(G)
F
(C)
- gard - less of dan - ger, the Lord in a
knelt down be - fore him, so let us a -
B♭
(F)
F/C
(C)
C7
(G7)
F
(C)
C
(G)
man - ger, the babe with - out peer. 2 O coun - sel of
- dore him and wor - ship our king. 4 O in - fin - ite
Dm7
(Bm7)
Gm
(Em)
C7
(G7)
F
(C)
splen-dour, O sac - ri - fice ten - der, that God should sur -
trea - sure, O love with - out mea - sure, it is God's good

Dm7 (Am7) C/G (G) G7 (D7) C (G) C7 (G7) F (C) C7 (G7)
- ren - der to us in this way – his pur - pose re -
plea - sure to give us his Son, the source of cre -
F (C) Gm7 (Em7) C (G)
- veal - ing, his pro - mi - ses seal - ing, the
- a - tion, the hope of each na - tion, the
F (C) B♭ (F) F/C (C) 8va C7 (G7) Fsus (Csus) F (C)
pledge of our heal - ing, the dawn of our day!
great ju - bil - a - tion of hea - ven be - gun!

305 The virgin Mary had a baby boy

The virgin Mary
Words: West Indian carol
Music: West Indian traditional melody
collected by Hal Evans and Edric Connor
arranged Noël Tredinnick
Capo 3(D)
With Carribean lilt
F(D)
Eb/F (C)
Em/F (C#m)
Introduction and link
organ
con ped.
Gm7 (Em7) C7 (A7) Bb/D (G) C7/E (A7) F (D) Gm (Em)
1 The vir - gin Ma - ry had a
2 The an - gels sang when the
3 The shep - herds came where the
C (A) Dm7 (Bm7) C/E (A) Gm7 (Em7) C7 (A7)
ba - by boy, the vir - gin Ma - ry had a
ba - by was born, the an - gels sang when the
ba - by was born, the shep - herds came where the
F (D) Gm7 (Em7) F/A (D) Cm7 (Am7) F7 (D7)
ba - by boy, the vir - gin Ma - ry had a
ba - by was born, the an - gels sang when the
ba - by was born, the shep - herds came where the

B♭
(G)
E♭9
(C9)
Gm
(Em)
C7
(A7)
ba - by boy___ and they say that his name is
ba - by was born___ and they sang that his name is
ba - by was born___ and they say that his name is
B♭
(G)
A♭
(F)
F♯
(E♭)
F
(D)
Chorus
Je - sus.
Je - sus. He come from the
Je - sus.
Gm7
(Em7)
C7
(A7)
F
(D)
Dm
(Bm)
Gm7
(Em7)
C7
(A7)
F
(D)
glo - ry,___ he come from the glo-ri-ous king-dom;
F♯9
(E♭9)
Gm
(Em)
C7
(A7)
Dm
(Bm)
G
(E)
A
(F♯)
(Yes!) he come from the glo - ry,___ he come from the

Dm (Bm) Gm7 (Em7) C7 (A7) F (D)
*
B♭ (G) Gm7 (Em7) C7 (A7) Am (F♯m)
glo - ri - ous king - dom:
f(p) O yes, be - lie - ver!
F/A (D) B♭ (G) C7 (A7) Am7 (F♯m7)
(+ perc.)
Gm7 (Em7) C (A)
p(f) O yes, be - lie - ver!
He come from the
Dm (Bm) G7dim5/D♭ (E7dim5) Am/C (F♯m) B7 (G♯7) B♭ (G) Gm7 (Em7) C7 (A7) F (D)
glo - ry,
he come from the glo - ri - ous king - dom.

West Indian percussion instruments may be used playing [rhythm] but should be tacet for 4 bars from *

306 The wise may bring their learning

Tyrolese Carol

Words: Unknown
in this version Word & Music
Music arranged David Peacock

G C D D7 Bm7 Em Am7 D7
1 The wise may bring their learn - ing, the rich may bring their
2 We'll bring the ma - ny du - ties we have to do each
3 We'll bring him hearts that love him, we'll bring him thank - ful
G D7 G C D D7 Bm7 Em Am7 D7
wealth, and some may bring their great - ness, and some their strength and
day, we'll try our best to please him, at home, at work, at
praise, and lives for ev - er stri - ving to fol - low in his
G D D7 G Am7 D7 G Em
health; we too would bring our trea - sures to of - fer to the
play; and bet - ter are these trea - sures to of - fer to the
ways; and these shall be the trea - sures we of - fer to the
D D7 G C D D7 Bm7 Em Am7 D7 G
king: how shall we greet our sav - iour, what pres-ents shall we bring?
king, than rich - est gifts with - out them - yet these we all may bring.
king, the gifts that now and ev - er our grate-ful hearts may bring!

307 There is a Redeemer

Words and music: Melody Green
Music arranged David Peacock

Flowing
optional 2nd part
D A/D D G/D D
1 There is a Re - deem - er,
2 Je - sus, my Re - deem - er,
3 When I stand in glo - ry,
con ped.
Em7 G/A A7 D Asus A7 D A/D D
Je - sus, God's own Son, pre - cious Lamb of
name a - bove all names, pre - cious Son of
I will see his face and there I'll serve my
G D/F♯ Em7 Asus A7 D D/F♯ G A7
God, Mes - si - ah, ho - ly One.
God, Mes - si - ah, Lamb for sin - ners slain:
king for ev - er in that ho - ly place.

Chorus
D D/F♯ G D Em7 G/A A7
Thank you, O my Fa - ther, for giv-ing us your
Thank you, O my Fa - ther, for giv-ing us your
D Em7/G A D Dmaj7/F♯ G D/F♯
Son, and leav - ing your Spi - rit till the
Son, and leav - ing your Spi - rit till the
1.2. 3.
Em7 Asus A7 D D/F♯ G A7 D
work on earth is done. done.
work on earth is done. done.

308 There's a bright sky over Bethlehem

Marloes

Quite slow

Words: Michael Perry
Music: Roger Mayor

obligato (violin, oboe, etc.)
G
Am7
Am7/D
D7
mp
mf
mp
1 There's a
G
G/B
C
bright sky o - ver Beth - le - hem, where
(2) sav - iour come to Beth - le - hem, a
(3) star high o - ver Beth - le - hem – the
(4) sign for us in Beth - le - hem, for
Bm
C
Dsus
D
shep - herds watch up - on the hill: and the
ba - by laid up - on the hay: in a
wise men start up - on the road: bear - ing
we re - joice at Christ-mas - tide to re -

Am/C
G/B
mp
mf
hea - vens ring as an - gels sing of
sta - ble bare no com - fort where the
gold and myrrh and in - cense rare they
- ceive our Lord, God's liv - ing Word, our
1.2.3
Asus A7 Am7/D D Gsus G
mp
peace on earth and God's good - will!
Christ is born this ho - ly day.
come to find the Son of God.
love, our light, our friend, our
mp
4.
Gsus
Am7 Am7/D D7 G
mf
2 There's a
3 There's a
4 There's a
guide!

309 There's a Saviour to see

Rise up shepherd and follow

Words: traditional
and in this version Word & Music
Music: traditional melody
arranged David Peacock

Lively
D
Bm
G
Asus
A
1 There's a Sav - iour to see on Christ - mas morn –
2 If you take good heed to the an - gel's words –
D
C
Asus
A
rise up, shep - herd, and fol - low; we will
rise up, shep - herd, and fol - low, you'll for -
Bm
G
D
G
E7
show you the place where the Child is born –
- get your flocks, you'll for - get your herds –
D/A
Em/A
G/D
D
D
D/C♯
D/B
D/A
rise up shep-herd and fol - low!
rise up, shep-herd, and fol - low!
Leave your sheep and

G D D C Asus A
leave your lambs – rise up, shep-herd, and fol - low;
D D/C♯ D/B D/A G A Bm E7 D/A G6
leave your sheep and leave your rams – rise up, shep-herd, and
G/D D G D
fol - low! Fol - low, fol - low,
C Asus A D D/C♯ D/B D/A
rise up, shep-herd, and fol - low, hark to the an - gels of
G F♯m/A Bm E7 D Em Em/A G/D D
Beth - le - hem – rise up, shep-herd, and fol - low!

310 These were the words

From Genesis 3 etc
Words and music: Chris Voke

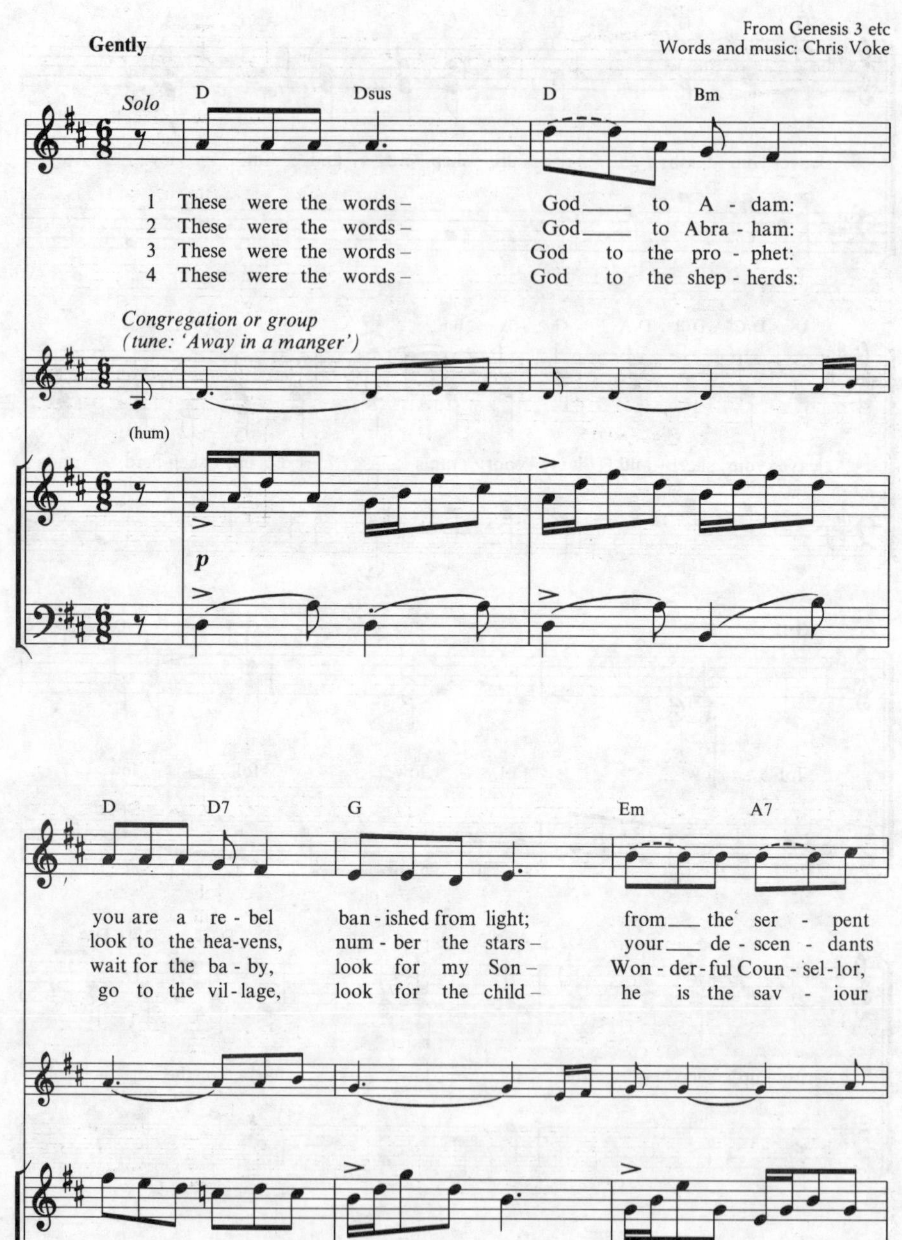

Gently
Solo
D Dsus D Bm
1 These were the words – God to A - dam:
2 These were the words – God to Abra - ham:
3 These were the words – God to the pro - phet:
4 These were the words – God to the shep - herds:
Congregation or group
(tune: 'Away in a manger')
(hum)
p
D D7 G Em A7
you are a re - bel ban - ished from light; from the ser - pent
look to the hea-vens, num - ber the stars – your de - scen - dants
wait for the ba - by, look for my Son – Won - der - ful Coun - sel - lor,
go to the vil - lage, look for the child – he is the sav - iour

D Bm E E7 A A7
and___ his e - vil___ you will find death and sor-row and night.
shall be as ma - ny; but One___shall shine much brigh-ter than all.
God___ so Migh - ty, E - ter - nal Fa-ther, yet Prince of peace.
born___ a-mong you,___ God in a sta - ble, far from the light.

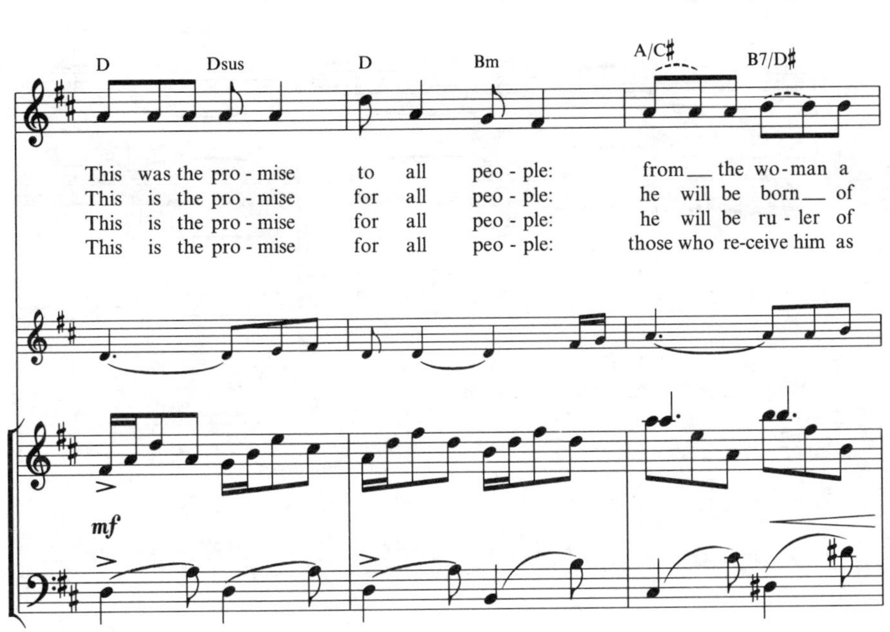
D Dsus D Bm A/C♯ B7/D♯
This was the pro - mise to all peo - ple: from___ the wo-man a
This is the pro - mise for all peo - ple: he will be born___ of
This is the pro - mise for all peo - ple: he will be ru - ler of
This is the pro - mise for all peo - ple: those who re-ceive him as
mf

Em
Em7
A7
D
Bm
sav - iour will come; by his liv - ing and his dy - ing
Ab - ra-ham's line, he will bring back the bless - ing of hea-ven to
hea - ven and earth; his great king - dom and his pow-er shall
Je - sus the Lord, he gives mer - cy, life, and pow-er to
1.2.3
4.
Dsus
D
he will bring life a - gain.
ev - ery fam - ily on earth.
ne - ver be ta - ken a - way.
be a child of God. (...the
(...the
pp
Dmaj7
lit - tle Lord Je - sus a - sleep on the hay.)
lit - tle Lord Je - sus a - sleep on the hay.)
dim.
ppp

311 Today the Christ is born

Hodie

Words and music: Anthony Greening

Brightly
Chorus (All)
D D/C♯ Bm Dmaj7/A Gmaj7 Em7 A A7 D C Am
*Sing in praise of God _ to - day: _ our sav - iour Christ is ___
D
Fine
born!
Verses (solo or choir)
D G Em D A/C♯
1 To - day the Christ is ___ born, to -
2 To - day the just re - joice, to -
3 To - day sing praise to ___ God – the
Bm Em Asus A D C D/F♯
- day our ___ sav - iour comes; to - day the an - gels
- day they ___ join in song – 'To God on high ___ be
Fa - ther ___ and the Son, who with the Spi - rit
G Em6 F♯m7 Bm Em7 A7 D
D.C.
sing, arch - an - gels chant ___ their joy.
praise, on earth as now ___ in heaven!'
reign for ev - er Three ___ in One:

*Original text: Jubilate Deo:/Salvator natus est.

312 This earth belongs to God

Trumpet Voluntary
Words from Psalm 24
Christopher Idle
Music: J Clarke (c.1674–1707)
arranged Noël Tredinnick
March style
1 This earth be - longs to God, the world, its wealth, and all its peo - ple; he formed the wa - ters wide and fash - ioned ev - ery sea and shore.
2 Lift high your heads, you gates, rise up, you ev - er - last - ing doors, as here now the king of glo - ry en - ters in - to full com - mand.
3 Lift high your heads, you gates, and fling wide o - pen the an - cient doors, for here comes the king of glo - ry tak - ing u - ni - ver - sal power.
4 All glo - ry be to God the Fa - ther, Son, and Ho - ly Spi - rit; from a - ges past it was, is now, and ev - er - more shall be.
Fine

Chorus
A
(G)
A
(G)
(GROUP A)
Who may go up the hill of the Lord and
Who is the king, this king of glo - ry,
Who is the king, this king of glo - ry,
A
E
stand in the place of ho - li - ness?
where is the throne he comes to claim?
what is the power by which he reigns?
(D)
E
(D)
(GROUP B)
On - ly the one whose heart is pure, whose
Christ is the king, the Lord of glo - ry,
Christ is the king, his cross his glo - ry,
E
F♯m
Bsus
B7
E
D.C.
hands and lips are clean.
fresh from his vic - to - ry.
and by love he rules.

313 This night a miracle happened

This night a miracle
Capo 3(A)
Words and music: Elaine Davies
Music arranged David Peacock
Rhythmically
Chorus
C(A) F(D) C(A)
This night a mi - ra - cle hap - pened – a
G7 (E7) C (A) Csus (Asus) C (A) Csus (Asus)
boy child was born.
C (A) F (D) C (A)
Go spread the news: from to - day a new
last time to Coda
B♭ (G) C (A) Csus (Asus) C (A) Csus (Asus)
e - ra will dawn.

Verses
Fm
(Dm)
Cm
(Am)
Fm
(Dm)
1 Glor-ious things to - night are hap - pen- ing – who can dis - be-lieve their
2 An - gels sing their heaven-ly cho - ru - ses to the babe, the King of
Cm
(Am)
Fm
(Dm)
Cm
(Am)
sight? roy - al kings will pay him hom - age, yes,
kings – he who is the truth and glo - ry, a
D.C.
Fm
(Dm)
G
(E)
com - ing to find this town to - night!
light to the dark-ness he will bring.
For,
CODA
C
(A)
Csus
(Asus)
C
(A)
Csus
(Asus)
C
(A)
dawn.

314 Though Mary of Nazareth

From Christmas Jazz
Words and music: Kenneth Cartwright

Capo 3(D)
Simply, but not too slowly
Gm7 (Em7) C7 (A7) Am7 (F♯m7) Dm7 (Bm7)
B♭ (G) D♭ (B♭) F9 (D9)
F (D) B♭maj7 (Gmaj7)
1 Though Ma - ry of Naz - ar - eth, that
2 They bor - rowed a don - key to
3 On a clear fros - ty night to this
4 At last in a sta - ble they
Em7 (C♯m7) Am (F♯m) Dm7 (Bm7)
mai - den so mild, was told by an
help get them there, their cloth - ing and
place in Ju - dea Ma - ry and
find room to rest. A place for a

Gaug (Eaug) C (A) Dm7 (Bm7) Em7 (C♯m7) Fmaj7 (Dmaj7)
an - gel that she was with child, to
bed - ding and lug - gage to bear. They
Jo - seph and don - key drew near. But
ba - by? It's hard - ly the best! But
Bm7 (G♯m7) B♭m (Gm) E♭7 (C7) A♭ (F)
Beth - le - hem ci - ty to go she was
tra - velled on foot on a rough dus - ty
when they ar - rived at the inn they did
there in that sta - ble that first Christ - mas
D♭ (B♭) Gm7 (Em7) Cm7 (Am7) Fm (Dm) D♭ (B♭)
told to jour - ney with Jo - seph through
road, for three days and nights they
find no com - fort or shield from the
morn, while peo - ple were sleep - ing,
Cm7 (Am7) 1.2.3. F(D) 4. F(D)
nights bleak and cold.
toiled with their load.
cold win - ter wind.
Je - sus was born.

315 Through our God

Victory Song
Capo 3(Am)
From Psalm 108
Words and music: Dale Garratt
Resolutely with steady pace
Cm(Am)
G7(E7)
(Descant (2nd time)) Ah
Through our God we shall do val - iant-ly, it is
Ah
he who will tread down our e - ne-mies; we'll
3rd time to Coda
Ah
sing and shout his vic - to - ry:
Cm(Am)
Bb(G)
Christ is king! For God has won the

E♭(C)
Fm(Dm)
B♭7(G7)
vic - to - ry and set his peo - ple
Cm(Am)
B♭(G)
E♭(C)
free, his word has slain the e - ne - my, the
Fm(Dm)
G7 (E7)
Fm (Dm)
F7 (D7)
G7 (E7)
earth shall stand and see that Through our
CODA
G7(E7)
Cm(Am)
G7(E7)
Christ is king! Christ is
Cm(Am)
G7(E7)
Cm(Am)
king! Christ is king!

316 To people of goodwill

Vreuchten

Words: after F Fletcher (1870–1954)
in this version Word & Music
Music: Dutch traditional melody
arranged C Wood (1866–1926)

Joyfully
E A Bsus B E A F♯m
1 To peo - ple of good - will, be peace on earth and
2 Through pain of sin's dis - tress, all world - ly pride un -
3 All you that bur - dens bear, come, take his yoke up -
4 O ho - ly, hum - ble birth – now sing the joy - ful
B7 E F♯m/A B E A
glad - - ness! Let joy - ful ca - rols
- heed - - ing, in paths of right - eous -
- on you: your work he comes to
sto - - ry! Good will, good will on
Bsus B E A F♯m B7 E F♯m/A B E
fill the world where once was sad - - ness.
- ness a lit - tle child is lead - - ing:
share, and lays his light load on you:
earth, and in the high - est glo - - ry!

Chorus
B E A E B A Bm A E F♯sus F♯
So let us on this morn lift up our hearts to hea -
B G♯m A B7 C♯ C♯7 F♯m E
- ven: to us a Child is born, to
B E A B C♯m
us a Son is gi - ven: O praise him, O
B B7 E A B7 E F♯m/A B E
praise him, O praise him!

317 To us a child of royal birth

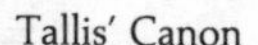
Tallis' Canon

Words: C Wesley (1707–1788)
and in this version Word & Music
Music: T Tallis (c.1505–1585)

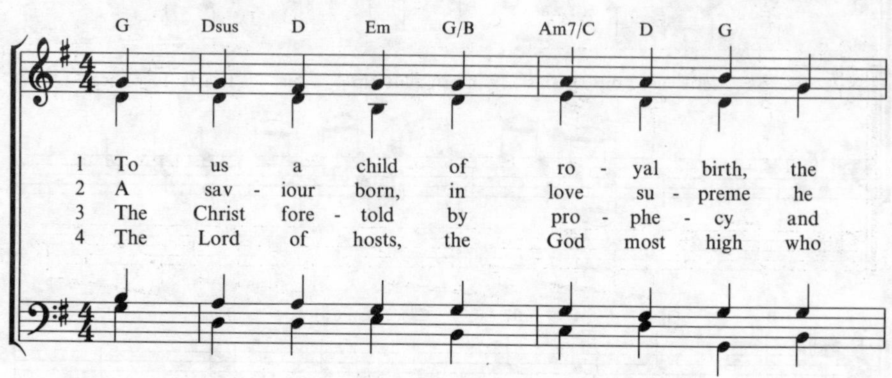
G Dsus D Em G/B Am7/C D G
1 To us a child of ro - yal birth, the
2 A sav - iour born, in love su - preme he
3 The Christ fore - told by pro - phe - cy and
4 The Lord of hosts, the God most high who

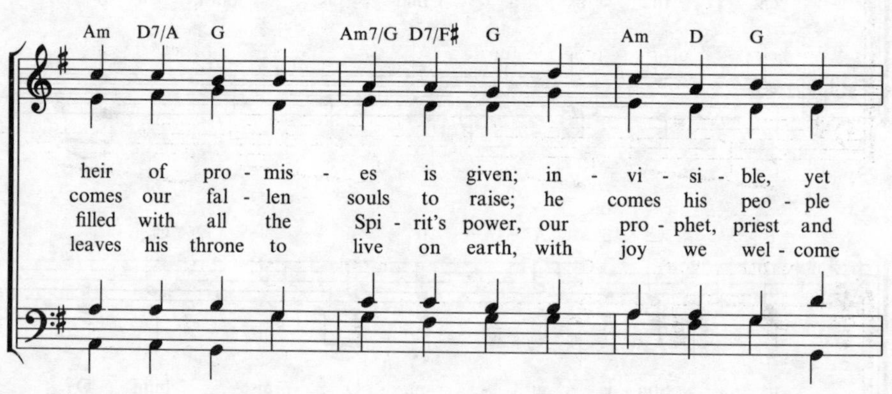
Am D7/A G Am7/G D7/F♯ G Am D G
heir of pro - mis - es is given; in - vi - si - ble, yet
comes our fal - len souls to raise; he comes his peo - ple
filled with all the Spi - rit's power, our pro - phet, priest and
leaves his throne to live on earth, with joy we wel - come

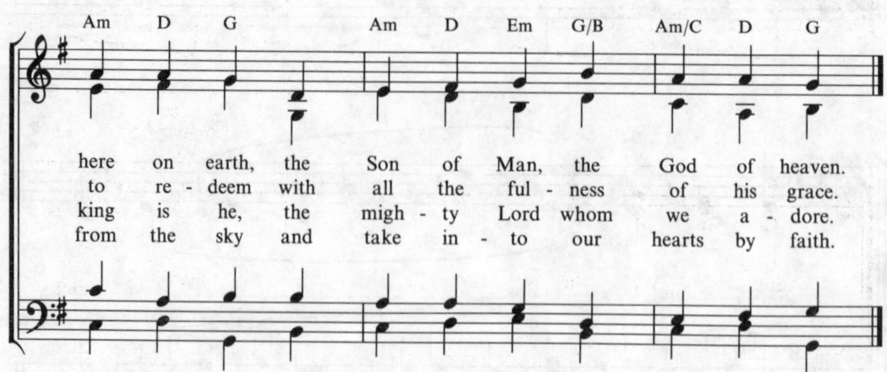
Am D G Am D Em G/B Am/C D G
here on earth, the Son of Man, the God of heaven.
to re - deem with all the ful - ness of his grace.
king is he, the migh - ty Lord whom we a - dore.
from the sky and take in - to our hearts by faith.

Suggested accompaniment when sung as a four-part round:

Smoothly
①
②
③
④
G Am7/G D7/G G Am7/G D7/G G
1 To us a child of ro - yal birth, the
Am7/G D7/G G Am7/G D7/G G
heir of pro - mis - es is given; in -
Am7/G D7/G G Am7/G D7/G G
- vi - si - ble, yet here on earth, the
to repeat
to end
Am7/G D7/G G Am7/D D7/G G Am7/D D7/G G
Son of Man, the God of heaven. 2 A hearts by faith.

318 We declare

Words and music: Graham Kendrick
Music arranged David Peacock

Triumphantly
Chorus
last time to Coda
D F Em D F Em
MEN We de-clare that the king-dom of God is here,
LADIES
We de-clare that the king-dom of God is

D F Em D F Em
we de-clare that the king-dom of God is here, a -
here, we de-clare that the king-dom of God is

D
among you,
a-
here, among you,
among you,
1.
2.
among you,
The
among you, among you, The
D
blind see, the deaf hear, the lame men are walk-ing, sick-nes-ses flee at his

D
voice; the dead live a-gain and the poor hear the good news:
Asus
A
D.C.
Je-sus is king – so re - joice!
CODA
D
F
Em
we de - clare that the king - dom of God is here!
here king - dom of God is here!

319 We believe this is Jesus

Words: traditional
Music: Spiritual
arranged Norman Warren

Lively
Chorus
D Gmaj7 Em7 D Asus A
f We be-lieve this is Je-sus – p come and see, come and see;
Fine
D G D A7 D
f we be-lieve this is Je-sus – p come and see, come and see.
Verses
D D/C♯ D/B D/A Gmaj7 F♯m7 Bm7 Em D A7
1 The light of God lights up his face – he
2 The love of God shines in his eyes – come and see, come and see; it
3 Did you ev-er see such love be-fore? –
D.C.
D Gmaj7/D A7/D D Gmaj7 F♯m7 G D
of-fers us re-deem-ing grace –
tells of glo-ry in the skies – come and see, come and see.
Go in peace and sin no more –

320 We have reason to rejoice

Words and music: Mosie Lister

Brightly

G
Am
D
A7
D
G
D
G
1 We have rea - son
We have rea - son
2 Tell the na - tions
Lift your voice and

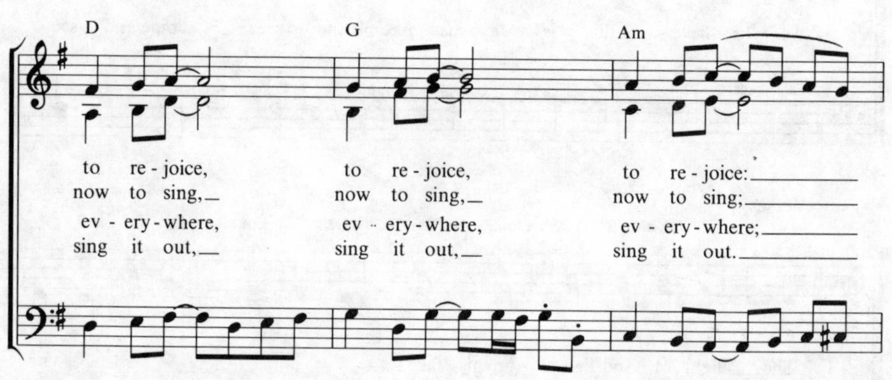
D
G
Am
to re - joice, to re - joice, to re - joice:
now to sing, now to sing, now to sing;
ev - ery - where, ev - ery - where, ev - ery - where;
sing it out, sing it out, sing it out.

D
D7
G
1.3.
Am
E
Am
A7
we have rea - son to re - joice:
we have rea - son now to sing:
tell the na - tions ev - ery - where:
Lift your voice and sing it out:
Christ the Lord is

2.4.
Dsus D Am E Am D G
born. Christ the Lord is born. Sing
C G D7 G D G
Al - le - lu - ia! Christ is born,
Em D7 G Am G/D D7
Christ is born. Al - le - lu - ia
1. 2.
D.S. Fine
Em G/D Em D D7 G D D7 G
Christ is born in Beth - le - hem! Beth - le - hem!

321 We three kings

Kings of Orient

Words and music: J H Hopkins (1820–1891)

Em B7/E Em B7/E Em B7/E Em B7/E
Em B7 Em
ALL 1 We three kings of or - i - ent are, bear - ing
FIRST 2 Born a king on Beth - le - hem's plain – gold I
SECOND 3 Frank - in - cense to of - fer have I – in - cense
B7 Em D
gifts we tra - vel a - far – field and foun - tain,
bring to crown him a - gain: king for ev - er,
tells of De - i - ty nigh; prayer and prais - ing
G Am6 Em/B B7 Em
moor and moun - tain – fol - low - ing yon - der star.
ceas - ing ne - ver, o - ver us all to reign.
all are rais - ing: wor - ship him – God most high!

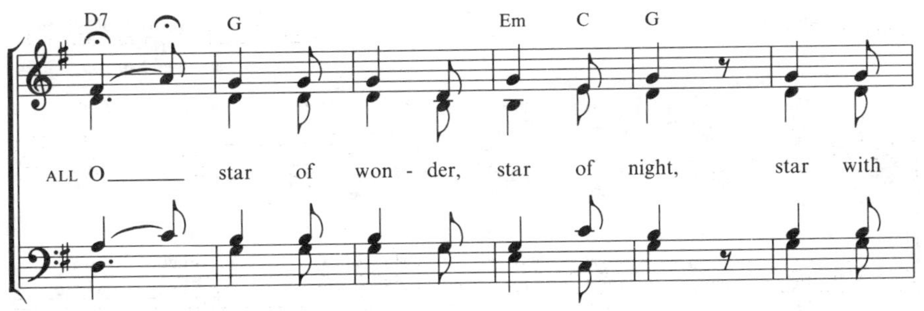
D7
G
Em
C
G
ALL O star of won - der, star of night, star with

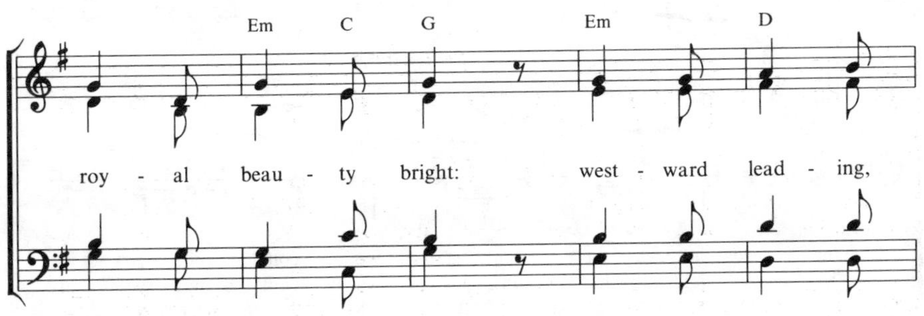
Em
C
G
Em
D
roy - al beau - ty bright: west - ward lead - ing,

C
G
Dsus
D7
G
C
G
still pro - ceed - ing, guide us to your per - fect light!

4 THIRD
Myrrh is mine – its bitter perfume
breathes a life of gathering gloom:
sorrowing, sighing, bleeding, dying,
sealed in the stone-cold tomb.
ALL O star of wonder . . .

5 ALL
Glorious now behold him arise –
king and God and sacrifice!
Heaven sings 'Alleluia!' –
'Alleluia!' the earth replies.
O star of wonder . . .

322 We were not there

In der wiegen
Capo 5(C)
With a lilt
Words: Paul Wigmore
Music: Austrian folk melody
arranged Norman Warren
1 We were not there in Beth - le - hem with shep - herds in the night; we could not see in star - ry sky the dawn of hea - ven's light and yet it shone for us.
2 We were not there in Beth - le - hem where Ma - ry laid her son; we could not see in man - ger bed his life on earth be - gun and yet he lived for us.

323 We worship and adore you

Words and music: D Trotter

Prayerfully with praise
Verse
D
Dsus
C/D
1 We wor-ship and a - dore you, we bow down be - fore you; you are the Lord, the King of kings, you are ex - alt - ed ov - er all things.
2 We lift our hands, we lift our hearts, we lift our voi-ces up to you, O Lord: all glo - ry and hon - our and praise, be yours for ev - er - more!
Chorus
Al - le - lu - ia, al - le - lu - ia, al - le - lu - ia!
G
Em7
1.
2.
- ia!

324 We wish you a merry Christmas

Words: in this version Word & Music
Music: traditional
arranged David Peacock

Joyfully

D7
G
C
E7
1&4 We wish you a mer - ry Christ - mas, we
2 We'll sing you a Christ - mas ca - rol, we'll
3 We'll tell you the Christ - mas sto - ry, we'll

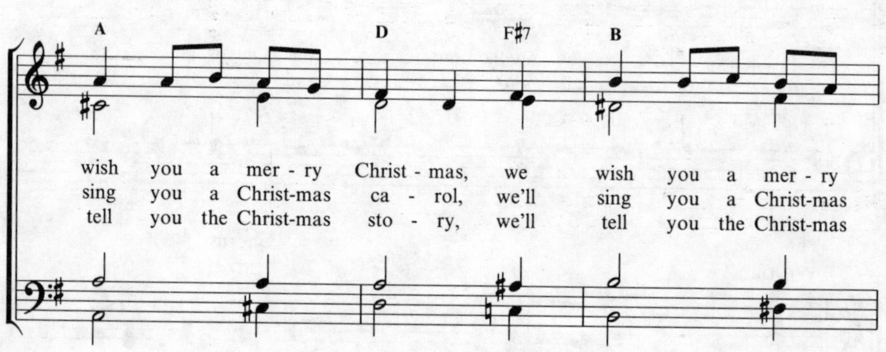

A
D
F#7
B
wish you a mer - ry Christ - mas, we wish you a mer - ry
sing you a Christ-mas ca - rol, we'll sing you a Christ-mas
tell you the Christ-mas sto - ry, we'll tell you the Christ-mas

Em
G
C
Am
D7
G
Christ - mas, and a hap - py new year!
ca - rol, so quick - ly draw near!
sto - ry, so make sure you hear!

Chorus

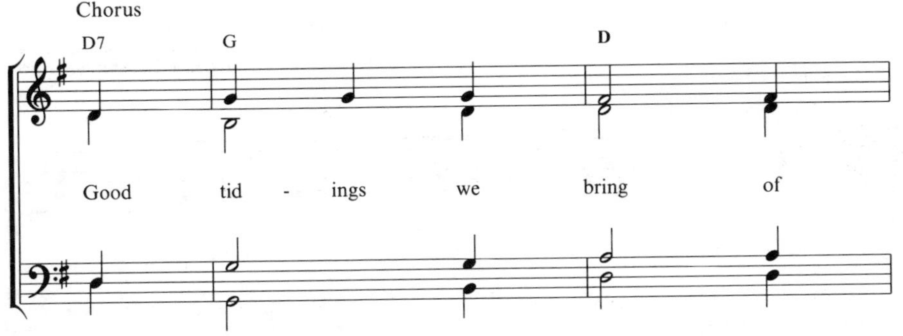
D7
G
D
Good tid - ings we bring of

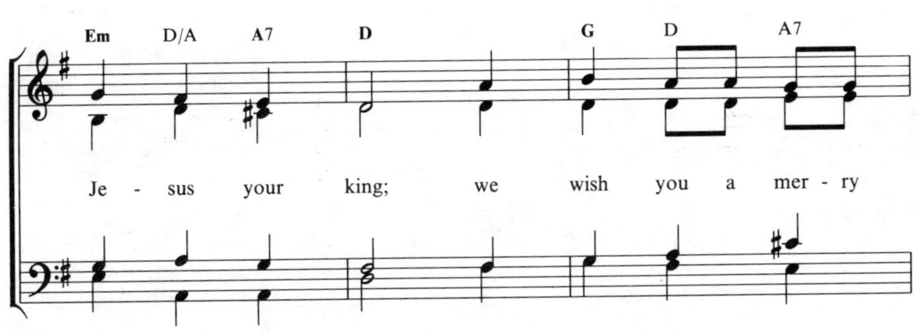
Em
D/A
A7
D
G
D
A7
Je - sus your king; we wish you a mer - ry

D
G/B
G
C
Am
D7
G
Christ - mas and a hap - py new year!

325 We'll sing a new song

Words and music: Diane Fung
Music arranged David Peacock

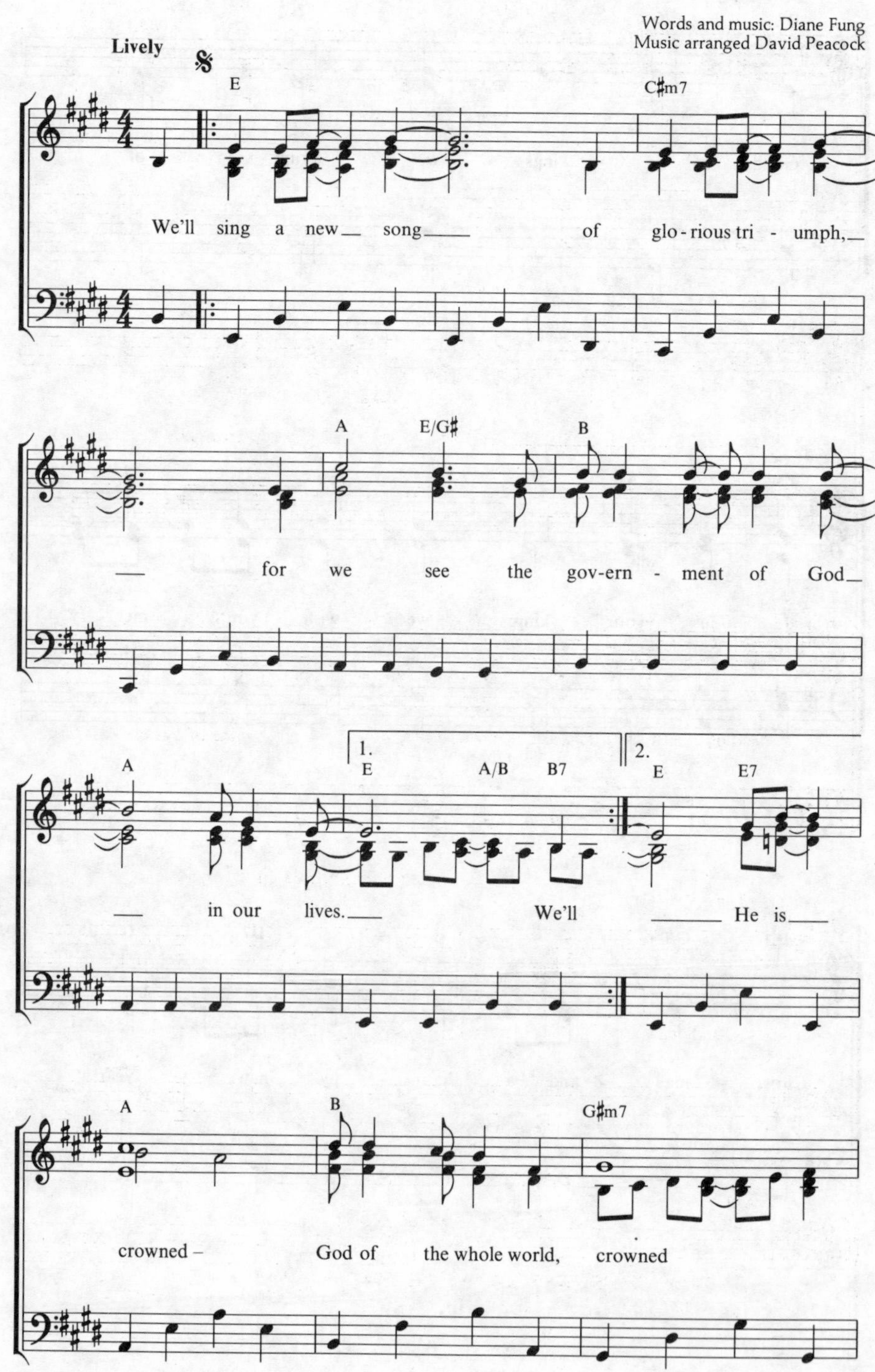

Lively
E
C♯m7
We'll sing a new song of glo - rious tri - umph,
A
E/G♯
B
for we see the gov-ern - ment of God
A
1.
E
A/B
B7
2.
E
E7
in our lives. We'll He is
A
B
G♯m7
crowned – God of the whole world, crowned

C♯
F♯m7
B
king of cre - a - tion, crowned –
rul-ing the na - tions
E
F♯m
E7/G♯
E
A
now.
Yes, he is
crowned –
B
G♯m7
C♯
God of the whole world, crowned
king of cre - a - tion,
last time to Coda
F♯m7
B
E
crowned –
rul-ing the na - tions now.
D.𝄋 al Coda
CODA
A/B
B7
We'll
now.

326 Welcome, Child of Mary

Nu zijt wellekome

Words: from the Dutch
Michael Perry
Music: Fifteenth-century Dutch melody
arranged John Barnard

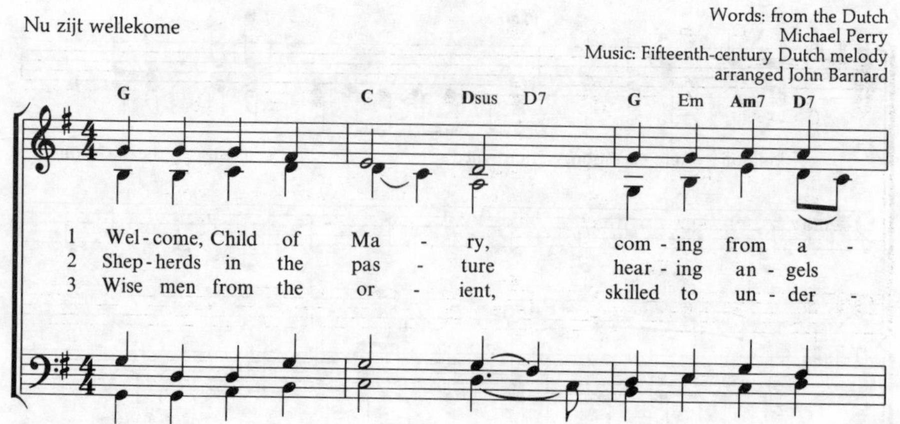

G C Dsus D7 G Em Am7 D7
1 Wel-come, Child of Ma - ry, com-ing from a -
2 Shep-herds in the pas - ture hear-ing an-gels
3 Wise men from the or - ient, skilled to un-der -

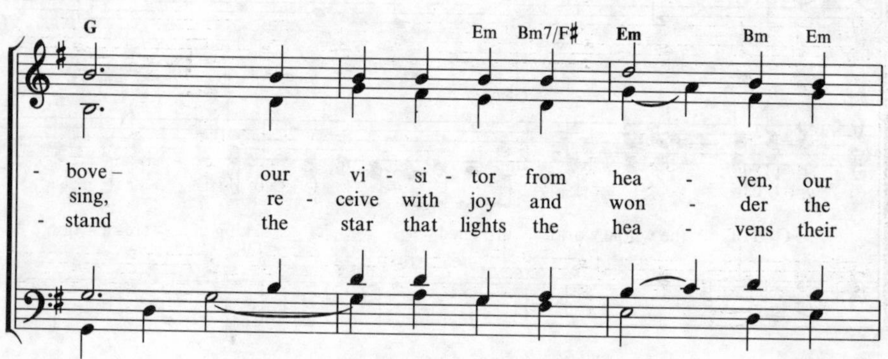

G Em Bm7/F♯ Em Bm Em
- bove – our vi - si - tor from hea - ven, our
sing, re - ceive with joy and won - der the
- stand the star that lights the hea - vens their

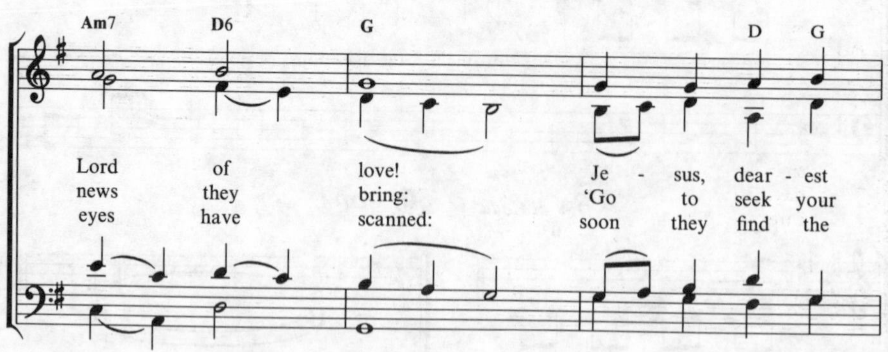

Am7 D6 G D G
Lord of love! Je - sus, dear - est
news they bring: 'Go to seek your
eyes have scanned: soon they find the

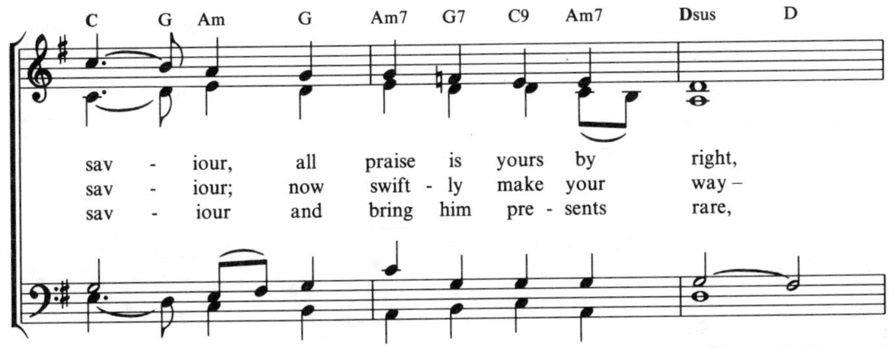
C G Am G Am7 G7 C9 Am7 Dsus D
sav - iour, all praise is yours by right,
sav - iour; now swift - ly make your way –
sav - iour and bring him pre - sents rare,

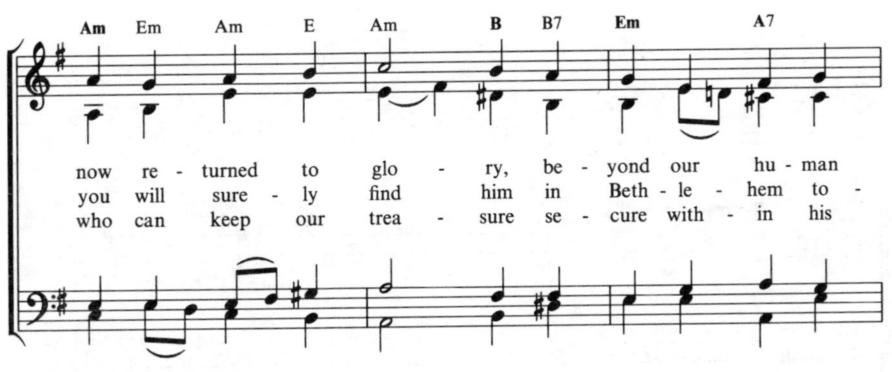
Am Em Am E Am B B7 Em A7
now re - turned to glo - ry, be - yond our hu - man
you will sure - ly find him in Beth - le - hem to -
who can keep our trea - sure se - cure with - in his

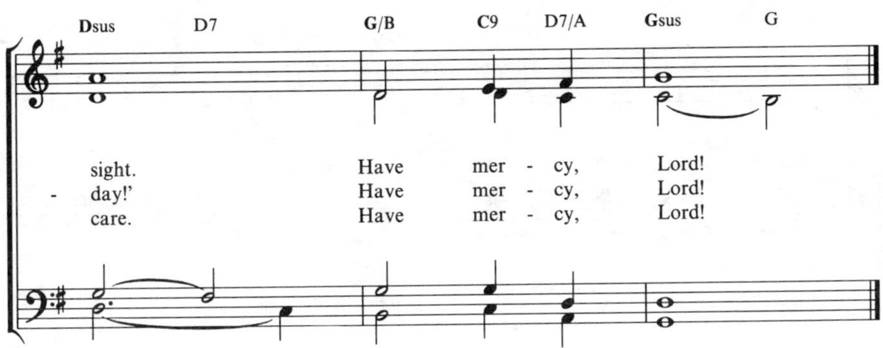
Dsus D7 G/B C9 D7/A Gsus G
sight. Have mer - cy, Lord!
- day!' Have mer - cy, Lord!
care. Have mer - cy, Lord!

327 Welcome the Christ-child

Words and music: F Roy Bennett

Crisp tango rhythm
G
Glockenspiel or chime bars
Em
1 Wel-come the Christ-child, Je-sus our Sav-iour,
2 Shep-herds on hill - sides hear of his com-ing,
Am
D7
G
born for us all this day:
swift-ly they leave their fold;
meek-ly he lies there,
wise men come rid - ing,
Em7
Am
D7
G
peace-ful - ly sleep - ing, cra-dled a - mid the hay.
rare gifts to bring him – fran-kin - cense, myrrh and gold.

Am
D7
B7
Em7
A
A7
Come now be-fore him, kneel and a-dore him, hon-our the King of
Hea-ven is ring-ing, an-gels are sing-ing, tell-ing of Je-sus'
D
D7
G
Em7
kings; wel-come the Christ-child, born in the man-ger –
birth: wel-come the Christ-child, born in the man-ger,
Am
D7
1.
G
2.
G
glad-ness and joy he brings!
king of all heaven and earth.

328 Welcome, Jesus

O du fröhliche

Words: Michael Perry
Music: Sicilian folk melody
arranged John Barnard

Joyfully
D G D G D
1 Wel - come, Je - sus child of Ma - ry,
2 Wel - come, Je - sus child of Ma - ry,
A/C♯ Bm A D A/E E7 A
Da - vid's son and Ju - dah's star!
come to us from realms a - far –
G/B A7/C♯ D G/B Asus A7
Al - le - lu - ia, al - le - lu - ia,
D G A Bm Em D G D/A A7 D
al - le - lu - ia, glo - ri - a!

329 Welcome your king

Words: Michael Perry
Music: Norman Warren

Lively Medieval style
Am (G7/A) Am (G7/A) Am
1 Wel-come your king – Al-le-lu-ia! lands of the sun-rise;
2 Fol-low his star – Al-le-lu-ia! Christ who en-thralls you;
3 In-cense and gold – Al-le-lu-ia! these you may bor-row;
Dm/A Am7 Dm/A Am
tra-vel-lers, sing, 'Al-le-lu-ia!', lift up your tired eyes:
seek him from far. Al-le-lu-ia, Beth-le-hem calls you!
priest-king fore-told – Al-le-lu-ia! myrrh for his sor-row.
Dm Am
Come and praise him, joy-ful raise him low-ly ca-rols of love;
Em C Em last time Am/E E
bow be-fore him and a-dore him – Lord from a-bove.

330 Welcome, welcome

Words: Michael Perry
Music: Norman Warren

Lively medieval style
G
Glockenspiel
[drum etc.]
Verses
G
Am7/G
G
descant v.3
Wel - come, wel - come, glo - ry,
1 Wel - come, wel - come, sav-iour born in Beth-le-hem; 'Glo - ry, glo - ry',
2 Wel - come, wel - come, God in our hu-ma-ni - ty; Glo - ry glo - ry,
3 Wel - come, wel - come – lift your voi-ces ev-ery-one; Glo - ry, glo - ry,

C/G
G
Am7/G
glo - ry.
Wel - come,
wel - come,
hea-ven's an-gels say:
praise him and a-dore:
sing with glad ac-claim:
Wel-come, wel - come – we shall join to sing with them,
wel-come, wel - come, spurn-ing prince-ly va - ni - ty,
Wel-come, wel - come, wel-come God's be-lov - èd Son:

Gmaj7
Am7/G
D7/G
G
to end
Glo - ry, glo - ry, glo - ry to his name!
to end
'Glo - ry, glo - ry: Christ is Lord to-day!'
Glo - ry, glo - ry, God a-mong the poor.
Glo - ry, glo - ry, glo - ry to his name!

331 What can I give to the King

Words: Barry McGuire
Music: Barry McGuire and Mike Deasy
arranged David Peacock

Gently
C Dm7/C C Dm7 G7 C Dm7/C
1 What can I give to the King, give to the one, who has
3 What can we give to the King, give to the one who has
C G/B Am C/G F C/E
ev - ery - thing; what can I give, what gift can I bring?
ev - ery - thing; what can we give, what gift can we bring?
Dm7 Em7 Fmaj7 Dm F/G G7
What can I give to the King; what can I give to the
What can we give to the King; what can we give to the
C Gm7 C7 F G
King?
King?
2 Give him a heart that's
4 Give him all glo-ry, his

C
Am7
F
G
C
Am7
o-pened up wide,
give him a life that's got nothing to hide,
peo-ple on earth;
give him all prai-ses this time of his birth;
F
G7/F
C
Am7
give him a love that's ten - der and true, and he'll
give him all hon - our in all that we do: as he's
Dm7
Em7
Fmaj7
Am/F♯
Dm7/G
G7
give it all back to you; yes, he'll give it all back to
giv - en his life to you, as he's giv - en his life to
C
1.
Fm7
F/G
2.
Fm7
F/G
you.
you.

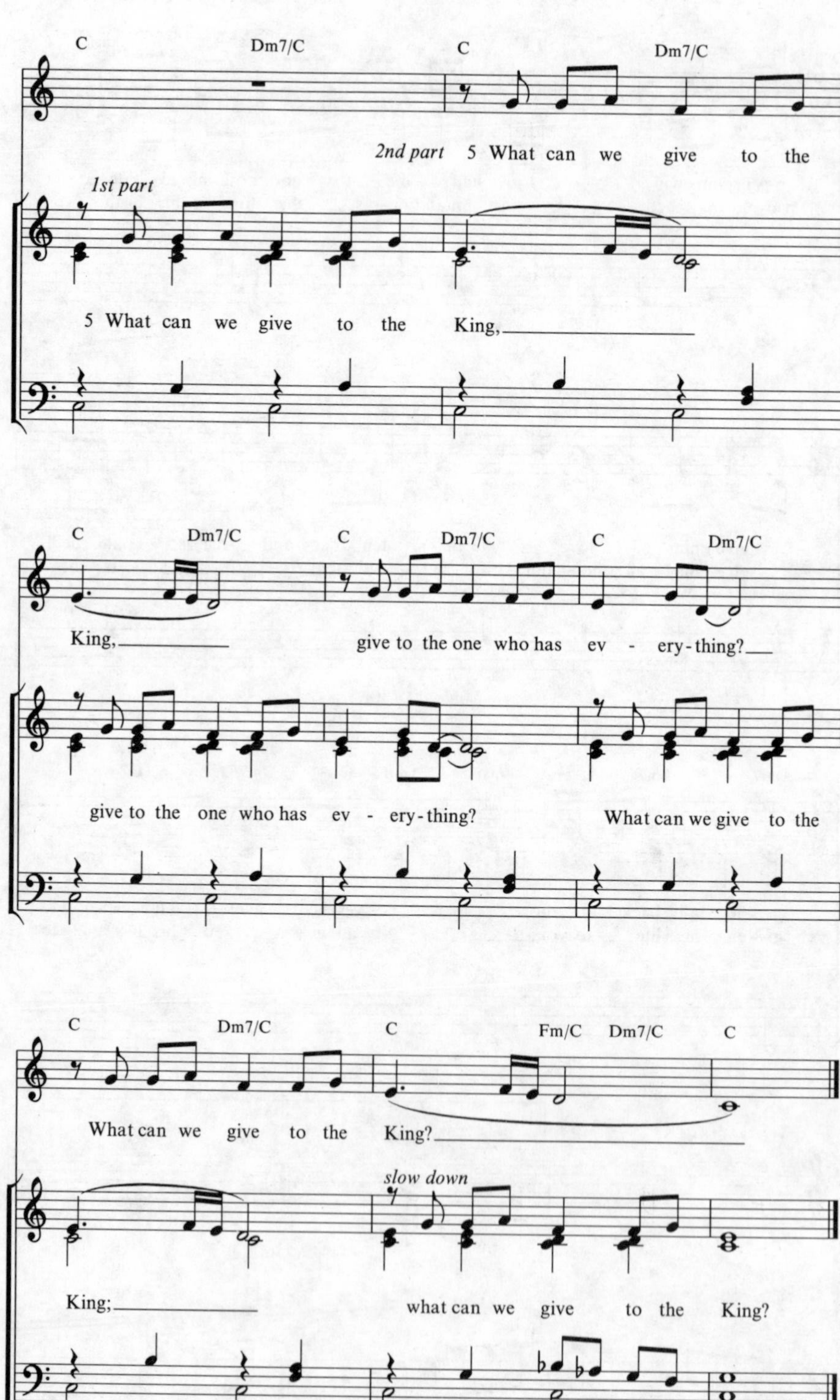
C
Dm7/C
C
Dm7/C
2nd part
5 What can we give to the
1st part
5 What can we give to the King,
C
Dm7/C
C
Dm7/C
C
Dm7/C
King,
give to the one who has ev - ery-thing?
give to the one who has ev - ery-thing?
What can we give to the
C
Dm7/C
C
Fm/C
Dm7/C
C
What can we give to the King?
slow down
King;
what can we give to the King?

332 When God from heaven to earth came down

I saw three ships
Words: Michael Perry
Music: English traditional melody
arranged David Iliff
G D G D7
ALL 1 When God from heaven to earth came down on
WOMEN AND GIRLS 2 For Christ was born to save us all, on
MEN AND BOYS 3 The shep - herds heard the an - gels sing on
ALL 4 Now joy is ours and all is well, on
G Em G D D7
Christ - mas Day, on Christ - mas Day, the
Christ - mas Day, on Christ - mas Day, and
Christ - mas Day, on Christ - mas Day, to
Christ - mas Day, on Christ - mas Day, so
Em C D7/A G D G Am
songs rang out in Beth - lehem town on
laid with - in a man - ger stall on
tell them of the sav - iour - king on
sound the or - gan, chime the bell on
G/D Em Am/C D G
Christ - mas Day in the morn - ing.
Christ - mas Day in the morn - ing.
Christ - mas Day in the morn - ing.
Christ - mas Day in the morn - ing.

333 When shepherds watched

Greensleeves

Words: Michael Perry
Music: English traditional melody
arranged Noël Tredinnick

F
Em
E♭m
Dm
Optional introduction
mp
C
B
Am
G
F♯m
Em
1 When
Verse
Em
D
C7
shep - herds watched and an - gels sang and Ju - dah's hills with
2 Jo - seph knelt and Ma - ry bowed and beasts of bur - den
3 wise men sought and He - rod feared and when a ro - yal
4 God no lon - ger calls in vain and hu - man hearts are
Bm
Em7
A7
Dmaj7
Gmaj7
glo - ry rang, then Christ was born the Son of Man on
brayed a - loud, there Christ was born for all our good on
star ap-peared, then Christ was born to be our Lord on
love's do-main, there Christ is born in us a - gain on

Chorus
C7
B7
Esus
Em
G
Em7
Christ - mas Day in the morn - ing: Christ was born the
Christ - mas Day in the morn - ing: Christ was born for
Christ - mas Day in the morn - ing: Christ was born to
Christ - mas Day in the morn - ing: Christ is born in
F♯m
Bm
Em
Am
Bm
Son of Man on Christ - mas Day, on Christ - mas Day;
all our good on Christ - mas Day, on Christ - mas Day;
be our Lord on Christ - mas Day, on Christ - mas Day;
us a - gain on Christ - mas Day, on Christ - mas Day;
G9
G/A
D9
Gmaj7
C7
B7
Christ was born the Son of Man on Christ - mas Day in the
Christ was born for all our good on Christ - mas Day in the
Christ was born to be our Lord on Christ - mas Day in the
Christ is born in us a - gain on Christ - mas Day in the
Fine
optional link
Am/E
Em
C
B
Am
Em
morn - ing.
morn - ing.
morn - ing.
morn - ing.
2 Where
3 When
4 Where

334 When the angel came to Mary

Sans Day Carol

Words: after the traditional carol
Michael Perry
Music: Cornish traditional melody
arranged Norman Warren

Not too slow

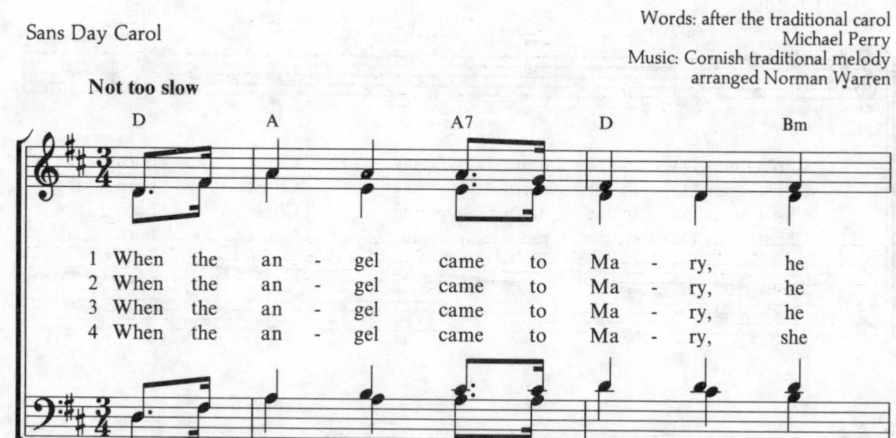
D
A
A7
D
Bm
1 When the an - gel came to Ma - ry, he
2 When the an - gel came to Ma - ry, he
3 When the an - gel came to Ma - ry, he
4 When the an - gel came to Ma - ry, she

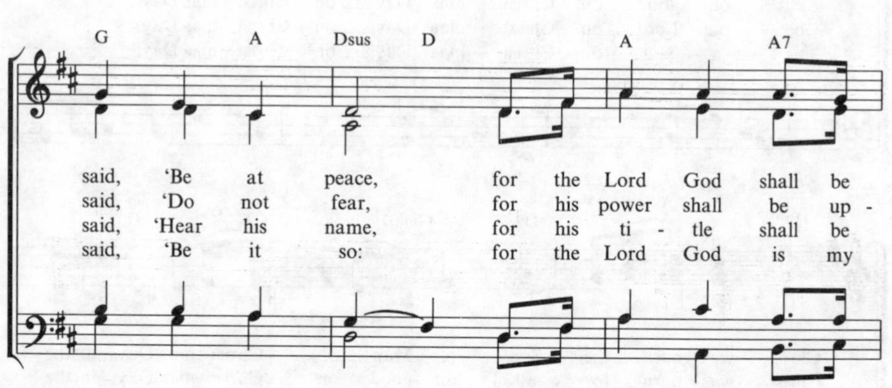
G
A
Dsus
D
A
A7
said, 'Be at peace, for the Lord God shall be
said, 'Do not fear, for his power shall be up -
said, 'Hear his name, for his ti - tle shall be
said, 'Be it so: for the Lord God is my

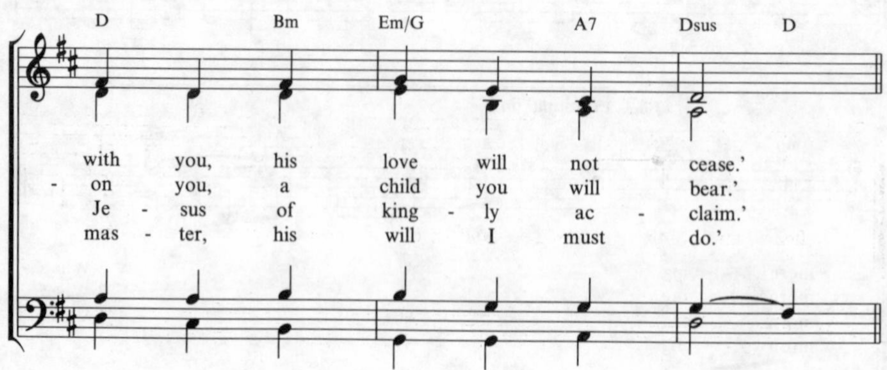
D
Bm
Em/G
A7
Dsus
D
with you, his love will not cease.'
- on you, a child you will bear.'
Je - sus of king - ly ac - claim.'
mas - ter, his will I must do.'

Chorus
A
G
D
F♯m7
Em
And___ Ma - ry bore___ Je - sus Christ, our sav - iour for to
Bm
D
Bm
be; and the first and the___ last and the
Em
A7
Dsus
D
A
Em
F♯m
Em7
great - est is he, is he, is he; and the
D
A7
Bm
Bm7/A
G
A
D
first and the___ last and the great - est is he.

335 When the King shall come again

Tempus adest floridum

Words: from Isaiah 35
Christopher Idle
Music: English traditional melody
arranged J Stainer (1840–1901)

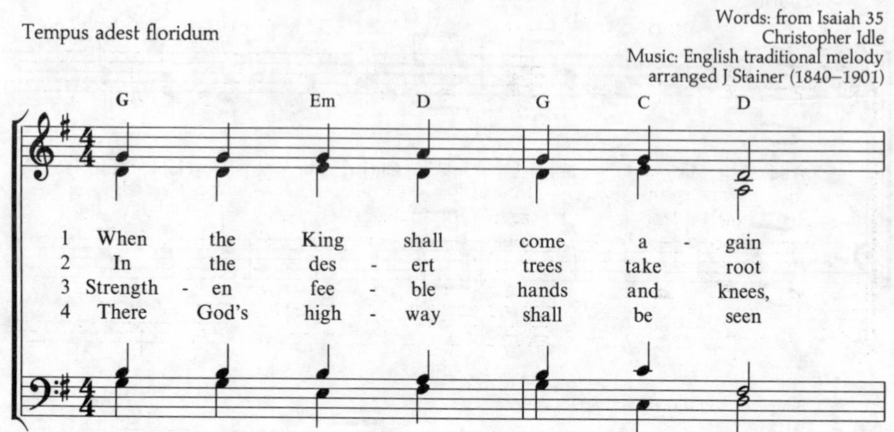

G Em D G C D
1 When the King shall come a - gain
2 In the des - ert trees take root
3 Strength - en fee - ble hands and knees,
4 There God's high - way shall be seen

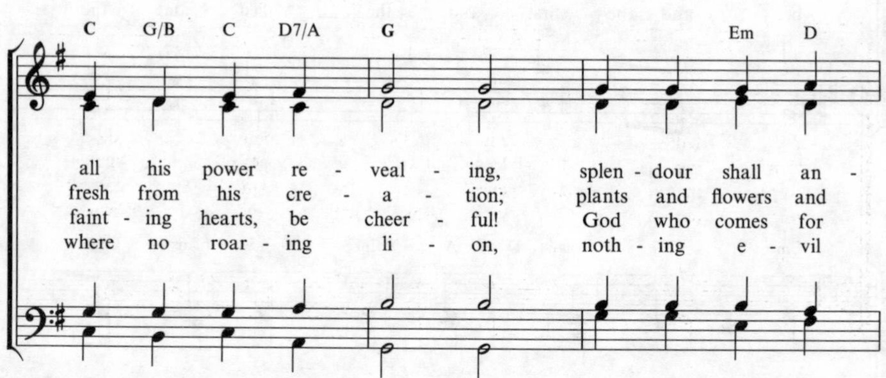

C G/B C D7/A G Em D
all his power re - veal - ing, splen - dour shall an -
fresh from his cre - a - tion; plants and flowers and
faint - ing hearts, be cheer - ful! God who comes for
where no roar - ing li - on, noth - ing e - vil

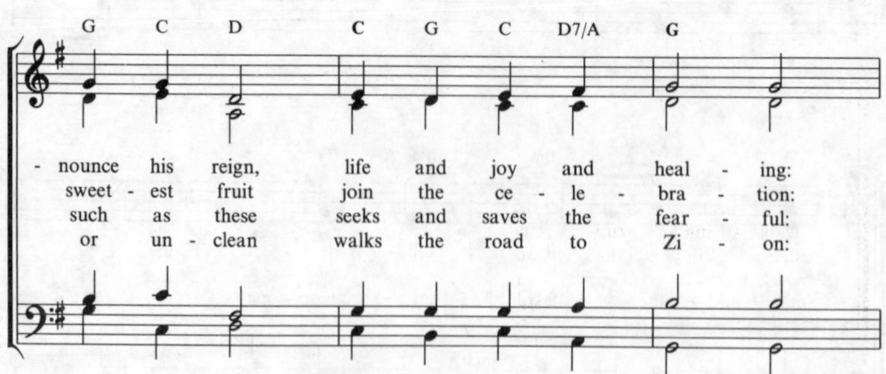

G C D C G C D7/A G
- nounce his reign, life and joy and heal - ing:
sweet - est fruit join the ce - le - bra - tion:
such as these seeks and saves the fear - ful:
or un - clean walks the road to Zi - on:

For another arrangement of this melody see number 109

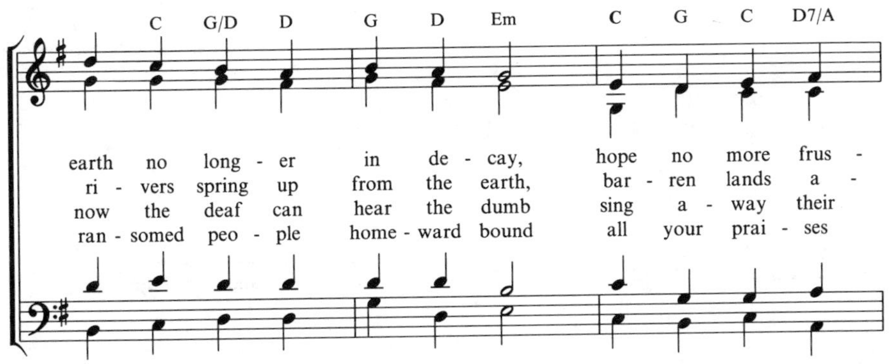
C G/D D G D Em C G C D7/A
earth no long - er in de - cay, hope no more frus -
ri - vers spring up from the earth, bar - ren lands a -
now the deaf can hear the dumb sing a - way their
ran - somed peo - ple home - ward bound all your prai - ses

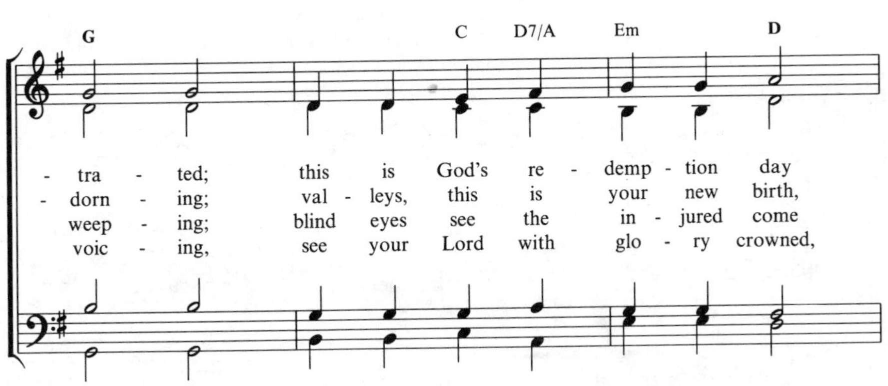
G C D7/A Em D
- tra - ted; this is God's re - demp - tion day
- dorn - ing; val - leys, this is your new birth,
weep - ing; blind eyes see the in - jured come
voic - ing, see your Lord with glo - ry crowned,

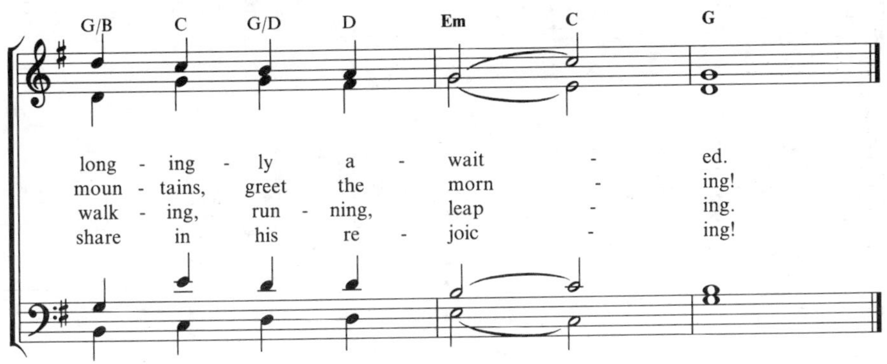
G/B C G/D D Em C G
long - ing - ly a - wait - ed.
moun - tains, greet the morn - ing!
walk - ing, run - ning, leap - ing.
share in his re - joic - ing!

336 When the Lord came to our land

Words: Kim Miller
Music: American folk melody
arranged David Peacock

C F C G7 C G7 C
When the Lord came to our land, he was not a wealth-thy man;
F A7 Dm7 G7 C
he was born in po-ver-ty
1 and the stars looked down to see: and the
2 and the an - gels came to see: and the
3 and the shep-herds came to see: and the
4 and the wise men came to see: and the
5 and the don - keys came to see: and the
* F C G7 C C Dm7 A7
bright - est star of all was his.
an - gels sang their joy - ful news, and the
shep - herds knelt and wor-shipped him, and the
wise men brought rare gifts for him, and the
don - keys gave their stall for him, and the
Je-sus was the Son of God, and he
Dm7 G7 1–4. C Dm7 G 5. C
came to earth for me.
me.

* From verse 2 onward repeat these 2 bars in cumulative fashion, starting with the last verse you have sung and working your way back to "...the brightest star."

337 When the sun is darkened

Advent Psalm

Words: from Matthew 24
Christopher Idle
Music: Norman Warren

E Emaj7/D♯ C♯m E/B A6 F♯m7 Bsus B
1 When the sun is dark-ened and the moon gives no light
2 All the peo-ples of the world will cry and la - ment
3 He will send his an-gels with a loud trum-pet blast,
F♯m F♯m/F F♯m/E G♯m7/D♯ A A/F♯ B7
and the stars fall from the sky, then in hea-ven will ap-pear the
when they see the Son of Man com-ing in great power and glo-ry
from the far-thest bounds of heaven; from the four winds they will ga-ther
C♯m Emaj7 A E/B F♯m7/C♯ A Esus E
long-pro-mised sign that pro-claims the Son of Man.
high on the clouds with his an-gels serv-ing him.
his cho-sen ones who are rea-dy for their Lord.

4 None on earth can prophesy
the day or the hour
which the Father knows alone:
keep awake and well prepared,
for Jesus will come
at the time you least expect.

5 Happy is the servant
who is found keeping faith
when the master comes again;
heaven and earth will pass away,
but never the words
of the Lord, the Son of Man.

338 Where do Christmas songs begin

Mountain Heights
Capo 3(C)
With movement
Words: Timothy Dudley-Smith
Music: unknown
arranged David Peacock
1 Where do Christ-mas songs be - gin?
2 Who is this, whose hu - man birth
3 On - ly love can ans - wer why
4 Praise we then, in Christ-mas songs,
By the sta - ble of an inn
here pro - claims him Child of earth?
he should come to grieve and die,
him to whom all praise be - longs.
where the song of hosts on high min - gled
He it is who formed the skies, saw the
share on earth our pain and loss, bear for
Hear the an - gel host re - ply 'Glo - ry
with a ba - by's cry.
new - made stars a - rise:
us the bit - ter cross.
be to God on high,

E♭ (C) A♭ (F) Gsus (Esus) G7 (E7)
There, for joy and won - der, smiled
Life im - mor - tal, Light di - vine,
Love is come to seek and save,
joy and peace to mor - tals given,
Cm (Am) A♭/B♭ (F) B♭7 (G7)
man and maid and ho - ly Child.
blink - ing in the can - dle - shine;
Life to mas - ter death and grave,
peace on earth and peace with heaven!'
E♭ (C) D7 (B7) Fm (Dm) E♭/B♭ (C) B♭ (G)
Christ - mas songs be - gin with them: sing the
born our dark - ness to dis - pel, God with
so in Christ is all re - stored, ri - sen
Join we now, as one with them: sing the
Gm7 (Em7) Cm (Am) Fm7 (Dm7) B♭7 (G7) 1.2.3. E♭(C) 4. E♭(C)
songs of Beth - le - hem!
us, Em-man - u - el!
and re-deem - ing Lord!
songs of Beth - le - - hem!

339 Where's everybody going

Going to see a baby

Words and music: Al Vincent
Music arranged David Peacock

In joyful gospel style
E
F♯m7
Bsus
B
E
F♯m7
A
A/B
B7
1 (SOLO) Where's ev - ery - bo - dy go - ing – please tell me?
2 (SOLO) We've been a - look - ing for Ma - ry and Jo - seph –
E
A
B7
E
(CONG) Going to see a ba - by in - a Beth - a - le - hem.
(CONG) going to see a ba - by born in Beth - a - le - hem.
E
F♯m7
Emaj7
F♯m7
E
A
B7
(S) Why is ev - ery - bo - dy rush - ing – please tell me?
(S) Heard from an an - gel a - bout a lit - tle ba - by,

E
A
B7
E
(C) There's been a ba - by born in Beth - a - le - hem.
(C) born in a man - ger in - a Beth - a - le - hem.
E
Bm7
E
A7/B
3 (S) Born in the Spi - rit, born in glo - ry,
(S) Come from the Fa - ther – tell the sto - ry –
1.
2.
E
A
B7
E
A
B7
E
C7
(C) born in a man-ger in - a Beth-a - le - hem.
(C) come down from hea-ven to - a Beth-a - le - hem.
F
Gm7
B♭
B♭/C
C7
4 (S) Come to be our sav - iour – come in peace,
5 (S) See that star – it shines so bright,

F
Bb
C7
Gm7
Fmaj7
(C) born in a man-ger in-a Beth-a-le-hem.
(S) Here to bring the prison-
(C) shin-ing on a man-ger in-a Beth-a-le-hem.
(S) Bring to earth such joy
-ers re-lease,
(C) Je-sus the sav-iour in-a
and light,
(C) lit-tle ba-by Je-sus born in
Beth-a-le-hem.
6 (S) God looked down from up a-bove,
Beth-a-le-hem.
(S) Sent to us his per-fect love,
C
Cm7
Bb7/C
1.
2.
(C) gave to us a ba-by in-a Beth-a-le-hem.
(C) sent his son Je-sus to
Beth-a-le-hem.

340 Who is he in yonder stall

Who is he?

Words and music: B R Hanby (1833–1867)

Verses

A D A/E F♯m E7

1 Who is he in yon - der stall at whose feet the shep-herds fall?
2 Who is he in deep dis - tress fast-ing in the wil - der - ness?
3 Who is he to whom they bring all the sick and sor - row - ing?

Chorus

A A/E E E7/A A

It's the Lord – O, won-drous sto - ry! It's the Lord, the king of glo - ry!

A/C♯ D A/E E7 A

At his feet we hum-bly fall – crown him, crown him Lord of all!

4 Who is he the gathering throng
greet with loud triumphant song?
It's the Lord . . .

5 Who is he that on the tree
dies in shame and agony?
It's the Lord . . .

6 Who is he that from the grave
comes to heal and help and save?
It's the Lord . . .

7 Who is he that from his throne
rules through all the worlds alone?
It's the Lord . . .

341 While shepherds watched their flocks

(FIRST TUNE)

Winchester Old

Words: N Tate (1652–1715)
Music: T Este's *Psalms* (1592)
arranged W H Monk (1823–1889)
verse 6 arranged with descant John Barnard

Capo 5(C)

F (C)
C (G)
Dm (Am)
B♭ (F)
F (C)
C (G)
1 While shep - herds watched their flocks by night, all
2 'Fear not,' said he – for migh - ty dread had
3 'To you in Da - vid's town this day is
F (C)
Am (Em)
G (D)
C (G)
F (C)
B♭ (F)
F (C)
B♭ (F)
F (C)
seat - ed on the ground, the an - gel of the
seized their trou - bled mind – 'Glad tid - ings of great
born of Da - vid's line a sav - iour, who is
C (G)
Dm (Am)
A (E)
F (C)
C (G)
Dm (Am)
B♭ (F)
C (G)
F (C)
Lord came down and glo - ry shone a - round.
joy I bring to you and all man - kind:
Christ the Lord. And this shall be the sign:

4 'The heavenly babe you there shall find
to human view displayed,
all tightly wrapped in swathing bands
and in a manger laid.'

5 Thus spoke the seraph, and forthwith
appeared a shining throng
of angels praising God, who thus
addressed their joyful song:

Descant
F (C)
Dm/F (Am)
A7/E (E7)
Dm (Am)
Gm (Dm)
C7 (A7)
F (C)
C (G)
6 'All glo - ry be to God on high, and
6 'All glo - ry be to God on high, and
Dm7 (Am7)
Dm7/G
G7 (D7)
C (G)
Cm6 (Am6)
Gm/B♭ (Em)
D7/A (A7)
Gm (Dm)
F/A (C)
to the earth be peace; good will hence - forth from
to the earth be peace; good will hence-forth from
Gm/B♭ (Dm)
G7/B (D7)
C (G)
F7♯5 (C7♯5)
Gm/B♭ (Dm)
F (C)
Gm7 (Dm7)
C7 (G7)
F (C)
high - est heaven be - gin and ne - ver cease!'
high - est heaven be - gin and ne - ver cease!'

342 While shepherds watched their flocks

(SECOND TUNE)
Lyngham
Words: N Tate (1652–1715)
Music: T Jarman (1782–1862)
G C G/D D7
1 While shep - herds watched their flocks by
2 'Fear not,' said he – for migh - ty
3 'To you in Da - vid's town this
G D7/A G D/F♯ A7/E D
night, all seat - ed on the ground, all
dread had seized their trou - bled mind – had
day is born of Da - vid's line, is
G Em D/A A D
seat - ed on the ground,
seized their trou - bled mind –
born of Da - vid's line
G D7/A G D/F♯ A7/E
the an - gel of the Lord came
'Glad tid - ings of great joy I
a sav - iour, who is Christ the

D G C
down
bring
Lord.
and glo - ry shone a -
to you and all man -
And this shall be the
and glo - ry shone a - round, and
to you and all man - kind, to
And this shall be the sign, and
G D D7 G
- round, and glo - ry shone a - round, and
- kind, to you and all man - kind, to
sign, and this shall be the sign, and
glo - ry shone a - round, and glo - ry shone a -
you and all man - kind, to you and all man -
this shall be the sign, and this shall be the
C G/B D7/A G Dsus D D7 G
glo - ry shone a - round.
you and all man - kind:
this shall be the sign:
- round, and glo - ry shone a - round.
- kind, to you and all man - kind:
sign, and this shall be the sign:

4 'The heavenly babe you there shall find
to human view displayed . . .
all tightly wrapped in swathing bands
and in a manger laid . . .

5 Thus spoke the seraph, and forthwith
appeared a shining throng . . .
of angels praising God, who thus
addressed their joyful song . . .

6 'All glory be to God on high,
and to the earth be peace . . .
good will henceforth from highest heaven
begin and never cease . . .

343 While shepherds watched their flocks

(THIRD TUNE)
Ilkley Moor
Words: N Tate (1652–1715)
Music: English traditional melody
arranged David Peacock
Capo 3(G)
With gusto
B♭ (G)
F7 (D7)
E♭ (C)
B♭/F (G)
F (D)
F/C
C7 (A7)
1 While shep - herds watched their flocks by night, all seat - ed on the ground, the an - gel of the Lord came down, the an - gel of the Lord came
2 'Fear not,' said he - for migh - ty dread had seized their trou - bled mind – 'Glad tid - ings of great joy I bring, glad tid - ings of great joy I
3 'To you in Da - vid's town this day is born of Da - vid's line a sav - iour, who is Christ the Lord, a sav - iour, who is Christ the
flocks by night,
migh - ty dread
town this day
the an - gel of the Lord came down,
'Glad tid - ings of great joy I bring,
a sav - iour, who is Christ the Lord,

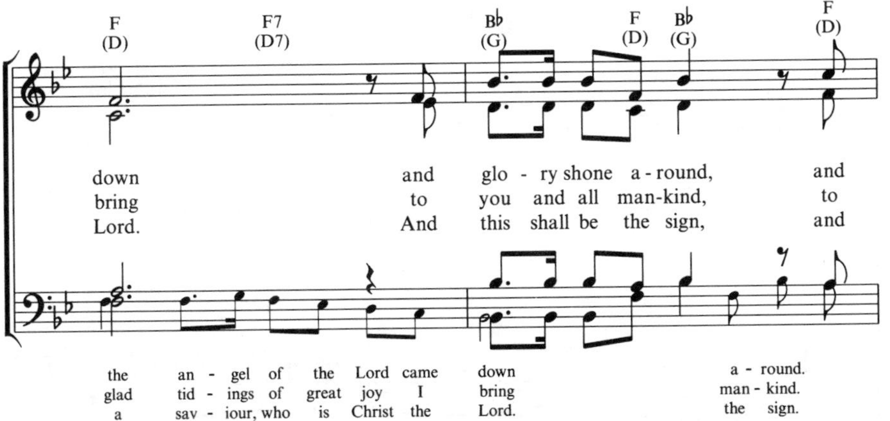
F (D)
F7 (D7)
Bb (G)
F (D)
Bb (G)
F (D)
down and glo - ry shone a - round, and
bring to you and all man-kind, to
Lord. And this shall be the sign, and
the an - gel of the Lord came down a - round.
glad tid - ings of great joy I bring man - kind.
a sav - iour, who is Christ the Lord. the sign.

Bb (G)
F (D)
Bb (G)
Bb7 (G7)
Cm7 (Am7)
Bb/F (G)
F7 (D7)
Bb (G)
glo - ry shone a - round, (a - round) and glo - ry shone a - round.
you and all man-kind, (man-kind) to you and all man - kind:
this shall be the sign, (the sign) and this shall be the sign:

4 'The heavenly babe you there shall find
to human view displayed,
all tightly wrapped in swathing bands,
all tightly wrapped in swathing bands
and in a manger laid,
and in a manger laid,
and in a manger laid.'

5 Thus spoke the seraph, and forthwith
appeared a shining throng
of angels praising God, who thus,
of angels praising God, who thus
addressed their joyful song,
addressed their joyful song,
addressed their joyful song:

6 'All glory be to God on high,
and to the earth be peace;
good will henceforth from highest heaven,
good will henceforth from highest heaven
begin and never cease,
begin and never cease,
begin and never cease!'

344 While shepherds watched their flocks

(FOURTH TUNE)

Capo 3(D)

Words: N Tate (1652–1715)
Music: Herbert Chappell

Relaxed and smooth
D♭maj7
(B♭maj7)
F
(D)
(SOLO) 1 While
F
(D)
shep - herds watched their flocks by night, all
(2) not,' said he – for migh - ty dread had
(4) heaven - ly babe you there shall find to
(6) glo - ry be to God on high, and
seat - ed on the ground, the
seized their trou - bled mind – 'Glad
hu - man view dis - played, all
to the earth be peace; good -

an - gel of the Lord came down and
ti - dings of great joy I bring to
tight - ly wrapped in swath - ing bands and
- will hence - forth from high - est heaven be -
Bm7 (G♯m7)
Em7 (C♯m7)
v.6 to Coda
glo - ry shone a - round.
you and all man - kind:
in a man - ger laid.'
- gin and ne - ver cease!'
R.H.
Bm7 (G♯m7)
1. C7 (A7)
2.3. E♭7 (C7)
(ALL) shone a - round.
(ALL) all man-kind:
(ALL) man - ger laid.'
(SOLO) 2 'Fear
(ALL) 3 'To
(ALL) 5 Thus
R.H.
A♭ (F)
D♭ (B♭)
you in Da - vid's town this day is
spoke the se - raph, and forth - with ap -

A♭
(F)
D♭
(B♭)
A♭
(F)
born of Da-vid's line a sav-iour, who is Christ
- peared a shi-ning throng of an-gels prais-ing God,
D♭
(B♭)
A♭
(F)
C7
(A7)
B♭/C
(G)
the Lord. And this shall be the sign:
who thus ad - dressed their joy-ful song:
C7
(A7)
D.S.
CODA
Bm7
(G♯m7)
(SOLO) 4 'The
(SOLO) 6 'All
(ALL) ne - ver cease,
Em7
(C♯m7)
N.C.
slow
ne - ver cease!
R.H.

345 Winds through the olive trees

Words: from the French
Unknown
Music: Gascon traditional carol
arranged Norman Warren

Gently
D
Dmaj7
G
A
D
1 Winds through the o - live trees soft - ly did blow,
3 Then from the hap - py skies an - gels bent low
Dmaj7
Gmaj7
A
Dsus
D
round lit - tle Beth - le - hem long, long a - go.
sing - ing their songs of joy long, long a - go:
A7
D
A7
D
Em7
2 Sheep on the hill - side lay, white as the snow;
4 For, in his man - ger bed cra - dled, we know
D/F♯
A7/E
D
Gmaj7
A
D
shep - herds were watch - ing them long, long a - go.
Christ came to Beth - le - hem long, long a - go.

346 Who is this child

Londonderry Air

Words: Michael Perry
Music: Irish traditional melody
arranged Noël Tredinnick

1 Who is this child that lies in hum-ble splen - dour, and spurns the night, and braves the win-ter wild? Was ev - er babe so low-ly and so ten - der, yet full of grace? Who is this lit - tle child?
2 What shall we sing to ce - le-brate his sto - ry, to praise our Lord and glo - ri - fy our king? How shall we tell the peo-ple of his glo - ry, and share his grace? What shall his peo-ple sing?
Chorus
This is the Christ, in whom we are for - giv - en; this is the Lord, the migh-ty Son of

1.
Dsus/A D7 G7 Am G/B C E7 Am F♯dim7
Man; this is our God, who comes to us from
C/G Am F G7 C C7/E Dm G7 Am F C
hea - ven — the liv-ing Word who was be-fore the world be - gan!
2.
Dsus/A D7 G7 G/F E Am F♯dim7
Man; this is our God, who comes to us from
C/E Am D7♭5 D7/A♭ Em7 A7 D7 G7 Am Fm7 C
hea - ven — the liv-ing Word who was be-fore the world be - gan!

347 Wise men, they came to look for wisdom

Neumark
Capo 3(Em)

Words: Christopher Idle
Music: G Neumark (1621–1681)
arranged E Routley (1917–1982)

Gm (Em) D (B) Gm (Em) Dm (Bm) E♭ (C) Cm6 (Am6)
1 Wise men, they came to look for wisdom, finding one wiser than they knew; rich men, they met with one yet richer–
2 Pilgrims they were, from unknown countries, searching for one who knows the world; lost are their names, and strange their journeys,
3 Magi, they stooped to see your splendour, led by a star to light supreme; promised Messiah, Lord eternal,
4 Guests of their God, they opened treasures, incense and gold and solemn myrrh, welcoming one too young to question
D (B) B♭ (G) Cm (Am) D (B) Gm (Em)
Dsus (Bsus) D (B) Gm (Em) E♭ (C) Cm6 (Am6)
B♭ (G) Dm (Bm) E♭ (C) Cm6 (Am6) D (B)

Dm (Bm) F7 (D7) B♭ (G) E♭ (C) Gm/D (Em) D7 (B7)
King of the kings, they knelt to
famed is their zeal to find the
glo - ry and peace are in your
how came these gifts, and what they
Gm (Em) B♭ (G) F (D) B♭ (G)
you: Je - sus, our wis - dom
child: Je - sus, in you the
name: Joy of each day, our
were: Gift be - yond price of
Cm (Am) F (D) B♭ (G) Cm6 (Am6) Cm (Am)
from a - bove, wealth and re -
lost are claimed, a - liens are
Song by night, shine on our
gold or gem, make a - mong
D (B) Gm (Em) Cm (Am) D7 (B7) Gm (Em)
- demp - tion, life and love.
found, and known, and named.
path your ho - ly light.
us your Beth - le - hem.

348 Within a crib my saviour lay

Lord of love

Words: Timothy Dudley-Smith
Music: Norman Warren

G Em Bm7 Em Am7 Dsus D G
1 With - in a
2 Up - on a
3 A vic - tor's
D7/G G D7/A G B7 C Em7
crib my sav - iour lay, a wood - en man - ger
cross my sav - iour died, to ran - som sin - ners
crown my sav - iour won, his work of love and
Am7 Dsus D F Em Em7 Am
filled with hay, come down for love on Christ - mas
cru - ci - fied, his lov - ing arms still o - pen
mer - cy done, the Fa - ther's high - a - scend - ed
B♭ D7/A G G7 Am/C G
Day: all glo - ry be to Je - sus!
wide: all glo - ry be to Je - sus!
Son: all glo - ry be to Je - sus!

349 Wonderful Counsellor, Jesus

From Isaiah 9
Words and music: Bill Yarger
Music arranged David Peacock

Tenderly

C/G C *Optional instrumental obligato* G/A Am7

C/D Dm F/G G C/G C

Verses

1 Won - der - ful
2 Migh - ty God,
3 Ev - er - last - ing
4 Prince of peace,
5 Won - der - ful

G/A Am7 C/D Dm7

Coun - sel - lor, Je - sus:
Son of God, Je - sus;
Fa - ther, Je - sus;
rule my heart, Je - sus;
Coun - sel - lor, Je - sus;

F/G
C/D
Dm7
search me,
name a - bove all
ho - ly and un -
know my ev - ery
Migh - ty God,
C/G
Dm7
Dm/C
C
know me,
Je - sus;
o - ther names,
Je - sus:
- change - a - ble,
Je - sus:
an - xious thought,
Je - sus;
Son of God,
Je - sus;
Gm7
Gm7/C
C7
G/A
Am
lead me,
glo - ri - fy,
fill me with your
calm my fears,
Ev - er - last - ing

G Am Fmaj7 F
guide me, Je - sus
mag - ni - fy, Je - sus
pre - sence, Je - sus
dry my tears, Je - sus
Fa - ther, Je - sus
Dm7 F/G G7 G/C C
Won - der - ful
Migh - ty God,
Ev - er - last - ing
Prince of peace,
Prince of peace,
1–4.
5.
C/D Dm7 F/C C G/C C
Coun - sel - lor, Je - sus.
Son of God, Je - sus.
Fa - ther, Je - sus.
rule my heart, Je - sus.
rule my heart, Je - sus!

350 Word of the Father everlasting

Bergers

Words: David Mowbray
Music: French traditional melody
arranged David Iliff

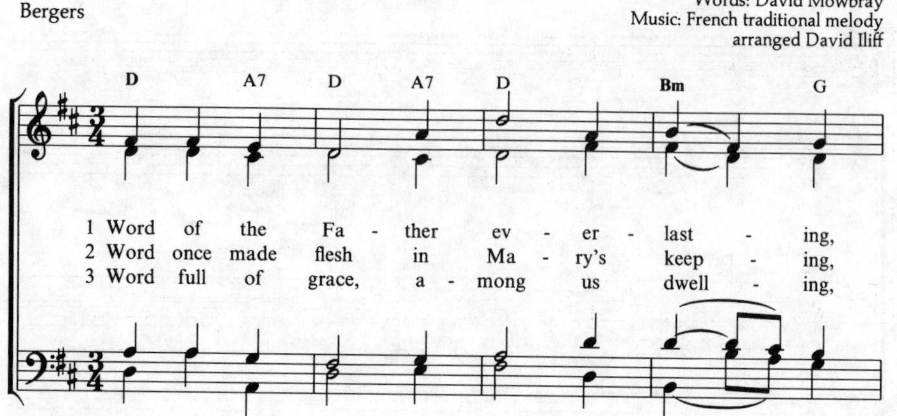

D A7 D A7 D Bm G
1 Word of the Fa - ther ev - er - last - ing,
2 Word once made flesh in Ma - ry's keep - ing,
3 Word full of grace, a - mong us dwell - ing,

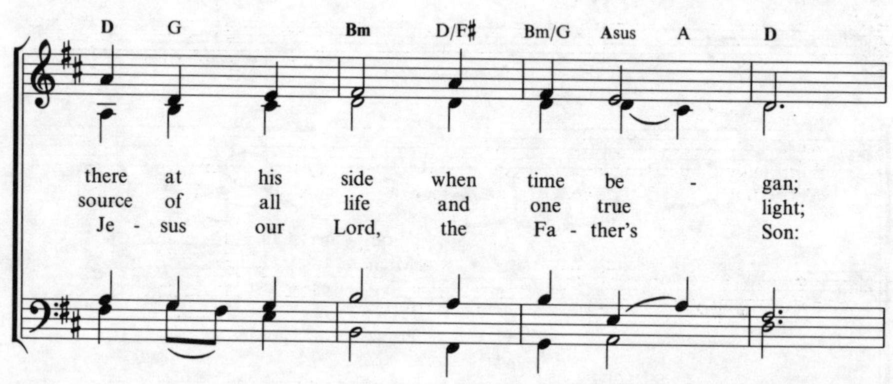

D G Bm D/F♯ Bm/G Asus A D
there at his side when time be - gan;
source of all life and one true light;
Je - sus our Lord, the Fa - ther's Son:

Bm F♯m G A D G A
who but the Word re - flects his glo - ry,
who of his own will dare re - ceive him,
give us the power, your name con - fess - ing,

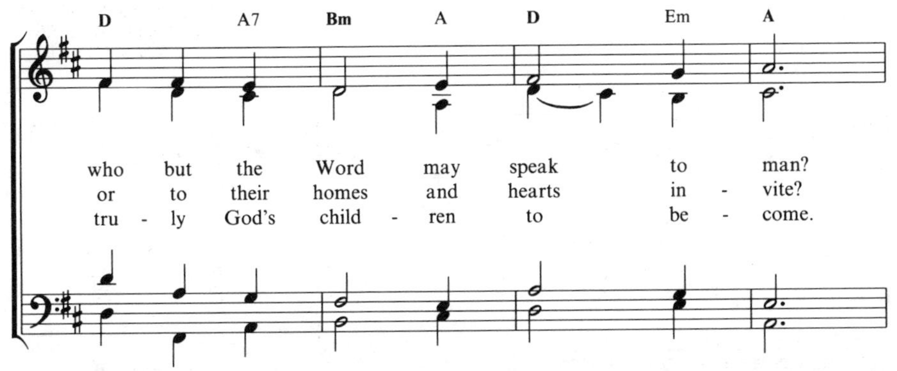
D A7 Bm A D Em A
who but the Word may speak to man?
or to their homes and hearts in - vite?
tru - ly God's child - ren to be - come.

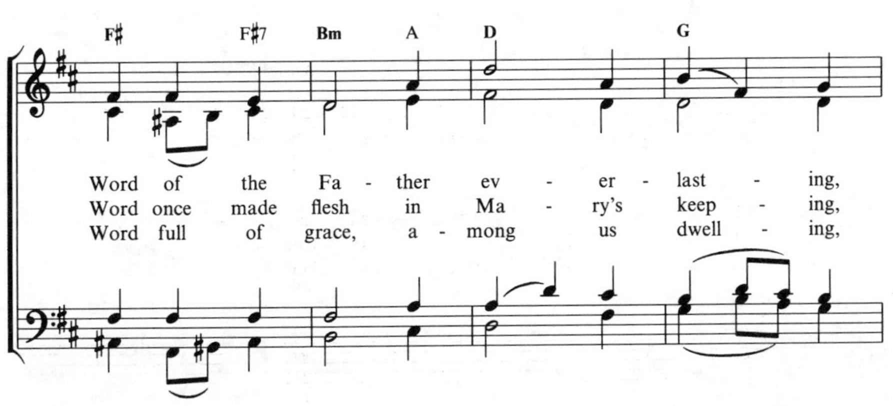
F♯ F♯7 Bm A D G
Word of the Fa - ther ev - er - last - ing,
Word once made flesh in Ma - ry's keep - ing,
Word full of grace, a - mong us dwell - ing,

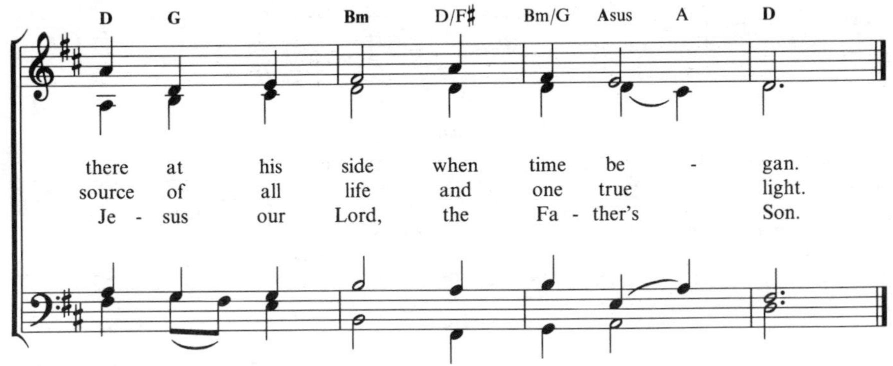
D G Bm D/F♯ Bm/G Asus A D
there at his side when time be - gan.
source of all life and one true light.
Je - sus our Lord, the Fa - ther's Son.

For piano version see number 351

351 Word of the Father everlasting

(PIANO VERSION)

Bergers

Words: David Mowbray
Music: French traditional melody
arranged for piano David Peacock

Flowing
D A D A Bm A
1 Word of the Fa - ther ev - er -
2 Word once made flesh in Ma - ry's
3 Word full of grace, a - mong us
Gmaj7 Em7 D G A/E D A
- last - ing, there at his side when
keep - ing, source of all life and
dwell - ing, Je - sus our Lord, the
Bm Em A D Bm F♯m7
time be - gan; who but the
one true light; who of his
Fa - ther's Son: give us the
G A Bm E7 A
Word re - flects his glo - ry,
own will dare re - ceive him,
power, your name con - fess - ing,

D A/C♯ Bm A D G/B
who but the Word may speak to
or to their homes and hearts in -
tru - ly God's child - ren to be -
A D A Bm A
man? Word of the Fa - ther
- vite? Word once made flesh in
- come. Word full of grace, a -
D Gmaj7 D Bm Gm6/B♭
ev - er - last - ing, there at his
Ma - ry's keep - ing, source of all
- mong us dwell - ing, Je - sus our
D/A B7 E9 Asus A
1.2. D
3. D
side when time be - gan.
life and one true light.
Lord, the Fa - ther's Son.

This arrangement is not compatible
with the harmonisation of number 350

352 You are the King of glory

From Isaiah 9
Words and music: Mavis Ford
Music arranged Noël Tredinnick

Triumphantly
marcato
G Bm Em Am7 Am7/D D7 G C G/B D7/A
Verse
G D7/A Bm B7 C A9 D F♯7/C♯
You are the King of glo - ry, you are the Prince of peace,
Am Bsus B7 Em Asus Am
you are the Lord of heaven and earth, you're the Sun of right - eous -
D Bsus B7 D♯dim/E Em Am
- ness! An - gels bow down be - fore you, wor - ship and a -
D F♯7/C♯ Bm C9 D9 Em
- dore, for you have the words of e - ter - nal life

Chorus
Bm Em Am D7 C/G G F♯dim7
you are Je - sus Christ the Lord! Ho - san - na to the Son of
Em Dm G7 C Am D G G7
Da - vid, ho - san - na to the King of __ kings: glo - ry in the high - est
C9 Bm Am9 D7 G C/D G B7
hea - ven, for Je - sus the Mes - si - ah reigns! Ho - san - na to the Son of
Em Dm G7 Am Am7 D G D7/A
Da - vid, ho - san - na to the King of __ kings: glo - ry in the high - est
Bm Em Am C/D D7 G G7 C Cm G
hea - ven, for Je - sus the Mes - si - ah reigns!

353 You servants of the Lord

Narenza

Words: from Luke 12
P Doddridge (1702–1751) and in this version Word & Music
Music: adapted from J Liesentritt *Catholicum Hymnologum* (1584)
arranged W H Havergal (1793–1870)
verse 5 arranged with descant John Barnard

Capo 3(G)

B♭ (G) F (D) B♭ (G) E♭ (C) F7 (D7) B♭ (G)
1 You ser - vants of the Lord who
2 Let all your lamps be bright and
3 A - wait your Lord's com - mand – the
4 O hap - py ser - vants they who
C (A) Dm (Bm) B♭ (G) C (A) F (D) B♭ (G) F7 (D7) B♭ (G) E♭ (C) F7 (D7)
for his com - ing wait: ob - serve with care his
guard the liv - ing flame; be rea - dy al - ways
bride - groom shall ap - pear: for his re - turn - ing
wide a - wake are found to greet their mas - ter
Gm (Em) E♭ (C) D (B) B♭ (G) F (D) Gm (Em) Cm7 (Am7) F (D) B♭ (G)
hea - venly word – be watch - ful at his gate.
in his sight, for awe - some is his name.
is at hand, and while we speak he's near.
on that day, and be with hon - our crowned!

Descant
B♭ (G)
F (D)
B♭ (G)
E♭ (C)
F7 (D7)
B♭ (G)
C9 (A9)
5 Christ shall the ban - quet spread with
5 Christ shall the ban - quet spread with
F (D)
Dm (Bm)
Gm (Em)
C (A)
Fsus (Dsus)
F (D)
B♭ (G)
F7 (D7)
B♭ (G)
E♭ (C)
F7 (D7)
his own roy - al hand,
and raise each faith - ful
his own roy - al hand, and raise each faith - ful
Gm (Em)
E♭ (C)
D (B)
B♭ (G)
F (D)
Gm (Em)
C7 (Am7)
F (D)
B♭ (G)
ser - vant's head a - mid the an - gel - ic band.
ser - vant's head a - mid the an - gel - ic band.

354 You shall go out with joy

From Isaiah 55
Words and music: Stuart Dauermann
Music arranged D J Langford

Lively
Intro.
Em C7 B7 Em C7 B7
You shall go
Em6 Em6 D7
out with joy and be led forth in peace; and the
G D B7
moun-tains and the hills shall break forth be - fore you, sing - ing

Em
C7
B7
songs of joy, and the trees of the field shall clap, shall clap their
Em
D7
G
D
hands; and the trees of the field shall clap their hands, and the
B7
Em
D7
G
trees of the field shall clap their hands, and the trees of the field shall
D
B7
Em6
clap their hands, as you go out with joy!

355 Your kingdom come

Irish

Capo 3(C)

Words: F L Hosmer (1840–1928)
and in this version Word & Music
Music: melody from *Hymns and Sacred Poems*, Dublin (1749)

E♭ (C) B♭ (G) Cm (Am) B♭ (G) E♭ (C) A♭ (F) E♭/B♭ (C) B♭ (G)
1 Your king - dom come! On bend - ed
2 The hours of wait - ing through the
3 And there al - rea - dy in the
E♭ (C) B♭ (G) E♭ (C) A♭ (F) E♭ (C) Cm (Am) Fm (Dm) B♭ (G) E♭ (C)
knee through pass - ing years we pray: all
night no less to God be - long; the
skies the dawn's first rays ap - pear – you
A♭ (F) E♭ (C) B♭7 (G7) E♭ (C) A♭ (F) Fm (Dm) E♭ (C)
faith - ful peo - ple long to
stars de - clare the e - ter - nal
pro - phets of our God, a -
E♭/B♭ (C) B♭ (G) Cm (Am) A♭ (F) E♭ (C) A♭ (F) E♭/B♭ (C) B♭ (G) E♭ (C)
see on earth that king - dom's day.
right and shame the crea - ture's wrong.
- rise, pro - claim the day is near:

4 The day in whose clear shining light
the Lord shall stand revealed,
and every wrong be turned to right,
and every hurt be healed:

5 When justice joined with truth and peace
make straight the Saviour's road –
the day of perfect righteousness,
the promised day of God!

ACKNOWLEDGEMENTS

We thank all those who contributed to the compilation of *Carol Praise*:

The 'Jubilate Hymns' team for the application of their immense expertise – especially in this case Noël Tredinnick, Norman Warren and Clifford Roseweir.

The 'Word & Music' team – especially Bunty Grundy and her assistants, Ann Darlington and Sylvia Bleasdale, for their efficiency and skill in getting material ready for publication.

The 'Marshalls' team – notably Debbie Thorpe, Stanley Grant, Jim Girling, and Tim Sanders – for believing in us before we sell the first million!

Our long-suffering wives, Beatrice and Jane, who have been enduring Christmas solidly for three years.

And we are grateful to all who have bought this book in order to share the vision of proclaiming Christ to the world at the season when hearts are most readily open to receive him.

Michael Perry and David Peacock

LEGAL INFORMATION

Those seeking to reproduce outside North America works in this book which are the property of Jubilate Hymns or associated authors (attributed '.. / Jubilate Hymns') may write to The Copyright Manager, Jubilate Hymns Ltd, 61 Chessel Avenue, Southampton SO2 4DY (telephone 0703 30038). In the United States of America, these same copyrights, along with those of Timothy Dudley-Smith, are administered by Hope Publishing Company, Carol Stream, IL 60188.

A number of publishers of UK Christian music have uniform concessions and rates. There is normally no charge for 'once off' use of an item provided that permission is obtained and proper acknowledgement made in print. Reproduction for permanent use, or re-sale, does attract a small charge in most cases. Details are available from The Copyright Manager, Jubilate Hymns Ltd.

Most of these publishers also combine to offer a licencing scheme for limited term reproduction. Where this is felt to be an advantage, application should be made to the Christian Music Association, Glyndley Manor, Stone Cross, Eastbourne, East Sussex BN24 5BS (telephone 0323 841419).

Items copyrighted Stainer & Bell may not be photocopied or reprinted under any blanket licencing scheme, and should only be cleared individually with Stainer & Bell.

As with all the major copyright holders represented in this collection, Jubilate Hymns with their associated authors and composers, and Word & Music, are members of the Mechanical Copyright Protection, and Performing Rights Societies. Appropriate application should be made to these bodies as follows: The Mechanical Copyright Protection Society, Elgar House, 41 Streatham High Road, London SW16 1ER (01 769 4400); The Performing Rights Society, 29–33 Berners Street, London W1P 4AA (01 580 5544).

ADDRESSES

From which permission to reproduce copyright items should be obtained

A & C Black, Howard Road, Eaton Scoton, Huntingdon, Cambridgeshire PE19 3EZ
Anfield Music Ltd, 201 Monument Road, Edgbaston, Birmingham, B16 8UU
Berea College, Berea, Kentucky 40404, USA
Bible Society, Stonehill Green, Westlea, Swindon, SN5 7DG
Blandford Press, Link House, West Street, Poole, Dorset BH15 1LL
Boosey & Hawkes, 295 Regent Street, London W1R 8JH
Bourne Music, 34/36 Maddox Street, London W1R 9PD
Breitkopf und Hartel, Buch und Musikverlag, Walkmuhlstrasse 52, Wiesbaden 1, West Germany
Cherry Lane Music (and Cherry Pie Music), 75 High Street, Needham Market, Ipswich, Suffolk IP6 8AW
Christian Fellowship of Columbia, 4600 Christian Fellowship Road, Columbia, Missouri 65203, USA
Clifton Music, Clifton Cathedral House, Clifton Park, Bristol BS8 3BX
Columbia Pictures Music, 3500 West Olive Avenue, Burbank, California 91505, USA
Coronation Music, c/o 32 St Alban's Road, Westbury Park, Bristol BS6 7ST
Ears & Eyes Music, Kerygma House, Canal Road, Leeds LS12 2PL
Glory Alleluia Music, Tempo Music Publications, 2712 W 104th Terrace, Leawood, Kansas 66206, USA
Gordon V Thompson Music Ltd, 29 Birch Avenue, Toronto, Ontario M4V 1E2, Canada
High-Fye Music, c/o Campbell Connelly, 8–9 Frith Street, London W1V 5TZ
Hodder & Stoughton, 47 Bedford Square, London WC1B 3DP
Hope Publishing Company, Carol Stream, Illinois 60188, USA
Hymns Ancient and Modern, St Mary's Works, St Mary's Plain, Norwich, Norfolk NR3 3BH
Integrity's Hosanna! Music, Integrity Communications, PO Box Z, Mobile, Al. 36616 USA
International Music Publications, Woodford Trading Estate, Southend Road, Woodford Green, Essex IG8 8HN
Josef Weinberger, 12/14 Mortimer Street, London W1N 7RD
Jubilate Hymns Ltd, c/o 61 Chessel Avenue, Bitterne, Southampton SO2 4DY
Lindsay Music, 23 Hitchin Street, Biggleswade, Bedfordshire SG18 8AX
Magnificat Music, St Thomas More Centre, The Burroughs, Hendon, London NW4 4TY
Mustard Seed Music, 9 Holdom Avenue, Bletchley, Milton Keynes MK1 1QU
New Song Ministries, PO Box 11662, Costa Mesa, California 92627 USA
Overseas Missionary Fellowship, Belmont, The Vine, Sevenoaks, Kent
Oxford University Press (London), Ely House, 37 Dover Street, London W1X 4AH
Oxford University Press (Oxford), Walton Street, Oxford OX2 6DP
Parish of Eastbourne Trust, PO Box 41026, Eastbourne, Wellington, New Zealand
Religious and Moral Education Press, Hennock Road, Exeter EX2 8RP
Renewal Servicing, PO Box 366, Addlestone, Weybridge, Surrey KT15 3UL
Restoration Music Ltd, Harvestime House, 136 Hall Lane, Bradford, West Yorkshire BD4 7DG
Royal School of Church Music, Addington Palace, Croydon, Surrey CR9 5AD
Salvationist Publishing and Supplies Ltd, 117/121 Judd Street, Kings Cross, London WC1H 9NN
St Paul's Outreach Trust, PO Box 6349, Wellesley Street, Auckland 1, New Zealand
Stainer & Bell Ltd, 82 High Road, London N2 9PW
Thankyou Music, PO Box 75, Eastbourne, East Sussex BN23 6NW
Tree International, 8 Music Square West, PO Box 1273, Nashville, Tennessee 37203, USA
Tro Essex Music Ltd, Essex House, 19/20 Poland Street, London W1V 3DD
William Elkin Music Services, Station Road Industrial Estate, Salhouse, Norwich, Norfolk NR13 6NY
Word & Music, c/o Jubilate Hymns, 61 Chessel Avenue, Bitterne, Southampton SO2 4DY
Word Music (UK), 9 Holdom Avenue, Bletchley, Milton Keynes MK1 1QU
Word of God Music, PO Box 8617, 840 Airport Blvd, Ann Arbor, Michigan 48107, USA

FURTHER COPYRIGHT INFORMATION

relating to copyright ascriptions marked † in the text

1 Used by permission of A & C Black (publishers) Ltd
2 Used by permission of Magnificat Music
9 Words: administered in North America by Hope Publishing Company
12 © 1981 Glory Alleluia Music. International copyright secured. All rights reserved. Used by permission only
15 © 1978 Thankyou Music
16 Music: Composer and copyright-holder sought
17 Copyright-holder sought
18 Used by permission of Magnificat Music
19 © 1975 administered in Europe by Thankyou Music
23 Arrangement and descant: used by permission of the Royal School of Church Music
24 © 1982 Thankyou Music
26 Music: © 1974 Chappell Music Ltd, London W1Y 3FA. Reproduced by permission of Chappell Music Ltd and International Music Publications
28 © administered by Religious and Moral Education Press
31 © 1984 Thankyou Music
32 Music: reprinted by permission of Gordon V Thompson Music, Toronto, Canada
35 Music arrangement: copyright-holder sought
36 Author and composer sought
40 © 1964/1987, used by permission of Stainer & Bell Ltd. A leaflet version for SSSA is published and available from them
45 Music arrangement used by permission of Oxford University Press (London)
50 Used by permission of Oxford University Press (Oxford)
53 Music: © 1961, 1987, used by permission of Stainer & Bell Ltd
55 © 1974 Chappell Music Ltd, London W1Y 3FA. Reproduced by permission of Chappell Music Ltd and International Music Publications
60 © Christopher Walker / Clifton Music. Adapted and used by permission
61 © 1972, and music arrangement © 1987 High-Fye Music Ltd. Used by permission. All rights reserved
65 © 1981 Thankyou Music
66 © 1981 Thankyou Music
68 Used by permission of Ears and Eyes Production Company Ltd
69 © 1984 Thankyou Music
72 Words: administered in North America by Hope Publishing Company. Music: used by kind permission of Breitkopf and Hartel, Wiesbaden
73 © 1975 administered in Europe by Thankyou Music
74 Used by permission of Magnificat Music
76 © 1985 Thankyou Music
78 Used by permission of Salvationist Publishing and Supplies Ltd
79 © 1985 Thankyou Music
80 © 1979 Thankyou Music
81 © 1976 administered by Word Music (UK) (A division of Word (UK) Ltd)
83 Words: administered in North America by Hope Publishing Company
84 © 1985 Word Music (UK) (A division of Word (UK) Ltd)
86 Music: used by permission of Hymns Ancient & Modern Ltd
88 © 1985 Thankyou Music
89 © 1984 Restoration Music Ltd
91 © 1983 Thankyou Music
92 © Bible Society
93 Words: administered in North America by Hope Publishing Company
94 Words: used by permission of Oxford University Press (Oxford)
97 © 1980 Lesley Neal
98 © Glory Alleluia Music. International copyright secured. All rights reserved. Used by permission only
101 © 1982 Word Music (UK) (A division of Word (UK) Ltd)
102 © 1984 Thankyou Music
103 © 1966 Willard F Jabusch, St Mary of the Lake, Mundelein, Illinois 60060, USA
104 © 1982 Thankyou Music
106 Music: © 1954 Chappell Music Ltd, London W1Y 3FA. Reproduced by permission of Chappell Music Ltd and International Music Publications
116 © 1983 administered in Europe by Thankyou Music
117 © 1980 administered by Word Music (UK) (A division of Word (UK) Ltd)
118 Words: author sought
119 © 1978 Thankyou Music
120 Used by permission of Cherry Lane Music Ltd
121 Words: administered in North America by Hope Publishing Company
123 Words: administered in North America by Hope Publishing Company
124 Words: administered in North America by Hope Publishing Company
125 © 1974, 1978 Thankyou Music
127 Words: administered in North America by Hope Publishing Company
130 © 1984 Integrity's Hosanna! Music. All rights reserved. International copyright secured. Used by permission only
133 © 1984 Mustard Seed Music
136 © 1973 administered in Europe by Thankyou Music
142 Music: used by permission of Berea College, Kentucky
145 © 1983 Thankyou Music
148 Used by permission of Magnificat Music
149 © 1974, 1979 administered in Europe by Thankyou Music
151 © 1960 used by permission Josef Weinberger Ltd
154 Words: © 1980 administered by Word Music (UK) (A division of Word (UK) Ltd)
155 Reproduced from *Merrily To Bethlehem* by permission of A & C Black (publishers) Ltd
158 © 1985 Thankyou Music
159 © 1984 Thankyou Music
160 © 1982 administered in Europe by Thankyou Music
161 Used by permission of Cherry Lane Music Ltd
162 © 1983 Thankyou Music
163 Music: used by permission of Oxford University Press (London)
166 © 1983 Restoration Music
167 Used by permission of Ears and Eyes Production Company Ltd
169 © 1985 Word Music (UK) (A division of Word (UK) Ltd)
170 © Used by permission of Coronation Music
171 Words (verse 1): © 1968 Boston Music Co Inc, USA. Reproduced by permission of Chappell Music Ltd and International Music Publications
172 © 1959, 1987 Chappell Music Ltd, London W1Y 3FA
173 © 1970 B Feldman & Co Ltd, trading as Freeman & Co Ltd. Reproduced by permission of EMI Publishing Ltd and International Music Publications
174 © 1970 used by permission of Oxford University Press (Oxford)
175 © Schumann Music Corp. administered by Bourne Music Ltd
178 © 1984 Thankyou Music
179 Music: © 1984 Mustard Seed Music, from whom a choral version of this piece is available
182 Words: administered in North America by Hope Publishing Company

184 Words: used by permission of the Overseas Missionary Fellowship. Music: copyright-holder sought
186 Words: copyright-holder sought
188 Music: used by permission of Oxford University Press (London)
194 © 1984 Mustard Seed Music
197 © 1986 Thankyou Music
198 © 1986 Thankyou Music
199 © 1984 Springtide / Word Music (UK) (A division of Word (UK) Ltd)
200 © 1975 administered in Europe by Thankyou Music
202 © 1935, 1977 Anfield Music Ltd. International copyright secured
203 © 1982 Christian Fellowship of Columbia, Inc
204 Words: by kind permission of Blandford Press
208 © 1981 Springtide / Word Music (UK) (A division of Word (UK) Ltd)
212 Words: used by permission of Oxford University Press (Oxford)
213 Music arrangement: used by permission of Oxford University Press (London)
215 Music: used by permission of Oxford University Press (London)
216 Music: © 1984 Philip Trumble, 33 Recreation Road, Guildford, Surrey GU1 1HQ
217 © 1981 Meadowgreen Music Company. This arrangement © 1984. All rights administered by Tree International. International copyright secured. All rights reserved. Used by permission
218 Words: administered in North America by Hope Publishing Company
221 © 1980 Thankyou Music
223 Words: © 1967 Hope Publishing Company, Carol Stream, Illinois 60188, USA. All rights reserved. Used by permission
225 Music: by kind permission of Blandford Press
229 Words: administered in North America by Hope Publishing Company
230 © 1981 Thankyou Music
231 Words: based on the New International Version (copyright © 1973, 1978, 1984 by International Bible Society) published by Hodder and Stoughton. Music: © Peter Lawry / Music for the King, Holly Cottage, 34 Stockers Lane, Kingfield, Woking, Surrey GU22 9DB
232 © 1984 Mustard Seed Music
234 Music: used by permission of Hymns Ancient & Modern Ltd
238 Music: © 1960, arrangement © 1987 by permission of Josef Weinberger Ltd
239 © 1983 Thankyou Music
240 © 1984 Mustard Seed Music
241 © 1983 Restoration Music
242 Used by permission of Renewal Servicing
243 Used by permission of Ears and Eyes Production Company Ltd
246 Used by permission of Cherry Lane Music Ltd
247 © 1983 Thankyou Music
248 © 1976, 1984 administered in Europe by Thankyou Music
249 © 1981 Thankyou Music
253 Used by permission of Cherry Pie Music
254 © administered by R Stockwell Esq, 22 Palmer Avenue, Cheam, Surrey SM3 8EG
255 © 1983. Reproduced by permission of Boosey & Hawkes Music Publishers Ltd
259 Words: © administered in North America by Hope Publishing Company
260 Music: used by permission of Oxford University Press (London)
263 Words: used by permission of Lindsay Music
268 Used by permission of Ears and Eyes Production Company Ltd
269 © 1976 administered in Europe by Thankyou Music
270 © 1974 Linda Stassen, New Song Ministries. All rights reserved. Used by permission only
271 Words: © administered in North America by Hope Publishing Company
273 Used by permission of Ears and Eyes Production Company Ltd
275 Words: administered in North America by Hope Publishing Company
278 Music: © Columbia Pictures Music, used by permission
279 © 1976 Lexicon Music Inc / Crouch Music USA. Administered by Word Music (UK)
280 © John McNeil, 38 Stourbridge Street, Christchurch 2, New Zealand
282 © 1963 Tro Essex Music Ltd. International copyright secured. All rights reserved. Used by permission
285 Words: © administered in North America by Hope Publishing Company. Music: used by permission of Oxford University Press (London)
286 Music: reproduced by permission of EMI publishing Ltd and International Music Publications
287 © 1976 Thankyou Music
288 Used by permission of Salvationist Publishing and Supplies
289 Words: administered in North America by Hope Publishing Company
290 Words: administered in North America by Hope Publishing Company
291 Used by permission of Ears and Eyes Production Company Ltd
294 Used by permission of Cherry Pie Music
296 © 1974 The Word of God Music. All rights reserved
299 © 1983 Thankyou Music
301 Used by permission of Cherry Pie Music
302 From *Carols for Christmas* © 1969. Reproduced by permission of Boosey & Hawkes Music Publishers Ltd
303 © 1975 St Paul's Outreach Trust
305 From *The Edric Connor Collection* © 1945. Reproduced by permission of Boosey & Hawkes Music Publishers Ltd
307 Used by permission of Cherry Lane Music Ltd
313 © 1984 Mustard Seed Music
314 © 1969. Reproduced by permission of Boosey & Hawkes Music Publishers Ltd
315 © 1979 administered in Europe by Thankyou Music
316 Words: used by permission of Oxford University Press (London)
318 © 1986 Thankyou Music
319 Words: copyright-holder sought
320 © 1983 administered in Europe by Thankyou Music
323 Words: copyright-holder sought. Music arrangement © 1983 Thankyou Music
325 © 1979 Springtide / Word Music (UK) (A division of Word (UK) Ltd)
327 Used by permission of William Elkin Music Services
331 Used by permission of Cherry Lane Music Ltd
336 Words: used by permission of Parish of Eastbourne Trust, New Zealand
338 Words: administered in North America by Hope Publishing Company
339 © 1980, 1983 administered by Thankyou Music
344 Music: © 1974 Chappell Music Ltd, London W1Y 3FA. Reproduced by permission of Chappell Music Ltd and International Music Publications
347 Words: administered in North America by Hope Publishing Company
348 Words: administered in North America by Hope Publishing Company
349 © 1982 Maranatha! Music USA / Word Music (UK) (A division of Word (UK) Ltd)
352 © 1978 Springtide / Word Music (UK) (A division of Word (UK) Ltd)
354 © 1975 administered in Europe by Thankyou Music

INDEX TO AUTHORS, ORIGINATORS AND ADAPTORS OF TEXTS

INDEX TO COMPOSERS, ARRANGERS AND SOURCES OF TUNES

Italicised numbers indicate arrangements

'STORY' INDEX TO CAROLS

This index assists users in the preparation
of Christmas carol events by setting out the carols
in thematic and 'chronological' order

Come to worship

Everybody must know

Jesus' life is threatened

Jesus is recognised . .

We wonder at God's love

We sing his praise

INDEX TO BIBLE REFERENCES

INDEX TO CAROLS SUITABLE FOR SATB SINGING

INDEX TO CAROLS WITH DESCANTS AND OTHER VOCAL ARRANGEMENTS

INDEX TO CAROLS ARRANGED AS ROUNDS

INDEX TO RESPONSE CAROLS

INDEX TO CAROLS WITH INSTRUMENTAL PARTS

* indicates B♭ arrangements

INDEX TO SEASONAL HYMNS

INDEX TO SEASONAL WORSHIP SONGS

INDEX TO CAROLS BASED ON FOLK TUNES OR OTHER NATIONAL TUNES

INDEX TO NEW CAROLS SET TO EXISTING TUNES

Tunes (First line in brackets)

INDEX TO CAROLS PARTICULARLY SUITABLE FOR CHILDREN

CHORD CHART

A♭ A♭7 A♭maj7 A A6

A7 A9 Amaj7 Asus Am

Am6 Am7 Am9 B♭ B♭7

B♭9 B♭maj7 B♭m B♭m7 B♭dim

B B7 B7♭5 Bno3 Bsus

B7sus Bm Bm6 Bm7 Bm9

Bdim C C6 C7 C9

Caug Cmaj7 Csus Cm 3fr. Cm6

Cm7 3fr. Cdim C♯m 4fr. C♯m7 4fr. C♯dim

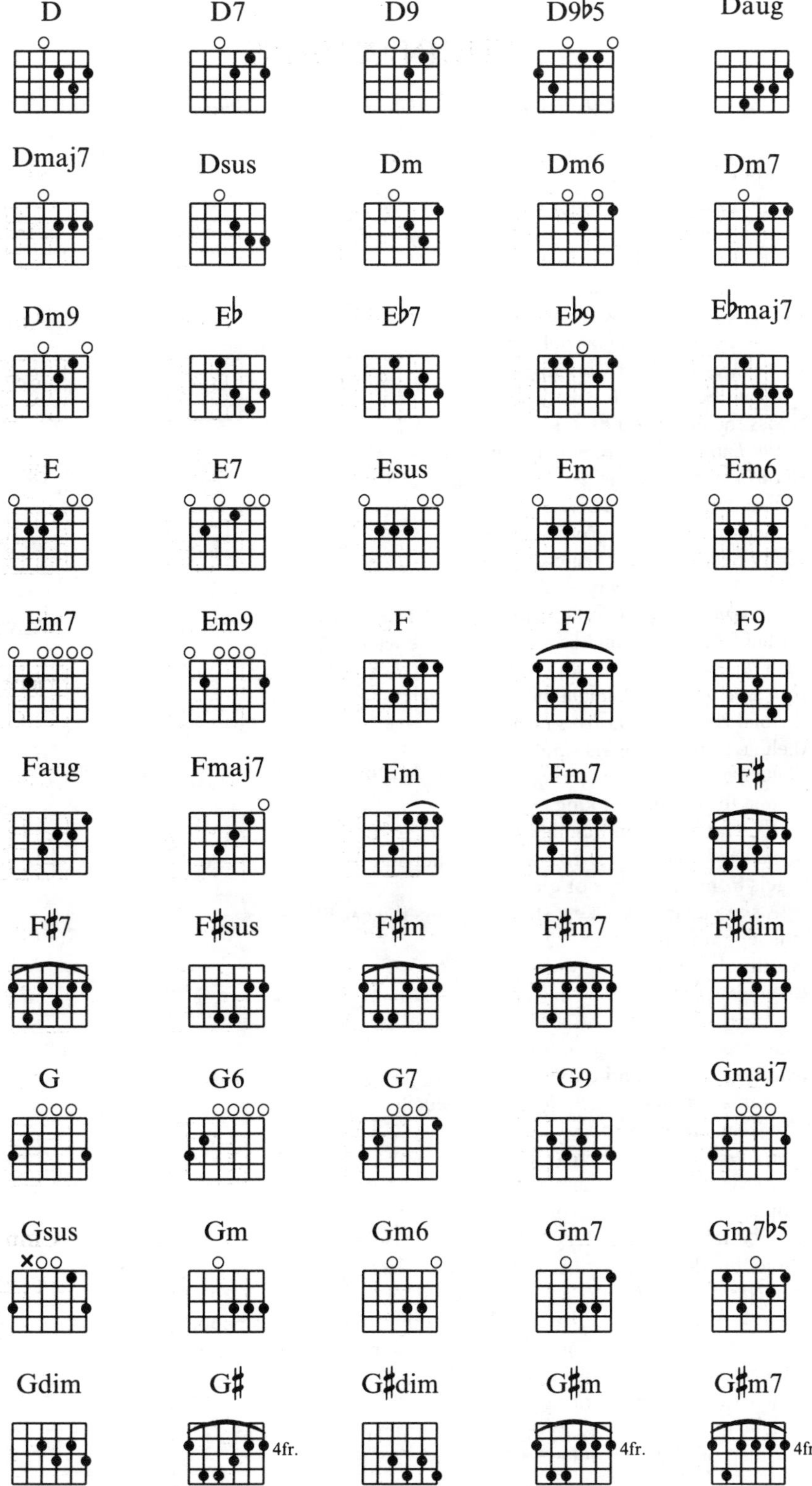
D
D7
D9
D9♭5
Daug
Dmaj7
Dsus
Dm
Dm6
Dm7
Dm9
E♭
E♭7
E♭9
E♭maj7
E
E7
Esus
Em
Em6
Em7
Em9
F
F7
F9
Faug
Fmaj7
Fm
Fm7
F♯
F♯7
F♯sus
F♯m
F♯m7
F♯dim
G
G6
G7
G9
Gmaj7
Gsus
Gm
Gm6
Gm7
Gm7♭5
Gdim
G♯
4fr.
G♯dim
G♯m
4fr.
G♯m7
4fr.

MAIN INDEX

Italics indicate translations, versions and titles